9/67

TP
482
53

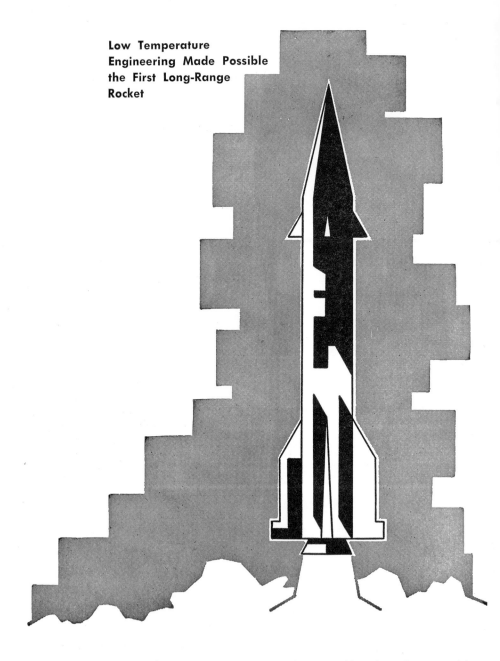

Low Temperature Engineering Made Possible the First Long-Range Rocket

For over fifteen years liquid oxygen has been used as an oxidant in rocket propulsion. In the future other cryogenic liquids may prove useful as rocket fuels or oxidants.

CRYOGENIC ENGINEERING

by

RUSSELL B. SCOTT

Chief, National Bureau of Standards
Cryogenic Engineering Laboratory

PREPARED FOR THE ATOMIC ENERGY COMMISSION

D. VAN NOSTRAND COMPANY, INC.

PRINCETON, NEW JERSEY

TORONTO   LONDON

NEW YORK

D. VAN NOSTRAND COMPANY, INC.
120 Alexander St., Princeton, New Jersey (*Principal office*)
24 West 40th Street, New York 18, New York

D. VAN NOSTRAND COMPANY, LTD.
358, Kensington High Street, London, W.14, England

D. VAN NOSTRAND COMPANY (Canada), LTD.
25 Hollinger Road, Toronto 16, Canada

First Published March 1959
Reprinted October 1959
August 1960, May 1962
November 1963, April 1966

PRINTED IN THE UNITED STATES OF AMERICA

BY THE COLONIAL PRESS INC., CLINTON, MASS.

PREFACE

Cryogenic engineering is concerned with developing and improving low-temperature processes and equipment; determining the physical properties of structural and other materials used in producing, maintaining, and using low temperatures; and the practical application of low-temperature techniques and processes. Such practical applications have become so widespread in recent years that there are now a large number of specialists in this type of work and the field has attained a degree of recognition as a minor branch of engineering. National conferences on cryogenic engineering were held at Boulder, Colorado, in 1954, 1956, 1957 and at Massachusetts Institute of Technology in 1958—the last of which was attended by 560 delegates. Present plans call for annual conferences.

This book is intended primarily as an introduction to cryogenic, or low-temperature, engineering. It has been written for engineers and others unfamiliar with cryogenic techniques who must employ them in their designs and investigations. Low-temperature processes and methods have already been used very successfully as adjuncts to other developments. For example, low-temperature propellants are used in nearly all long-range rockets and space vehicles. It is hoped that work on applications such as these will help smooth the way and contribute in some measure to future efforts of this kind.

Cryogenic Engineering should also be useful to students who intend to specialize in cryogenics, since it consolidates in a single text information selected from numerous sources.

Historically speaking, the National Bureau of Standards was asked in 1950 to assist the Los Alamos Scientific Laboratory (operated for the U.S. Atomic Energy Commission by the University of California) on a major research project involving the application of low-temperature techniques. For this purpose the NBS Cryogenic Laboratory was established in Boulder, Colorado, starting actual operations in the spring of 1952. As far as is known this was the first major laboratory designed solely for research in cryogenic engineering.

During the course of the joint NBS–Los Alamos research project, scientists and engineers, experts in other fields, found it necessary to familiarize themselves with cryogenic processes and techniques. As the original assignment drew to a close, additional specialists came to the NBS Cryogenic Laboratory for advice and assistance on low-temperature problems. Noting the increasing need for a treatise on cryogenic engineering, M. G. Holloway (then with

v

the Los Alamos laboratory and now president, Nuclear Energy Products Division, ACF Industries, Inc.) urged its preparation. Earl A. Long, Director of the Institute of Metals, University of Chicago, and E. F. Hammel, Jr., of the Los Alamos laboratory supported Dr. Holloway's recommendation and made many valuable suggestions about the type of material to be included.

Since a treatise of this type is without precedent, the selection of material to be included constituted a major problem. In general, the material presented is that which is found to be most valuable in helping others with their cryogenic engineering problems and in carrying on daily operations of the laboratory. Another factor which influenced both the selection and arrangements of subject matter was the frequent requests by engineers new to the field for lists of references on low-temperature engineering. This indicated the probable value of including some background facts such as the review of gas liquefaction and separation processes.

The entire staff of the National Bureau of Standards Cryogenic Engineering Laboratory has assisted in one way or another in preparing this book for the Atomic Energy Commission. Of course, the scientific evaluations of the data herein contained are those of the author and his acknowledged contributors.

Advice of NBS staff members has been freely sought and generously given. The author has tried to give proper credit in the text for the unpublished and published data which they supplied. Any omissions are sincerely regretted.

The following staff members deserve special mention for their contributions: James A. Brennan for compiling most of the data on properties of fluids and structural materials, and Lewis J. Ericks for preparing most of the illustrations, charts, and graphs.

In addition, the author is indebted to the following for contributing original data and ideas, or for helping to edit and organize these data:

R. W. Arnett
Paul L. Barrick
B. W. Birmingham
William R. Bjorklund
Edmund H. Brown
William W. Bulla
Mahlon D. Bunch
Dudley B. Chelton
R. J. Corruccini
Marion M. Fulk
Thomas M. Flynn
Robert D. Goodwin
Robert B. Jacobs
Victor J. Johnson

J. E. Jensen (now with Brookhaven
    National Laboratory)
Richard H. Kropschot
R. M. McClintock
John Macinko
Douglas B. Mann
Kenneth B. Martin
Orlo E. Park
Robert L. Powell
Robert J. Richards
Alan F. Schmidt
Lynn E. Scott
K. D. Timmerhaus
Donald A. Van Gundy

P. C. Vander Arend (now with Air
   Products, Inc.)
Daniel H. Weitzel
William A. Wilson

W. T. Ziegler (part-time consultant to
   National Bureau of Standards, and
   Professor of Chemical Engineering,
   Georgia Institute of Technology)

Finally, acknowledgment is made of the very valuable editorial assistance of William E. Boardman of the Atomic Energy Commission's Technical Information Service, Industrial Information Branch.

Inquiries on and criticisms of this text are cordially invited. These will be of considerable value in planning future revisions.

Russell B. Scott

Boulder, Colorado
March 1959

CONTENTS

Chapter I

INTRODUCTION

1.1. Cryogenic engineering deals with the practical application of very low-temperature processes and techniques. These temperatures are below those usually encountered in refrigerating engineering.

It is rather difficult to assign a definite temperature which will serve as the dividing point between refrigerating and cryogenic engineering, but it will probably conform to present usage to say that cryogenic engineering is concerned with temperatures below $-150°$C. Another equally acceptable division is to assign to cryogenic engineering the temperature region reached by the liquefaction of gases whose critical temperatures are below terrestrial temperatures.

There is ample reason for treating cryogenics as a special field. The physical properties of materials at very low temperatures differ so drastically from those commonly encountered that the engineer cannot rely on his ordinary experience. The following examples illustrate this:

(a) *Some materials become very brittle at low temperatures.* This is true of carbon steel and of several other materials. Disastrous failures of engineering structures have been attributed to this cause. On the other hand, many non-ferrous metals and alloys such as aluminum, copper and nickel behave very well at low temperatures. Austenitic stainless steels are also good.

(b) *The heats of vaporization of low-boiling liquids are quite small.* Therefore such liquids can be preserved only in very well-insulated storage vessels. In the case of liquid helium the heat of vaporization is so small that it has very little cooling power. In cooling an apparatus to the temperature of liquid helium the experimenter usually relies on the heat capacity of the helium vapor to furnish the major part of the refrigeration required to cool his equipment.

(c) *The electrical resistances of pure metals are extremely small at low temperatures.* Some metals have zero resistance below a certain temperature—the phenomenon known as superconductivity. There have been some practical uses of superconductivity, and it seems probable that this striking phenomenon will continue to find applications.

1

Gas Liquefaction Facility, National Bureau of Standards Cryogenic Engineering Laboratory at Boulder, Colorado, houses equipment for producing large quantities of liquid nitrogen, hydrogen, and helium used in research in low-temperature engineering. Large roof ventilators completely change the air in the building every two minutes, preventing hazardous concentrations of gaseous hydrogen. Foothills of the Rocky Mountains are in the background.

(d) *The thermal conductivity of most pure metals and monocrystalline solids increases greatly at low temperatures* and has a maximum value which may be many times the room-temperature value. On the other hand, most alloys exhibit a progressive decrease of thermal conductivity with decreasing temperature. The thermal conductivity of all materials approaches zero as the absolute zero of temperature is approached.

(e) *The specific heats of all liquids and solids decrease with decreasing temperature* and become extremely small at very low temperatures.

(f) In all low temperature apparatus and equipment, proper insulation is of paramount importance, and since one of the best insulators is a vacuum, *high-vacuum techniques are of great importance in low-temperature technology.*

(g) When employing a high vacuum as insulation it often happens that nearly all the residual heat transfer is by thermal radiation across the insulating vacuum, so the *study and control of energy transfer by radiation is very important to the cryogenic engineer.*

(h) *Many practical thermometers are quite useless at very low temperatures.* For a great part of the temperature range commercial thermometers are not available; hence the low-temperatures investigator often has to provide his own thermometer and have means of calibrating it.

I. Advances in Cryogenic Technology

1.2. There have been two principal sources of advances in cryogenic technology: (1) laboratories employing low temperatures for basic studies in physics or chemistry and (2) suppliers of industrial gases. The developments contributed by the gas suppliers have been directed toward new cryogenic processes for separating and purifying gases and improving the over-all efficiencies of their plants in order to reduce the cost of the product. The research laboratories have been primarily concerned with convenient methods of producing the low temperatures needed in their experiments. In some instances, however, research workers have concentrated upon the development of commercial equipment for temperatures much lower than those of interest to the industrial gas suppliers. One of the most noteworthy recent accomplishments of this kind is the development, by S. C. Collins of the Massachusetts Institute of Technology, of the Collins Helium Cryostat (p. 68). This machine, now commercially available* constitutes a complete facility for the liquefaction of helium. It will also maintain temperatures at any desired level between room temperature and approximately 2°K.

II. Industrial Application of Cryogenics

1.3. By far the greatest industrial application of cryogenics is the separation of gases. Large-scale plants in which air is liquefied and the constituents separated by distillation have been in regular use for many years. Some plants produce more than 200 tons of gaseous oxygen per day for use in steel making. Large quantities of liquid oxygen and liquid nitrogen are being produced and shipped in insulated railroad tank cars. By processing very large amounts of air, sizable quantities of the rare-gas constituents neon, argon, krypton, and xenon are being separated and marketed. Pure helium gas, obtained from helium-bearing natural gas by a low-temperature separation process, is now a standard article of commerce, available in large quantities —subject to the regulations of the U.S. Bureau of Mines.

III. Cryogenics in Rocketry

1.4. A noteworthy example of a major use of cryogenics in a separate specialized field is in the science of rocketry. Liquid oxygen is extensively used as the oxidant in rocket research and was employed in the first practical long-range rocket, the German V-2. It seems probable that other cryogenic liquids may be useful as rocket fuels or oxidants.

IV. Engineering Research and Development at Low Temperatures

1.5. In 1952 the National Bureau of Standards, with financial support from the Atomic Energy Commission, established a laboratory at Boulder, Colorado,

* Manufactured by Arthur D. Little, Inc., Cambridge, Mass.

specifically designed for engineering research and development at low temperatures. The laboratory is equipped to make investigations at temperatures as low as 1°K. Research facilities occupy 21,500 square feet. The supporting liquefaction facility includes a liquid-nitrogen plant delivering about 450 liters per hour, a hydrogen liquefier producing 240 liters of liquid parahydrogen per hour, and a helium liquefier producing 15 liters per hour.

This laboratory has served not only the AEC but has helped the U.S. Army, Navy, and Air Force on projects involving low-temperature techniques.

In addition, the laboratory, in 1955, started its own long-range program of basic cryogenic engineering research with the broad objective of providing information of general usefulness in the field.

1.6. The selection of the material presented in this book is based partly upon the experience of this laboratory. The wide variety of problems encountered has indicated the type of information that may be expected to be most useful in the future. Also, several of the developments of the laboratory are described in some detail, since they illustrate methods and techniques that may be applied elsewhere.

Although the practical aspects of cryogenic processes and equipment are emphasized and detailed, an effort has been made to include the theoretical discussions that are required for proper understanding. A knowledge of basic physics, chemistry, and thermodynamics is assumed. An attempt has been made to select for consideration the most important and the most useful developments and to give detail on those features which seem likely to have other applications. Most attention is given to the latest developments because they utilize the most advanced techniques. The large number and generous detail of these descriptions are believed to be the most effective way of illustrating the practical application of cryogenic techniques and indicating the capabilities and limitations thereof. The chapter on the low-temperature properties of cryogenic fluids (pp. 268-321) includes a modest amount of handbook material for the convenience of the design engineer. The chapter on the properties of structural materials (pp. 322-352) also includes handbook material, but its principal objective is to present the outstanding characteristics of these materials at low temperatures and to list references which may be used in obtaining more complete information.

In selecting the handbook type of material to present the physical properties of materials of construction and cryogenic fluids, it has been necessary to exercise a strict selectivity in order to keep the material to a reasonable volume. For this reason the data presented on the physical properties of structural materials are usually restricted to those materials which at this time appear to have the greatest usefulness in low-temperature construction. In some instances the materials are simply those most likely to be available. Also data are given on the most-used cryogenic fluids. In every case an attempt is made to present the data in a readily usable form, convenient for rapid preliminary computation and estimates. Wherever necessary and feasible, these data are supplemented by equations which permit higher accuracy at the expense of additional computational effort. For example, vapor pressure–temperature relations are often presented both as tables and equations. A great amount of the data is presented in the form of graphs and charts. Where these yield acceptable accuracy, no supplementary material is given. Although an effort has been made to select reliable data, a critical review was not made. The data presented are not necessarily "best values." The cryogenic fluids whose properties are given greatest attention are limited to those most commonly used: air, oxygen, nitrogen, hydrogen, and helium.

While extensive references are given, there has been no attempt to prepare a complete bibliography. Wherever possible the references are to readily available literature. They are intended to indicate sources of additional information.

V. Summary

1.7. Throughout the preparation of this book an objective always considered was to present the necessary information in such a manner that an investigator with a new idea involving cryogenic techniques can assess the feasibility of his project and gain some idea about the difficulties that he should expect. Because *this book is intended primarily for the reader who is unfamiliar with low temperatures,* the treatment is deliberately elementary, but it is not trivial. It is believed that considerations of practical importance can be presented in language that is easily understood. There is little or no attempt to deal with either the esoteric concepts of modern cryogenic physics or the refinements that engineering practice has established in some disciplines used by cryogenists such as heat exchange, distillation, or adsorption. References to authoritative information on such subjects are given. The emphasis here is upon both basic and applied information most important in engineering research and development at low temperatures.

Since this treatise emphasizes the practical aspects of low-temperature technology, it is hoped that the information will be most useful to the design engineer who has the responsibility of making "practical" equipment work. Accordingly, suggestions, questions, criticisms, and comments are most earnestly solicited.

The units of measurement used in this book are those commonly employed by cryogenic research workers who received their training in physics or chemistry. There is an occasional incongruity; for example, gas volume given in cubic feet and liquid volume in liters. This and similar inconsistencies may be noted. This mixing of units by cryogenic workers probably came about because the investigators were used to the metric system and yet employed commercial equipment rated in British units, such as gas compressors rated in cubic feet per minute. Care has been exercised to avoid confusion or ambiguities from this source. American engineers, chemists, and physicists should not be unduly inconvenienced by the use of more than one system of units, because this is common practice. For example the common energy units employed by engineers include kilowatt-hours (partly metric), British thermal units, horsepower hours, and foot-pounds or foot-poundals, while the physicist or chemist uses ergs, calories, liter-atmospheres, and electron volts. Several tables of conversion factors are given in the appendix for the reader's convenience (see pp. 353-358).

Chapter II

LIQUEFACTION OF GASES

2.1. The liquefaction of any gas is accomplished by cooling it until its condensation temperature is reached and then removing the latent heat of vaporization. Thus the only basic requirement for gas liquefaction is suitable refrigeration; that is, a refrigerative process that is effective in removing heat from a sufficiently low temperature. As will presently be shown, if one could employ a perfect (ideal) refrigerating process without losses, the energy required for gas liquefaction would be much less than that for even the best existing liquefier. The reasons for this shortcoming of actual liquefiers are the inefficiencies of the practical refrigerative processes and the imperfections of methods of conserving refrigeration. Nearly all the complexities of modern gas liquefiers are principally concerned with practical methods for the efficient production and conservation of refrigeration.

It is planned in this chapter first to discuss the ideal liquefaction process and determine the least work required to liquefy a unit quantity of gas. Following this, there will be a brief discussion of air liquefiers to provide technical and historical background for the study of the liquefaction of hydrogen and helium. Practical liquefiers will be discussed first, starting with the relatively simple Hampson process and then taking up the various improvements and modifications which have increased the efficiency. The critical components which have the greatest influence on efficiency will be discussed, and some of the modern developments in this field will be described.

Historically, the first concern of cryogenics was the liquefaction of gases, and still today gas liquefaction is employed in nearly all processes requiring quite low temperatures. Thus the study of the liquefaction of gases constitutes not only a logical but also a very practical introduction to cryogenic engineering.

The liquefaction of air will be considered first because it offers the best opportunity for tracing the various developments and improvements which have occurred since the liquefaction of "permanent" gases was first accomplished. There has been a great amount of effort devoted to improving the efficiency and lowering the cost of producing liquid air because of its com-

7

mercial importance in the production of oxygen, nitrogen, and rare gases. Thus a study of air liquefaction processes will include and compare several practical liquefaction methods.

The present-day research worker in cryogenics is not, as a rule, concerned with the details of the design of air liquefiers, because he can either purchase a complete air liquefaction plant or buy liquid oxygen or nitrogen as required. Accordingly, there will be no attempt here to present very detailed descriptions of air liquefiers. The discussion will deal with general descriptions and basic principles, enlarging on those items which have a wider usefulness in liquefying other gases.

On the other hand, hydrogen and helium liquefiers will be described more thoroughly, because the user of these liquids is normally concerned with the design and operation of the liquefying equipment. The liquefaction of hydrogen was first achieved in 1898 and that of helium in 1908, but since there has been no extensive commercial demand for these liquids, their liquefaction is still essentially a laboratory process.

For a more detailed and comprehensive treatment of the liquefaction of gases, the reader is referred to two excellent review articles in the *Encyclopedia of Physics* (or *Handbuch der Physik*). The first, by Daunt [1], deals with the general subject of the production of low temperatures down to the temperature of liquid hydrogen. The second, by Collins [2], is principally concerned with helium liquefaction.

I. IDEAL GAS LIQUEFACTION PROCESS

2.2. It is obvious that the goal of perfection in gas liquefaction is to liquefy a unit quantity of gas with the least possible expenditure of energy. Since the liquefaction of a gas can be accomplished by refrigeration only, the theoretical optimum performance of a liquefier is that which would be attained by a thermodynamically reversible process. Such a process is indicated by the cycle shown on the temperature-entropy diagram, Figure 2.1. It is assumed that this is a continuous flow process. A gas entering at a certain initial pressure is compressed isothermally, the heat of compression being absorbed by a heat sink. The isothermal compression is followed by an isentropic expansion in which the work produced by the expansion engine is returned to help with the isothermal compression. The pressure is chosen to yield liquid after the expansion. The simple thermodynamic analysis is as follows:

The energy of a unit quantity of the gas entering the compressor is

$$h_1 = u_1 + p_1 v_1 \tag{2.1}$$

where h is the specific enthalpy, u the specific internal energy, p the pressure and v the specific volume.

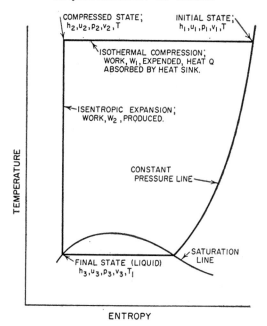

FIGURE 2.1. An ideal theoretical liquefaction process.

The energy of the unit quantity of gas leaving the compressor is

$$h_2 = u_2 + p_2 v_2 \qquad (2.2)$$

Therefore

$$h_2 - h_1 = W_1 - Q \qquad (2.3)$$

where W_1 is the work of compression and Q is the heat which flows into the heat sink.

For the isentropic expansion, similar reasoning shows that (since heat is neither added nor extracted)

$$h_2 - h_3 = W_2 \qquad (2.4)$$

where W_2 is the work supplied by the expansion engine.

Therefore

$$h_1 - h_3 = W_2 - W_1 + Q \qquad (2.5)$$

However $Q = T\Delta S$
where $\Delta S = S_1 - S_2$. Hence the net work $W = W_1 - W_2 = h_3 - h_1 + T\Delta S$
or

$$-W = \Delta h - T\Delta S \qquad (2.6)$$

This process bears little relation to that used in any liquefier thus far devised, not only because perfect isothermal compression and isentropic expansion are unattainable, but because a fantastically high pressure would be required to compress the gas to such a density that, after isentropic expansion, it would be converted completely to the liquid phase. The analysis is presented only to show the minimum theoretical work required for gas liquefaction.

TABLE 2.1.   THE ENERGY REQUIRED FOR THE LIQUEFACTION
OF SEVERAL GASES USING THE IDEAL, THERMODYNAMICALLY
REVERSIBLE PROCESS, $-W = \Delta h - T\Delta S$

Gas	Energy required for liquefaction starting with gas at 25°C (298.15°K) 1 atm		
	Joules per mole	Kilowatt-hours per kg	Kilowatt-hours per lb
Air	20,900	0.20	0.091
Nitrogen	21,400	0.21	0.096
Oxygen	20,300	0.18	0.080
Hydrogen	23,800	3.30	1.50
Helium	27,200	1.89	0.86

II. LIQUEFACTION OF AIR

2.3. Hampson Process. The Hampson process for liquefying air is illustrated schematically in Figure 2.2. Clean dry air at a pressure of 2000 to 3000 pounds per square inch enters the high-pressure passages of the counterflow heat exchanger, flows through the exchanger, and is expanded to approximately atmospheric pressure upon passing through the expansion valve. The Joule-Thomson cooling upon expansion causes a lowering of temperature, and the cool expanded air is constrained to pass back through the low-pressure passages of the heat exchanger, where it cools the incoming high-pressure stream. Thus the temperature at the valve is progressively lowered until the liquefaction temperature is reached.

The yield of the Hampson liquefier can readily be computed in terms of the thermal properties of the gas:

Let h_1 = specific enthalpy of high-pressure air at the inlet to the exchanger,

h_2 = specific enthalpy of high-pressure air just before expansion,

h_3 = specific enthalpy of the unliquefied part of the expanded air at the cold end of the process,

h_{liq} = specific enthalpy of the liquid,

x = fraction of total flow which is liquefied,

h_4 = specific enthalpy of the low-pressure air as it leaves the warm end of the heat exchanger.

If we neglect heat leaking in from the surroundings, the heat given up by the ingoing stream is received by the outgoing stream

$$h_1 - h_2 = (1 - x)(h_4 - h_3) \tag{2.7}$$

Since the steady-flow, throttling process is isenthalpic,

$$h_2 = x h_{\text{liq}} + (1 - x) h_3 \tag{2.8}$$

Substituting this value of h_2 in Equation 2.7, we obtain

$$x = \frac{h_4 - h_1}{h_4 - h_{\text{liq}}} \tag{2.9}$$

From the temperature-entropy diagram for air, Chapter 9, the values of enthalpy needed to evaluate Equation 2.9 can be obtained. It will be noted that h_4 must be greater than h_1; otherwise this process will not work. This is just another way of saying that the Joule-Thomson coefficient must have a positive value at the temperature and pressures existing at the warm end of the heat exchanger. It is worth noting that the fraction liquefied is independent of what happens below the top of the heat exchanger; as long as no heat or external work enters or leaves below this point, the fraction liquefied is determined solely by the specific enthalpies of the ingoing and outgoing streams of air and that of the liquid. Of course, the temperatures of the ingoing and outgoing streams can never be made exactly equal, and it will be seen later that in some cases the properties of the gases flowing in the

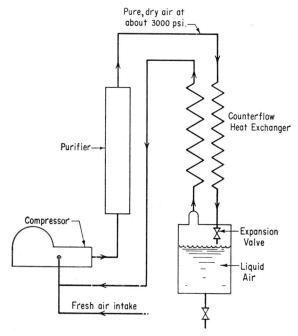

FIGURE 2.2. Schematic diagram of Hampson air liquefier.

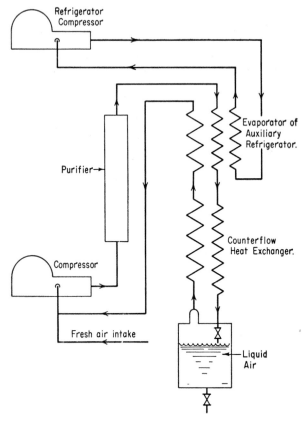

FIGURE 2.3. Hampson air liquefier with precooler.

heat exchanger are such that, no matter how perfect the heat exchanger, a large temperature difference at the top is inevitable. This latter difficulty, however, is not experienced in the air exchanger just described.

2.4. Precooling. The efficiency of the Hampson process can be improved by using a separate refrigerating system to lower the initial temperature of the air admitted to the heat exchanger in Figure 2.2. For example, a refrigerator using carbon dioxide, ammonia or Freon® can be inserted as illustrated in the flow diagram, Figure 2.3. This auxiliary refrigerator is inherently a more efficient heat pump than that represented by the primary air liquefaction cycle because condensation and evaporation processes are more nearly reversible than gas throttling processes. This preliminary refrigeration is, of course, usable in all liquefaction processes. The Joule-Thomson part of this process can again be evaluated by Equation 2.9, using values of enthalpy, h_1 and h_4, at the temperature and pressure at which the air enters the top of the final heat exchanger. It will be noted that lowering the temperature causes a substantial increase in the numerator of the right hand member of Equation 2.9 $(h_4 - h_1)$, and reduction of the denominator $(h_4 - h_{liq})$ and thus the fraction liquefied is considerably increased.

2.5. Linde High Pressure Process. A further advance in efficiency is represented by the Linde process, Figure 2.4, wherein most of the air circulated is expanded from 200 atmospheres down to about 40 atmospheres and then returned via heat exchangers to the compressor. Since the work of compression is approximately proportional to the logarithm of the pressure ratio, p_2/p_1, while the Joule-Thomson cooling is roughly proportional to the pressure difference, this process, by increasing p_1, produces refrigeration more cheaply than the Hampson process.

2.6. Claude Process. In the Claude liquefier a large part of the air is expanded in an engine which transfers the energy produced by the expansion out of the system. In the most efficient design, the energy produced by the expansion engine is used to help compress the incoming air. The energy thus removed from the expanding air represents extra refrigeration produced in the cycle. Figure 2.5 is a diagram of the essentials of the Claude process.

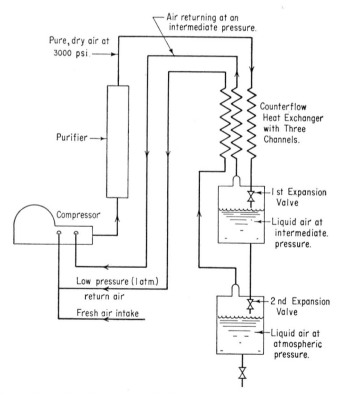

FIGURE 2.4. Schematic diagram of the Linde dual-pressure liquefaction system.

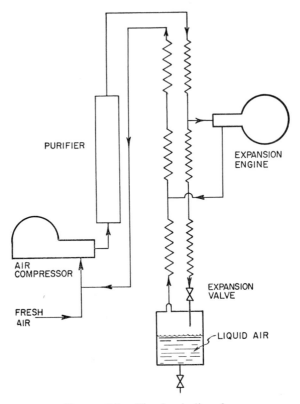

FIGURE 2.5.   Claude air liquefier.

Claude's expansion engine was of the reciprocating type, but more recently turbines have been used.   This process is one that can conceivably be made to approach the ideal reversible cycle because it utilizes an expansion engine which aims at an isentropic behavior.   If a sufficient number of expansion engines are used, the approach to thermodynamic reversibility is limited only by the imperfection of the engines and the losses caused by imperfect heat exchange and insulation.

2.7. Kapitza Air Liquefier.   In 1939 Kapitza [3] described a small air liquefier utilizing a turbine expander and regenerators which served the dual purpose of cooling and purifying the air.   In essence this is a variation of the Claude cycle, but because it introduced many innovations and included information unavailable elsewhere, it deserves a separate treatment.   The flow diagram of Kapitza's cycle is shown in Figure 2.6.   Air from the compressor at room temperature and a pressure of about 7 atmospheres enters the bottom of one of the two parallel regenerators, where it is progressively cooled and impurities (water and CO_2) are deposited on the cold surfaces of

the regenerator. After passing through the regenerator, the air is divided
into two streams. The major part of the air passes through the temperature
equalizer and then through the expansion turbine, where its temperature is
further reduced by doing work. (If the turbine were perfect this would be
an isentropic expansion.) The very cold air exhausted from the turbine at
a pressure a little above 1 atmosphere filters over the condensing coil into
which the remainder of the incoming high-pressure air has been routed. This
heat exchange results in the condensation of the 7-atmosphere air in the condensing coil and a warming of the low-pressure, turbine-exhaust air to near
the temperature at the cold end of the regenerator. The low-pressure air
then returns through the other regenerator cooling it. The air liquefied in
the condenser passes through the expansion valve, where its pressure is reduced to near atmospheric, resulting in a further decrease in temperature and
a little additional evaporation. After about 1 to 5 minutes of operation, the
reversing valve is operated so that the high-pressure and low-pressure streams
change regenerators. The functions of the regenerators are now apparent.
The incoming high-pressure impure air is cooled and its impurities are condensed on the surfaces of the first regenerator, while in the other regenerator
the pure cold low-pressure exhaust air is evaporating and removing impurities;

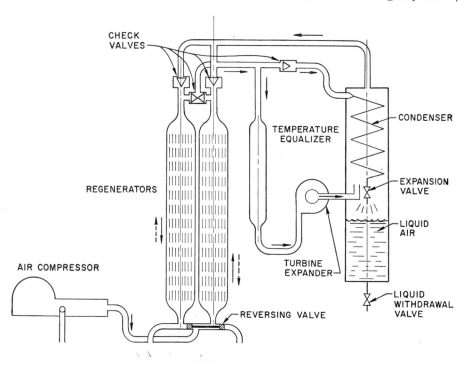

FIGURE 2.6. Kapitza air liquefier.

at the same time it is cooling the regenerator. The circumstance which allows this scheme to work is the fact that the impurities are being evaporated into a much greater volume of air than that from which they were deposited, because the return stream is at a lower pressure. In other words the partial pressures of the impurities are a greater fraction of the total pressure in the low-pressure exhaust air than they are in the incoming high-pressure air.

The temperature equalizer consists of a few kilograms of charcoal which adsorb or desorb air when there is a tendency for the temperature to fall or rise caused by reversing the regenerators. The high heat of adsorption of air on charcoal tends to maintain a constant temperature. The purpose of the equalizer is to keep the temperature of the air supplied to the turbine from rising to the value where it can carry an objectionable amount of CO_2, which could be deposited in the turbine nozzles and interfere with the operation.

2.8 Cascade Process. Before leaving the subject of air liquefaction, mention should be made of the cascade system wherein a series of liquids of progressively lower boiling points are condensed under pressure at the temperature produced by the evaporation of the next higher boiling liquid. Keesom [4] has proposed such a scheme for liquefying nitrogen and computes a

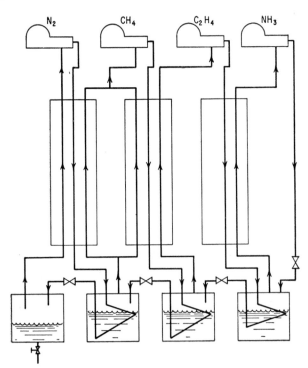

FIGURE 2.7. Keesom's cascade air liquefier.

"practical" power consumption much lower than that achieved by any of the preceding processes. Keesom's cascade is shown schematically in Figure 2.7. The refrigerants are ammonia, ethylene, and methane. The theoretical aspects of the cascade system are discussed by Ruhemann [5], and the conclusion is reached that it is "profitable, wherever possible to employ refrigerants near a state of saturation." Ball [6], at Los Alamos, described a partial cascade system for air liquefaction which employed two of the commercial Freon® refrigerants.

2.9. Performance of Air Liquefiers. Table 2.2 gives data on the performance of several air liquefaction systems.

TABLE 2.2. A COMPARISON OF AIR LIQUEFIERS

Air Liquefaction System	Work Required to Liquefy 1 lb, kwh	
Ideal reversible process	0.095	(Calculated)
Hampson or simple Linde process	1.3	(Observed) [5]
Hampson precooled to −45°C	0.7	(Observed) [5]
High-pressure Linde	0.8	(Observed) [5]
High-pressure Linde precooled to −45°C	0.4_5	(Observed) [5]
Claude	0.4_5	(Observed) [5]
Heylandt	0.4_2	(Observed) [5]
Los Alamos cascade (Ball)	0.41	(Observed) [6]
Cascade system of Keesom	0.2_7	(Calculated for N_2) [5]

III. CRITICAL COMPONENTS OF LIQUEFIERS

2.10. It was stated earlier that the fundamental requirement for gas liquefaction is a refrigerative process capable of removing heat from the gas until the liquefaction temperature is reached. In the quest for better liquefaction processes the principal goals are (1) the development of a refrigerator with the highest possible efficiency and (2) the design of equipment which will not waste the refrigeration that has been produced.

In the preceding pages the refrigerative processes have included the Joule-Thomson cooling in the Hampson liquefier, the improvement introduced by Linde which reduces the compressor power needed for a given amount of Joule-Thomson refrigeration, the cascade system in which gases are condensed by compressing them at a temperature realized by evaporating other liquids, and finally the expansion engine refrigerator which, in theory, can approach the isentropic expansion phase of the ideal reversible Carnot cycle. The equipment for conserving refrigeration has been exemplified by the counterflow heat exchangers and the regenerator used in the Kapitza liquefier. The other development which is concerned with conservation of refrigeration is the insulation which minimizes the flow of heat from the ambient to the cold parts of the liquefier. Insulation will be discussed in a later chapter. It is only necessary to remark here that, in an ordinary air liquefier, the amount of refrigeration produced is so great that the insulation would have to be poor indeed if it were to cause the loss of an appreciable fraction of the refrigeration. In the liquefaction of hydrogen and helium, insulation assumes an increasing importance.

Some of the devices which have been developed to improve the efficiency of air liquefaction may be applicable to other cryogenic processes; so, in the following few pages, descriptions are presented of some of the more successful practical developments as well as a very ingenious but as yet untried refrigerating device which seems to have promise of future usefulness. Although the gas compressor is actually a part of the refrigerative cycle and its efficiency has a direct influence on the over-all efficiency of a gas liquefier, it will not be considered here because compressors are not strictly cryogenic equipment. Compressor efficiencies can be found from the maker's specifications.

2.11. Heat Exchangers. The counterflow heat exchanger is one of the most important devices used in cryogenics. It constituted the final touch that permitted the continuous-flow liquefaction of the "permanent" gases. It now exists in a multitude of forms, but its purpose is always to transfer heat from one fluid stream to another and thus in cryogenic processes, to conserve "cold" by using the outgoing cold fluid to cool the incoming warm stream. If this can be done with negligible temperature differences and no appreciable resistance to flow, the process approaches thermodynamic reversibility. Thus the designer of a heat exchanger tries to provide large surface for heat flow and yet tries to avoid excessive pressure drop. These two objectives are actually somewhat opposed, because increasing the surface area, and thus enhancing the opportunity for heat exchange of a channel of given

FIGURE 2.8.   Giauque-Hampson heat exchanger.

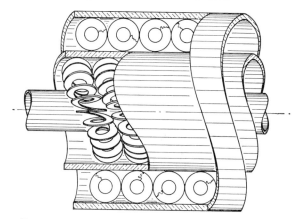

FIGURE 2.9. Heat exchanger designed by Collins.

cross section, also increases its resistance to flow. There is another practical consideration in heat-exchanger design; the heat capacity should be kept small. This reduces the time required to reach a steady thermal state.

Some Types of Heat Exchangers. It may be seen that there exists the possibility of almost infinite variation in heat-exchanger design. The form chosen depends upon several factors, among which are (1) the importance of avoiding pressure drop, (2) the need for low heat capacity, (3) the cost, (4) the pressures to be accommodated, and (5) the dimensions of the space available for the exchanger.

In the form used by Hampson the exchanger consisted of small copper tubes wound in a closely spaced coil. The high-pressure gas stream flowed in the tubes and the low-pressure stream filtered back outside the tubes through the interstices between the turns. Figure 2.8 is a photograph of a modern version of the Hampson heat exchanger, a design of W. F. Giauque of the University of California. Multiple-tube exchangers of rather similar design have been used in very large commercial installations. It is important in exchangers of this type to make the tube spacing quite uniform; otherwise the low-pressure return gas stream will tend to channel, that is, it will have a preferred path and will not be equally distributed over a cross section of the exchanger. This precaution is particularly important when the diameter of the exchanger is large.

One of the recent developments in heat exchangers is the design of S. C. Collins, Figure 2.9. It consists of several coaxial copper tubes, each closely wrapped with an edge-wound helix of copper ribbon. The helix is soft- soldered to the outside of the tube it surrounds and to the inside of the next outer tube. The helix thus greatly extends the surface for heat transfer and at the same time provides a lateral path for heat conduction. This heat-exchanger tubing is manufactured by the Joy Manufacturing Company of

Michigan City, Indiana, and is available with as many as three annular channels. The channels chosen for the ingoing and outgoing gas flows can be selected and combined to accommodate gas streams of different pressure and volumetric rate of flow.

A heat exchanger of good efficiency, low heat capacity, and relatively simple construction was described by Parkinson [7]. It consists of a number of helices (of small diameter and small pitch) of high-pressure copper tubing. These are wound as a multiple-thread helix on a central, poorly conducting thin-wall tube and are surrounded by a close-fitting sheath of low thermal conductivity as shown in Figure 2.10. The low-pressure counterflowing stream returns through the annular space bounded by the central tube and the outer sheath, and makes good contact with the high-pressure helices.

Heat exchangers have been made consisting of seven high-pressure tubes spaced inside the tube which constitutes the return passage of the low-pressure gas as shown in cross section in Figure 2.11. It will be noted that in this design all the surfaces contribute to heat exchange except the large-diameter outer tube. This will serve to illustrate a desirable objective in heat-exchanger design. Since all the surfaces bounding either gas stream cause frictional loss and thus contribute to the pressure drop, it is desirable to have them contribute also to heat exchange between the two streams, in order to have the most favorable ratio of heat-exchange efficiency to pressure drop. In the Hampson heat exchanger the thermally useless surface is the outer case.

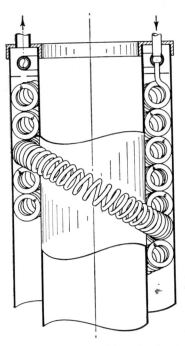

FIGURE 2.10. Parkinson's heat exchanger.

In the Collins exchanger the conducting helix provides thermal paths which make all the surfaces useful in heat exchange.

Determining Temperature Differences. Some general characteristics of counterflow heat exchangers can be derived by a simple application of the law of conservation of energy. If the exchanger is insulated so that losses to the surroundings may be neglected, the pressure drop in each channel is negligible, and the flow velocities are such that kinetic energies can be ignored, then the heat dq transferred in unit time from the warmer to the cooler stream in an element of the exchanger is

$$dq = m'c'dT' = m''c''dT'' \qquad (2.10)$$

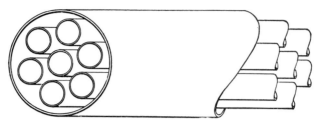

FIGURE 2.11. Multiple-tube heat exchanger.

where m is the mass rate of flow, c the specific heat at constant pressure, and T the temperature. Single primes denote the warmer stream and double primes the cooler. If the specific heats are independent of temperature,

$$m'c'T' = m''c''T'' + d \tag{2.11}$$

The temperature difference between the two streams is

$$\Delta T = T' - T'' = \left(1 - \frac{m'c'}{m''c''}\right) T' + d/m''c'' \tag{2.12}$$

where d is the constant of integration to be determined by the conditions existing for a specific application of this equation. If the heat capacity $m'c'$ of the warmer stream is greater than that of the cooler stream $m''c''$, the slope of the line ΔT versus T' will be negative; that is, ΔT will diminish as the temperature increases. This is the condition existing in the Hampson air liquefier. Since part of the air is condensed and removed as liquid, the heat capacity of the cold returning stream is less than that of the incoming stream. Thus in the Hampson liquefier the ΔT at the warm end can be made negligible if the heat exchanger is sufficiently large. However, if $m''c''$ is greater than $m'c'$, ΔT will increase at higher temperatures, and if $m''c'' = m'c'$, ΔT will not change.

When the specific heat of either stream varies, it is better to use the specific enthalpy h of the gas as given in temperature-entropy or Mollier diagrams. Thus, since $c\,dT = dh$, instead of Equation 2.10 we can write

$$dq = m'dh' = m''dh'' \tag{2.13}$$

and

$$m'h' = m''h'' + d \tag{2.14}$$

or

$$m'\Delta h' = m''\Delta h'' \tag{2.14a}$$

This relation is valid for any variation of specific heats and can be used to make a more detailed analysis of temperature differences along a counterflow heat exchanger when the specific heats of the fluid streams are changing.

It is recommended that the student of heat-exchanger design become thoroughly familiar with this concept because it is fundamental and is often the limiting factor in heat-exchanger efficiency, and the controlling consideration in selecting a liquefaction circuit. A practical application of Equation 2.14 is presented later in this chapter in discussing the liquefaction of helium. The usefulness of Equation 2.14 or its equivalent, 2.14a, can be illustrated graphically by plotting both $m'\Delta h'$ and $m''\Delta h''$ as ordinate with temperature as abscissa, as shown in Figure 2.12. Figure 2.12A illustrates the conditions usually encountered in the final exchanger of a Joule-Thomson liquefier, having a returning cold stream of much smaller mass rate of flow than that of the incoming warm stream. Figure 2.12B illustrates a difficult heat-exchanger situation. Here the specific heat of one of the streams has a temperature dependence such that large temperature differences are required at both ends of the exchanger in order to maintain a temperature difference in the center of the proper sign to transfer heat. By switching the gases of Figure 2.12B so that the cold stream consists of the gas which formerly occupied the warm channel, and vice versa, the very favorable situation illustrated by Figure 2.12C will result. Here the temperature difference is larger in the middle of the heat exchanger than it is at the ends.

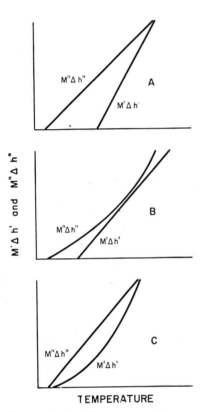

FIGURE 2.12. Three types of temperature distribution along a counterflow heat exchanger.

Heat Transfer Coefficient. In the analysis of heat exchangers an important concept is the heat transfer coefficient, here designated by the symbol U or u, and defined by Newton's differential equation of heat transfer.

$$dq = U\Delta T dA \qquad (2.15)$$

where dq is the element of heat transferred in unit time across an element of area dA when the temperature difference is ΔT. The capital U indicates the over-all coefficient, as from a fluid inside a pipe to another outside the pipe. The lower-case u is used to designate an individual coefficient, as between a fluid and a surface of a pipe. For a thin-wall tube, where the wetted areas inside and out may be considered equal, the over-all coefficient from the inside fluid to that outside may be obtained from the individual coefficients by the relation

$$1/U = 1/u_i + 1/u_w + 1/u_o \qquad (2.16)$$

where u_i is the heat-transfer coefficient between the wall and the inside fluid, u_o that between the wall and the outside fluid, and u_w the heat transfer coefficient through the tube wall; $u_w = $ (thermal conductivity)/(wall thickness). For thick tubes or finned tubes one must take account of the differences in areas wetted by the two fluids.

By substituting into Equation 2.15 the value of ΔT given by Equation 2.12, and integrating, it is found that

$$\ln \frac{\Delta T_w}{\Delta T_c} = \left(\frac{1}{m'c'} - \frac{1}{m''c''} \right) UA = \frac{1}{q_t} (\Delta T_w - \Delta T_c) UA \qquad (2.17)$$

or

$$q_t = \frac{(\Delta T_w - \Delta T_c) UA}{\ln (\Delta T_w / \Delta T_c)}, \qquad (2.17\text{a})$$

where A is the total area across which heat is transferred, ΔT_w the temperature difference at the warm end, ΔT_c that at the cold end, and q_t the total heat transferred per unit time; $q_t = m'c'(T'_w - T'_c) = m''c''(T''_w - T''_c)$.

If U varies markedly with temperature, the heat exchangers can be thought to consist of a number of exchangers in series, in each of which U is linear in temperature. Then for each such section

$$q_t = A \frac{U_c \Delta T_w - U_w \Delta T_c}{\ln (U_c \Delta T_w / U_w \Delta T_c)} \qquad (2.18)$$

The above discussion applies to parallel-flow or counterflow heat exchangers. There is a special case that is often of interest in low-temperature applications—that of constant temperature on one side of the exchanger, as, for example, when a gas is being cooled in a tube immersed in an evaporating liquid. In this case $m''c''$ may be considered infinite, since there can be no change in the temperature of the cold fluid; so Equation 2.17 becomes

$$\ln \frac{\Delta T_w}{\Delta T_c} = \frac{UA}{m'c'} = \frac{UA}{q_t} (T'_w - T'_c) \qquad (2.19)$$

Computing Heat-Transfer Coefficients and Pressure Drop. The computation of heat-transfer coefficients and pressure drop in actual heat exchangers is a complex subject. A large amount of data has been accumulated and empirical formulae, based upon the dimensional analysis of the experimental measurements have been developed. For a thorough treatment of the subject the reader is referred to texts by McAdams [8] and Jakob [9].

For convenience in making preliminary computations, two formulae from McAdams are given here together with auxiliary information needed for their application.

For turbulent flow* in a straight, smooth, cylindrical tube the heat-transfer coefficient between the fluid and the wall of the tube is given approximately by

$$\frac{uD}{k} = 0.023 \left(\frac{DG}{\mu}\right)^{0.8} \left(\frac{c_p\mu}{k}\right)^{0.4} \tag{2.20}$$

where the symbols have the following definitions:

u = coefficient of heat transfer between fluid and surface,
c_p = specific heat of fluid at constant pressure,
μ = viscosity of fluid,
G = mass velocity,
k = thermal conductivity of fluid,
D = diameter of tube.

The values of the physical properties of the fluid used in Equation 2.20 are those corresponding to the bulk temperature, that is, the mass-average temperature of a cross section of the passage. Any consistent system of units may be used in conjunction with Equation 2.20.

For gas passages of constant cross-section other than circular, it is possible to employ Equation 2.20 by substituting for D the quantity $4r_h$, where r_h is the hydraulic radius, defined as the cross-sectional area of the passage divided by the total wetted perimeter. By this means one can compute heat-transfer coefficients for such shapes as rectangular passages or annuli between coaxial tubes.

The pressure drop accompanying the turbulent flow of a gas in a tube is given by

$$p_1{}^2 - p_2{}^2 = 2RT_mG^2 \left[\ln\frac{v_2}{v_1} + \frac{f_mL}{2r_h}\right] \tag{2.21}$$

the symbols being defined as:

p = absolute pressure,
R = universal gas constant,
M = molecular weight,
T_m = mean temperature,

---

*The character of fluid flow in tubes depends upon several variables and may be predicted by determining the magnitude of the dimensionless number Re, the Reynolds number. (Re $= DG/\mu$) For values of Re greater than about 3000 the fluid flow is turbulent — the condition usually found in heat exchangers. The other type of flow, called laminar or viscous flow, is encountered at lower velocities or higher viscosities and is very regular in pattern, the velocity increasing monotonically from a value zero at the wall of the tube to a maximum velocity at the center. No eddies or vortices which would introduce a transverse velocity component are present.

G = mass velocity,
v = specific volume,
f_m = mean value of friction factor, dimensionless,
L = length of straight tube,
r_h = hydraulic radius.

Subscript 1 refers to the upstream end of the tube and subscript 2 to the downstream end.

The friction factor f can be computed from the empirical equation

$$f = 0.00140 + 0.125/\text{Re}^{0.32} \qquad (2.22)$$

If f varies appreciably, a mean value f_m may be used in Equation 2.21. The Reynolds number $\text{Re} = DG/\mu$, where D is the diameter of the tube and μ is the viscosity. Again any consistent system of units may be used. Table 2.3 lists three sets of units which can be properly used in Equations 2.20 and 2.21.

TABLE 2.3. UNITS COMMONLY USED FOR THE QUANTITIES
APPEARING IN EQUATIONS 2.20 AND 2.21

Quantity	Cgs System	British Units Commonly Used for Heat Transfer	British Units Commonly Used for Fluid Flow
u	watts cm$^{-2\circ}$ K^{-1}	Btu hr^{-1} ft^{-2} $^\circ$R^{-1}	—
D	cm	ft	ft
k	watt cm$^{-1\circ}$ K^{-1}	Btu hr^{-1} ft^{-1} $^\circ$R^{-1}	—
G	g sec^{-1} cm^{-2}	lb hr^{-1} ft^{-2}	lb sec^{-1} ft^{-2}
c_p	Joules g^{-1} $^\circ$K^{-1}	Btu lb^{-1} $^\circ$R^{-1}	—
μ	poises	lb hr^{-1} ft^{-1} = 242 $\times$ (μ in poises)	lb sec^{-1} ft^{-1} = 0.0672 $\times$ (μ in poises) poundals ft^{-2}
p	dynes cm^{-2}, or microbars	—	—
T_m	$^\circ$K	$^\circ$R	$^\circ$R
v	cm^3 g^{-1}	—	ft^3 lb^{-1}
R	ergs g^{-1} $^\circ$K^{-1}	—	ft-poundals lb^{-1} $^\circ$R^{-1}
L	cm	—	ft
r_h	cm	—	ft

The following example will serve to illustrate some of the procedures for analyzing heat exchangers:

PROBLEM

The coaxial-tube heat exchanger illustrated in Figure 2.13 is used with gaseous hydrogen in counterflow. Stream 1, 1 lb per minute at 5 atmospheres and 68°F, enters the central tube at the top end and leaves at −100°F at the bottom. Stream 2, 0.8 lb per minute, enters the annulus at the bottom end at 1.5 atmospheres.

(1) What is the pressure at the exit of stream 1?

(2) What are the entering and exit temperatures of stream 2?

Assume that hydrogen behaves as an ideal gas and that the following properties are constant for this temperature range:

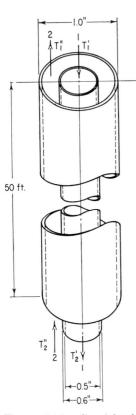

Viscosity $= 8 \times 10^{-3}$ centipoise,

Specific heat $c = 3.5$ Btu lb^{-1} deg F^{-1},

Thermal conductivity $k = 0.009$ Btu hr^{-1} ft^{-1} deg F^{-1}.

The molecular weight M of hydrogen is 2.016. (One pound-molecular weight of an ideal gas occupies 359 ft^3 at 32°F, 491.7°R.) Assume zero transverse thermal resistance in the inner tube and perfect insulation surrounding the outer tube. Assume also that heat is not conducted along the tubes.

SOLUTION

(a) The temperature change in stream 2 can be determined immediately from Equation 2.11. Since the specific heat is constant,

$$m'c(T_1' - T_2') = m''c(T_1'' - T_2''),$$

$$c(68 + 100) = 0.8c(T_1'' - T_2''), \text{ and}$$

$$T_1'' - T_2'' = 168/0.8 = 210 \text{ degrees.}$$

(b) The pressure at the exit of the central tube may be determined from Equation 2.21.

$$D = \tfrac{1}{24} \text{ ft,}$$

$$G = 12.2 \text{ lb sec}^{-1} \text{ ft}^{-2},$$

$$\mu = 6.72 \times 10^{-4} \times 8 \times 10^{-3} = 5.37 \times 10^{-6},$$

$$\text{Re} = DG/\mu = 0.95 \times 10^5,$$

$$R = 49720/M = 24663 \text{ ft poundals lb}^{-1} \text{ °R}^{-1},$$

$$p_1 = 5 \times 14.7 \times 32.17 \times 144 = 34 \times 10^4$$
$$\text{poundals ft}^{-2},$$

FIGURE 2.13. Coaxial-tube heat exchanger.

$$T_m = (460 + 68 + 460 - 100)/2 = 444°R$$

$$V_1 = \frac{359}{M} \times \frac{1}{5} \times \frac{460 - 68}{492} = 38.3 \text{ ft}^3 \text{ lb}^{-1},$$

$$V_2 = \frac{359}{M} \times \frac{1}{5} \times \frac{460 - 100}{492} = 26.2 \text{ ft}^3 \text{ lb}^{-1},$$

$$f_m = 0.00140 + \frac{0.125}{(0.95 \times 10^5)^{0.32}} = 0.0042,$$

$$L = 50 \text{ ft,}$$

$$r_h = D/4 = \tfrac{1}{96} \text{ ft.}$$

Substituting these values in Equation 2.21, $p_2 = 29 \times 10^4$ poundals ft^{-2} = 4.26 atmospheres. A more exact solution could be achieved now by using this value of p_2 to compute an improved value of V_2. However, in this case the final result will not be changed substantially. In some cases, however, successive approximations of this kind will be necessary.

(c) The heat transfer coefficient between stream 1 and the central tube can be determined from Equation 2.20.

$c = 3.5$ Btu lb^{-1} deg F^{-1},

$\mu = 2.42 \times 8 \times 10^{-3} = 19.4 \times 10^{-3}$,

$G = 44000$ lb hr^{-1} ft^{-2},

$k = 0.09$ Btu hr^{-1} ft^{-1} deg F^{-1},

$D = \frac{1}{24}$ ft.

With these values Equation 2.20 gives

$$u_c = 425 \text{ Btu hr}^{-1} \text{ ft}^{-2} \text{ deg F}^{-1}$$

(d) For computing the heat transfer coefficient of the annulus, the same values are used with the exception of G and D.

$$G = 13{,}750 \text{ lb hr}^{-1} \text{ ft}^{-2}$$

and for D we use $4r_h$. Since in this case the area for heat transfer is just the surface of the inner tube,

$r_h = \dfrac{\pi}{4 \times 12^2} (1 - 0.6^2)/\pi \times \dfrac{0.6}{12}$,

$r_h = 0.0222$,

$u_a = 144$ Btu hr^{-1} ft^{-2} deg F^{-1}.

(e) The over-all coefficient U can be obtained from Equation 2.16, but since the area of the outside of the central tube is 1.2 times that of the inner we need to refer the over-all coefficient to a specific surface. Either surface will do, so the inside will be chosen. Accordingly, the value of u_a should be raised by a factor of 1.2 so that it will correspond to a square foot of inner surface. Then

$1/U = 1/u_c + 1/1.2u_a$,

$U = 123$ Btu hr^{-1} ft^{-2} deg F^{-1}.

(f) The temperature differences between the two streams may now be computed from Equation 2.17.

$$m'c' = 60 \times 3.5 = 210 \text{ Btu hr}^{-1} \text{ deg F}^{-1},$$

$$m''c'' = 48 \times 3.5 = 168 \text{ Btu hr}^{-1} \text{ deg F}^{-1},$$

$$A = \pi DL = \pi 50/24 = 6.55 \text{ ft}^2,$$

$$q_t = 210 \times 168 = 35300 \text{ Btu hr}^{-1},$$

$$\ln \frac{\Delta T_w}{\Delta T_c} = \left(\frac{1}{m'c'} - \frac{1}{m''c''} \right) UA,$$

$$\ln \frac{\Delta T_w}{\Delta T_c} = -.959,$$

$$\frac{\Delta T_w}{\Delta T_c} = 0.383,$$

$$\ln \frac{\Delta T_w}{\Delta T_c} = \frac{1}{q_t} (\Delta T_w - \Delta T_c) UA,$$

$$(\Delta T_c - \Delta T_w) = 42.0°\text{F},$$

$$\Delta T_c - .383 \Delta T_c = 42.0°\text{F},$$

$$\Delta T_c = 68.0°\text{F},$$

$$\Delta T_w = 26.0°\text{F}.$$

So $T_2'' = -168°\text{F}$, and $T_1'' = 42°\text{F}$.

Reversing Heat Exchangers. The reversing heat exchanger was developed by Collins [10] for use in airborne oxygen plants. As in other counterflow exchangers, the reversing exchanger has at least two channels that are in good thermal contact with each other. These two channels are very similar as to surface area and resistance to flow. Incoming gas (air in Collins' machine) flows from the warm to the cold end in one channel, while waste gas flows in the opposite direction in the other. Collins used the finned-tube heat exchangers of his own design described earlier. The two inner annuli constituted the channel for one stream of gas and the outer annulus, of cross section equal to the sum of the two inner annuli, carried the counterflow stream. By means of appropriate valves these two streams are caused to exchange channels every few minutes. During one half-cycle the surfaces of the channel carrying the incoming air become coated with liquid water, ice, and finally, at the cold end, solid carbon dioxide. During the next half-cycle these impurities are evaporated into the outgoing relatively pure gas which being at a lower pressure, has a much greater volume rate of flow. It is seen that the reversing heat exchanger performs functions similar to those of the regenerators previously described. In the reversing exchanger, however, there is no necessity for a packing of high heat capacity to store heat and refrigeration. Also it is possible to provide a third channel which may carry a pure gas continuously in one direction. This is sometimes done in an air separation plant which delivers pure oxygen in the gaseous state. Also the third channel may be used to supply refrigeration from an independent source to a gas liquefaction system.

2.12. Regenerators. The regenerator, or cold accumulator, introduced by Fränkl in 1928, was an important advance in large-scale gas liquefaction and separation. In principle it is very similar to the "stove," "oven," or "checker chamber" used with blast furnaces, in which heat from waste gases is accumulated by a checkerwork of bricks during one part of the cycle and then utilized in the other phase to heat the air supplied to the furnace.

The applications of regenerators for gas liquefaction was briefly mentioned in connection with the description of Kapitza's air liquefier. A better understanding of the operation may be gained by reference to Figure 2.14. Warm,

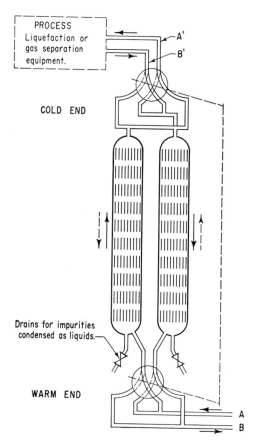

FIGURE 2.14. Regenerator for cooling and purifying air for liquefaction.

impure gas enters at A, is directed to the proper regenerator by the reversing valve I and is cooled by, and deposits its impurities upon, the cold surfaces of the packing of the regenerator. At valve II the cold, pure gas, A′, is directed to the correct channel of the processing device (e.g., a liquefier or gas separation column). The return cold stream B′ is directed by valve II to pass back through the other regenerator, cooling it and picking up and removing impurities which had been deposited earlier. It will be noted that the attitude of the regenerators is such that a readily condensible impurity such as water or oil vapor can condense and flow by gravity to the drains. If impurities condensed as liquids were allowed to flow to colder parts of the regenerator, there would be danger of their freezing and blocking the system.

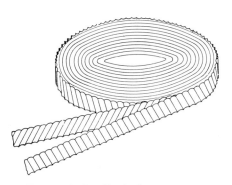

FIGURE 2.15. Typical regenerator packing.

The requirements for an effective regenerator are: (1) a large surface exposed to the gas, (2) a high heat capacity, (3) easy transfer of heat between the regenerator and the gas being circulated and (4) low resistance to flow of gas. The regenerators are usually packed with pancakes wound from thin corrugated aluminum ribbon 0.2 to 0.4 mm thick (Figure 2.15). The corrugations are 1.5 to 3.0 mm deep and slant in opposite directions on adjacent ribbons. Kapitza used alternately smooth ribbons and ribbons with small dimples punched at regular intervals.

Ruhemann [5] lists the following as very important advantages of alternating regenerators as compared with ordinary heat exchangers:

"1. They are relatively cheap and easy to manufacture.
2. They enable a very large surface to be concentrated into a small volume. Most regenerators have a surface of 1,000 to 2,000 sq. ft. per cu. ft.
3. Suitably designed regenerators have a low hydraulic resistance and thus allow the passage of large quantities of gas with a very small loss in pressure.
4. Regenerators allow some impurities to be deposited by the warm stream in one period and to be reevaporated by the cold gas in the other period. Thus eliminating the need for chemical purification in certain cases."

On the other hand Ruhemann points out certain inherent disadvantages of regenerators. First, since the regenerator contains a rather large volume of gas, the ingoing stream is periodically mixed with what was formerly the outgoing stream at the moment of reversal. This is objectionable in gas separation plants. Also satisfactory operation requires that there be approximately the same amount of gas in each stream and that there be not a great difference in temperature between the two streams. He sums up by saying that "regenerators are eminently suitable for the exchange of heat between two large and similar gas streams; conditions which occur very frequently in practice. They are not suitable when the streams are very dissimilar, either as regards pressure, temperature or rate of flow."

There is a further characteristic of regenerators which may limit their usefulness at very low temperatures; that is the heat capacity requirement. Since the specific heats of all metals become exceedingly small at quite low temperatures, while the heat capacities of most gases are nearly constant, the heat capacity of the regenerator packing may be too little to store the required heat. It may be argued that this shortcoming can be circumvented simply by shortening the cycle, reversing more often. This, however, is undesirable, because there is a loss attendant upon each reversal. It is best to maintain a reasonably long period. For use at very low temperatures it would help to pack the regenerators with a metal having a low Debye characteristic temperature, and accordingly, a higher heat capacity at low temperature. Lead is one of the best materials in this respect.

Ruhemann's requirement that the two gas streams be of comparable pressure seems to this writer subject to question. If the pressure drop in the low-pressure return gas stream (the gas being warmed) can be kept at an acceptable value, there is a distinct advantage in keeping the pressure of the return stream as low as is practical. The lower the pressure, and accordingly the greater the volume of the return stream, the more readily impurities are evaporated and removed from the surfaces of the regenerator packing. A low-pressure return stream, therefore, is an important factor in the purifying function of the regenerator.

2.13. Reciprocating Expansion-Engine Refrigerator. This device was introduced by Claude. In principle it is simply a reciprocating piston-and-cylinder engine similar to the steam engine which has been in use for over a century. The most difficult practical problem is that of providing lubrication that will remain effective at the low operating temperatures. Claude's first solution was the use of light hydrocarbons which remained fluid at the engine temperatures. More recently engines have been designed with pistons or piston rings made of special materials which operate unlubricated with little friction and little wear. Expansion engines used in the helium separation plants of the U.S. Bureau of Mines use plastic rings (Micarta®). Collins [11] described a liquid nitrogen generator which utilizes an air expansion engine with a Micarta® piston sleeve operating in a chromium-plated bronze cylinder. The Collins Helium Cryostat [12], which will be described later, uses expansion engines having cylinder and pistons of nitrided steel. It seems that in such engines the gas itself is the lubricant, a very thin layer of gas being always between the piston and cylinder during operation. Collins states that for air expansion machines, the chromium-plated-bronze–plastic combination is preferable to the nitrided steel cylinder-piston assemblies.

Not only is the former easier to manufacture but it is also less vulnerable to seizure from solid foreign matter. The efficiency of the Collins air engine is approximately 85 percent and was not diminished after several thousand hours of operation. Figure 2.16 shows the piston and cylinder of the Collins air engine. More recently Collins has constructed expansion engines with pistons which present a surface of laminated leather disks to contact the walls of the cylinder.

The thermodynamic analysis of the steam engine can be applied to the reciprocating expansion engine. Figure 2.17 shows a schematic representation of an expansion engine together with a parallel pressure-volume diagram which illustrates the events in both the ideal reversible process shown by solid lines, and a practical cycle shown by dashed lines.

In the ideal cycle the inlet valve opens instantaneously and completely at a and remains open while gas at the pressure p_i enters and the piston moves until the volume of gas indicated at b has entered the cylinder. Then the inlet valve closes and the gas undergoes an isentropic expansion bc as the piston moves to its extreme right-hand position. At c the exhaust valve opens and the gas is expelled at a constant pressure p_e. At d the exhaust valve closes and the gas remaining in the cylinder suffers an isentropic compression just sufficient to bring the pressure up to p_i as the piston reaches the extreme left of its excursion, completing the cycle. The work delivered

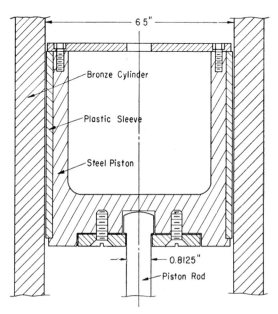

6 5"

Bronze Cylinder

Plastic Sleeve

Steel Piston

0.8125"

Piston Rod

FIGURE 2.16. Piston and cylinder of Collins' air expansion engine.

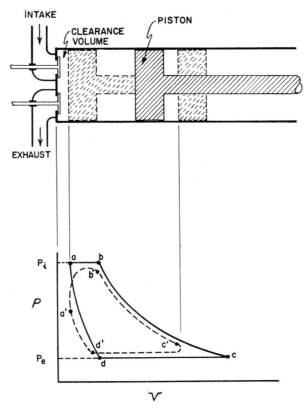

FIGURE 2.17. An illustration of the behavior of an ideal and a practical reciprocating expansion engine by means of a pressure-volume or "indicator" diagram.

during this cycle is represented by the area enclosed in the figure *abcd*. Since all the processes are reversible the thermodynamic efficiency is unity.

In an actual engine the pressure-volume relations are somewhat like those indicated by the dashed curve, where *a'b'c'* and *d'* again indicate the opening and closing of the valves. The practical cycle differs from the ideal cycle because (1) valves do not open and close instantaneously, (2) an irreversible pressure drop accompanies the flow of gas into and out of the engine, (3) there is an irreversible flow of heat between the gas and the walls of the cylinder, and (4) there is friction between the piston and the cylinder walls. These effects make it advisable to shorten the stroke and open the exhaust valve at *c'* rather than at *c* because the extra piston travel from *c'* to *c* accomplishes little net work and yet adds to the piston friction and heat flow between the cylinder and the gas. In fact the optimum pattern of valve action can best be determined by trial, so some of the more successful expansion engines have provision for adjusting the timing of the phases of the valve action. In some cases such adjustments can be made while the engine is running. Efficiencies as high as 85 percent of the ideal have been reported.

For the steady-flow operation of such an engine the work delivered can be computed as follows:

Let u, p, v, and h represent the specific internal energy, pressure, specific volume, and specific enthalpy respectively. Denote the ingoing gas by the subscript i and the exhaust gas by subscript e. Assume that the engine is thermally insulated and that kinetic energy of the gas can be neglected. Then the total energy entering with a unit quantity of gas is

$$u_i + p_i v_i = h_i$$

Likewise the total energy carried out by this unit quantity of gas is

$$u_e + p_e v_e = h_e$$

Since the system is thermally insulated, the law of conservation of energy requires that

$$h_i - h_e = W$$

the work delivered to the exterior by the engine. By reference to a temperature-entropy diagram for the gas being expanded, the expected temperature drop can be estimated.

2.14. Expansion Turbine. In 1934 Linde [13] published an article on the use of expansion turbines for cooling. Later Kapitza [14] published a thorough theoretical study of the application of the expansion turbine to the liquefaction of air. His analysis and subsequent development produced a radial-inflow, or centripetal, turbine having an efficiency of over 80 percent of theoretical. One of the arguments he presented in favor of the radial-inflow turbine for air liquefaction was that air, at the temperature and pressure existing in such an expansion turbine, had characteristics more like water than like steam, so the turbine should have some attributes similar to those of the very efficient modern water turbines. Kapitza's success was followed by further development, e.g., that described by Swearingen [15], so that today the radial-inflow expansion turbine is in regular use for air liquefaction.

Figure 2.18 is a diagram of a centripetal turbine: a cross section perpendicular to the axis. Gas enters at the inlet, is accelerated and directed by the turbine nozzles, and then enters the rotor passages with a high tangential velocity and a small radial velocity. As the gas passes through the rotor, its kinetic energy is transmitted to the rotor and it leaves with negligible velocity. Also, during its passage through the rotor, the gas is subjected to a strong centrifugal force; so it experiences an additional expansion as it traverses the diminishing centrifugal force field. The energy of this expansion also is transmitted to the rotor.

Let p, v, u, and T designate the pressure, molar volume, molar internal

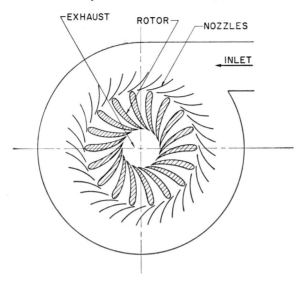

FIGURE 2.18. Schematic diagram of a radial-inflow or centripetal turbine. This is a cross section through the housing, nozzles, and blades, perpendicular to the axis of the shaft.

energy, and absolute temperature, respectively, of the gas. Let the subscript 1 refer to the entering high pressure gas, subscript 2 to the gas as it enters the rotor, and subscript 3 to the exhaust gas as it leaves the center of the rotor. Assume no losses. Assume also that this is a "zero angle" turbine—that the gas enters the rotor almost tangentially. This, of course, is an idealized case; if the inlet angle were really zero there would be zero radial velocity and no gas would pass through the turbine. However, the angle can be such that the radial velocity is as much as 10 percent of the tangential velocity without seriously departing from the characteristics of the zero-angle turbine. The tangential component of velocity will, even in this practical case, still be 99 percent of the total velocity.

For one mole of gas passing through the nozzles, the specific energy entering the nozzles can be equated to that leaving.

Entering:

(1) u_1 = internal energy entering with one mole,

(2) p_1v_1 = work done to inject one mole.

Leaving:

(3) u_2 = internal energy leaving with one mole,

(4) p_2v_2 = work done to expel one mole,

(5) $MV^2/2$ = kinetic energy of one mole, where M is the molecular weight of the gas and V its velocity as it leaves the nozzles.

Then
$$u_1 + p_1v_1 = u_2 + p_2v_2 + MV^2/2 \tag{2.23}$$

or since $h = u + pv$,
$$h_1 - h_2 = MV^2/2 \tag{2.24}$$

and, since $\Delta h = C_p \Delta T$,
$$C_p(T_1 - T_2) = MV^2/2 \tag{2.25}$$

where $h = u + pv$ is the molar enthalpy of the gas and C_p is the molar specific heat at constant pressure.

The energy relations of the gas passing through the rotor can be treated in a similar fashion.

Entering:

(1) u_2 = internal energy entering with one mole,

(2) p_2v_2 = work to inject one mole,

(3) $MV^2/2$ = kinetic energy entering with one mole.

Leaving:

(4) u_3 = internal energy leaving with one mole,

(5) p_3v_3 = work to expel one mole,

(6) $MV^2/2$ = kinetic energy of the gas which is absorbed by the rotor and transmitted to the shaft,

(7) $MV^2/2*$ = work done by the gas against the radial centrifugal force (also transmitted to the shaft).

Then $u_2 + p_2v_2 + MV^2/2 = u_3 + p_3v_3 + MV^2$, so
$$h_2 - h_3 = MV^2/2$$

or
$$C_p(T_2 - T_3) = MV^2/2 \tag{2.26}$$

Thus it is seen that the enthalpy change that occurs in the nozzles is the same as that accompanying the expansion in the rotor, and the total energy absorbed from one mole of gas is $C_p(T_1 - T_3) = MV^2$.

It should be noted that this centripetal turbine is similar to a reaction turbine; however, high velocities of the gas relative to the rotor passages are avoided because the exit ends of the rotor passages are near the axis and hence they are moving at a velocity much less than the peripheral velocity. In a reaction turbine the gas enters the moving blades with little relative velocity and is discharged in a backwards direction with a relative velocity

---

* The centrifugal force on a mole at radial distance r is $MV^2/r = M\omega^2 r$ where ω is the angular velocity of the rotor.   Then the work

$$W = \int f\,dx = \int_{r_1}^{r_2} M\omega^2 r\,dr = \tfrac{1}{2}M\omega^2(r_2{}^2 - r_1{}^2)$$

where r_1 and r_2 are the inner and outer radii of the rotor blades.   When $r_1 \ll r_2$, $W \cong \tfrac{1}{2}M\omega^2 r_2{}^2 = MV^2/2$.

equal to the forward velocity of the blades, so that its absolute exhaust velocity is practically zero.

The characteristic behavior of a loss-free reaction turbine having sonic* gas velocity at the nozzles ($V = V_c$) can be computed from well-known thermodynamic relations. These relations are:

$$pv^\gamma = \text{constant} \tag{2.27}$$

where $\gamma = C_p/C_v$, the ratio of the specific heat at constant pressure to that at constant volume;

$$pv = RT \tag{2.28}$$

$$V_c^2 = \frac{\gamma p_2 v_2}{M} \tag{2.29}$$

(V_c is the velocity of sound)

and Equations 2.25 and 2.26,

$$C_p(T_1 - T_2) = C_p(T_2 - T_3) = \frac{M V_c^2}{2} \tag{2.30}$$

From 2.27

$$\frac{p_1}{p_2} = \left(\frac{v_2}{v_1}\right)^\gamma \tag{2.31}$$

From 2.28

$$\frac{v_1}{v_2} = \frac{p_2}{p_1}\frac{T_1}{T_2} \tag{2.32}$$

Substituting 2.32 in 2.31 we have

$$\frac{p_1}{p_2} = \left[\frac{T_1}{T_2}\right]^{\gamma/(\gamma-1)} \tag{2.33}$$

Similarly

$$\frac{p_1}{p_3} = \left[\frac{T_1}{T_3}\right]^{\gamma/(\gamma-1)} \tag{2.34}$$

From Equations 2.28, 2.29, and 2.30

$$\frac{T_1}{T_2} - 1 = 1 - \frac{T_3}{T_2} = \frac{\gamma R}{2C_p} \tag{2.35}$$

$$\frac{T_1}{T_3} = \frac{1 + \gamma R/2C_p}{1 - \gamma R/2C_p} \tag{2.36}$$

For monatomic gases $\gamma = \frac{5}{3}$ and $C_p = \frac{5}{2}R$, so

$$\frac{T_1}{T_3} = 2 \quad \text{and} \quad \frac{p_1}{p_3} = 2^{\gamma/(\gamma-1)} = 5.64$$

For diatomic gases $\gamma = \frac{7}{5}$ and $C_p = \frac{7}{2}R$, so

$$\frac{T_1}{T_3} = 1.5 \quad \text{and} \quad \frac{p_1}{p_3} = (1.5)^{\gamma/(\gamma-1)} = 4.13$$

* Sonic velocity is chosen because it is the upper limit for normal design. Supersonic design introduces additional complexities and probable losses.

As a practical example consider a nitrogen expansion turbine operating at inlet conditions $T_1 = 120°K$, $p_1 = 6$ atm. Then $T_3 = 80°K$ and $p_3 = 1.45$ atm. From Equation 2.35

$$\frac{T_1}{T_2} = 1 + \frac{\gamma R}{2C_p} = \frac{6}{5}$$

so $T_2 = 100°K$. From Equation 2.30

$$V_c^2 = \frac{2C_p}{M} (T_1 - T_2)$$

and

$$V_c = 2.04 \times 10^4 \text{ cm/sec}$$

V_c is also the peripheral speed of the rotor.

This is a fair approximation of what may be expected of such a turbine. Of course the performance of an actual turbine is somewhat different because the losses tend to increase the pressure drop and reduce the temperature drop. Since excessive speed is a disadvantage of the expansion turbine it should be noted that the speed may be reduced by (1) using a heavy gas, (2) operating at a low temperature. The lower temperature may offset the disadvantage of a lighter gas. For example, a sonic expansion turbine using helium at an inlet temperature of 15°K would have a somewhat lower peripheral speed than the nitrogen turbine just analyzed. Of course another way to reduce speed is to provide a multistage turbine in which several rotors and sets of nozzles share the pressure drop in a series arrangement.

This discussion is intended only to give some idea of the physics and thermodynamics of expansion turbines. It is greatly oversimplified because a sophisticated turbine analysis is very complex. For example, a great variety of inlet and exit angles and blade shapes are possible which still yield good efficiencies. Also the velocity at which the gas leaves the rotor blades can be quite large, provided the accompanying pressure is sufficiently low; the excess kinetic energy is utilized in a diffuser which raises the pressure up to the exit pressure of the turbine in a process which approaches an isentropic one.

2.15. Roebuck's Refrigerating Device. In 1945 J. R. Roebuck [16] proposed a new type of refrigerator which has, in theory, some very desirable characteristics, although as yet a working model has not been developed. Because of its interesting and promising aspects a brief description is given.

The principle of operation may be understood by reference to Figure **2.19** which depicts a pipe, in the shape of a crank, being rotated rapidly. The gas to be cooled enters at A and is compressed by the centrifugal force as it traverses the arm B. A cooling medium surrounding B makes this an iso-

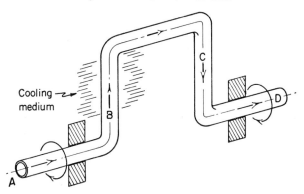

FIGURE 2.19.   Diagram illustrating the principle of the refrigerative device proposed
by J. R. Roebuck.

thermal compression.   The gas then returns to the axis of rotation through
arm C where it expands isentropically, with large cooling since C is insulated.
Finally the cycle is completed by sending the gas through an external isothermal
compressor which returns it to A.

It is apparent that work of isothermal compression must be supplied by
the crank as it accelerates the gas moving out arm B.   Likewise the work done
by the gas in expanding isentropically as it moves in arm C is delivered to the
crank.   Thus the work of expansion is delivered without loss to help compress the gas in arm B.   Another desirable feature is the fact that the speed
of the gas relative to the pipe is small; therefore, it is argued, flow friction is
much lower than in a gas turbine.   Since the gas is colder and therefore
denser in arm C than in arm B, the pressure at A will be greater than that
at D, so the external compressor will be a part of the isothermal compression
phase of the refrigerative cycle.

An objection to this device is the need for high peripheral speed and the
consequent design and structural difficulties.   The cooling to be expected
may be computed as it was for the centripetal expansion turbine.   The decrease in enthalpy taking place in arm C is exactly the same as that taking
place in a turbine rotor with the same peripheral speed or half the total
enthalpy decrease computed for the loss-free centripetal turbine.   Thus very
high peripheral speeds are necessary if substantial temperature changes are
to be achieved.   Roebuck has some suggestions regarding a practical design.

Another criticism of this device is the prediction that Coriolis forces will
cause turbulent losses even though the bulk velocity of the gas with respect
to the tube is quite low.

2.16. Vortex Tube.   Another device which produces refrigeration and
which may have some application to the liquefaction of gases is the Ranque

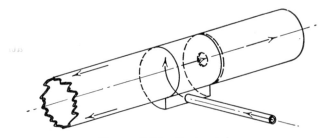

FIGURE 2.20.   Vortex tube.

Vortex Tube [17], sometimes called the Hilsch Tube because Rudolf Hilsch was the author of an article [18] describing it.   This invention is illustrated in Figure 2.20.   A gas at a moderately high pressure, e.g., 5 atmospheres, enters the tube tangentially, expands in the nozzle to nearly atmospheric pressure and thereby attains a very high velocity.   This produces a very rapid rotation of the gas in the tube near the nozzle.   The gas is permitted to escape by two avenues, to the left through the unobstructed full diameter of the tube and to the right through a small central aperture.   A throttling valve situated some distance (ca. 30 tube diameters) to the left of the vortex allows the operator to adjust the ratio of the amounts of gas which depart via the two exits.   It is found that the gas which emerges through the central aperture is cold, while that which departs through the unobstructed part of the tube is warm.   By proper adjustment of the flows in the two exists, cooling as great as 40°C can be obtained.

A quantitative solution to the performance of this device has not been advanced, probably because of the extreme complexity of the problem.   The following qualitative explanation may be of some value.

Any small element of gas in the vortex is expanding in an intense centrifugal-force field as it traverses the spiral path from the periphery of the tube to the center.   This expansion will produce energy which ordinarily would manifest itself as increased velocity.   However, the velocity must decrease (and actually approach zero) as the center is approached.   A velocity proportional to the radial distance is consistent with constant angular velocity and accordingly would not cause energy transfer between adjacent revolving layers by viscous shear.   However, in the vortex tube each layer of gas transmits some of its energy to the next outer layer by viscous interaction as it tends toward constant angular velocity.   Consequently the outer layers of the vortex gain energy; and when kinetic energy is lost, a temperature rise results.   For the same cause the inner layers of the vortex, having transferred their kinetic energy to the outer parts of the vortex, are reduced in temperature.   Thus the part of the gas which flows through the central aperture is colder than the average while that remaining is warmer.

It should be pointed out that the Ranque tube, in practical models thus far devised, does not have a very good thermodynamic efficiency. Turbines or reciprocating expansion engines are much more efficient. Also the Ranque tube cannot be used in a straightforward manner to improve the performance of a Hampson-type liquefier employing a counterflow heat exchanger. Since one of the gas streams which is discharged from the vortex tube is at a high temperature, only a fraction of the total flow is available to be used in the return stream to cool the incoming gas. A more general way of stating this limitation is to say that the refrigerative effect of the Ranque tube can be utilized only by transmitting the concurrent heating effect outside the thermodynamic boundary being considered.

IV. LIQUEFACTION OF HYDROGEN

2.17. The liquefaction of hydrogen can be accomplished by employing the same principles as those used for air liquefaction; however, there are several practical complications. The inversion temperature for the Joule-Thomson effect is at approximately $204°K$; therefore isenthalpic expansion will not produce cooling unless the hydrogen is first precooled below this temperature. Moreover all substances, other than hydrogen and helium, freeze well above the boiling temperature of hydrogen; so, unless the hydrogen being liquefied is extremely pure, the contaminating gases are likely to solidify and obstruct the passages of the liquefier. Particularly serious is a small oxygen impurity: explosions inside hydrogen liquefiers have been attributed to accumulations of solid oxygen in the tubes carrying cold high-pressure hydrogen.

Nearly all the hydrogen liquefiers in use at the present time employ the Joule-Thomson principle and use liquid nitrogen or liquid air for precooling. A flow diagram and a description of the fundamental hydrogen liquefaction process will be presented first and then some actual designs showing the nature of the components and their practical arrangement will be described.

2.18. Joule-Thomson Liquefaction Process with Precooling by Liquid Nitrogen. Figure 2.21 is the flow diagram of a hydrogen liquefier with liquid nitrogen precooling. Pure hydrogen at about 120 atmospheres enters the liquefier and the flow is divided between the two heat exchangers, E_1 and E_2. In E_1 the incoming high-pressure hydrogen is cooled by the outgoing low-pressure hydrogen; in E_2, by the nitrogen vaporized from the precooling chamber. Next the high-pressure streams unite and are cooled in the exchanger E_3, which is immersed in liquid nitrogen boiling at reduced pressure. The hydrogen then enters the final heat exchanger E_4, sometimes called the Joule-Thomson or J-T exchanger, where it is cooled by the returning stream of unliquefied hydrogen. At the bottom of this exchanger is the expansion valve where the pressure is reduced to slightly above atmospheric. At this point part of the hydrogen condenses and the rest returns through the low-pressure channels of exchanger E_1. The liquid hydrogen is drawn off through the transfer tube,

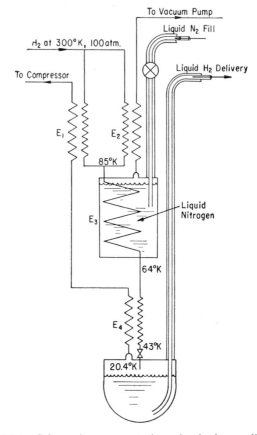

To Vacuum Pump

Liquid N_2 Fill

H_2 at 300°K, 100 atm.

Liquid H_2 Delivery

To Compressor

E_1

E_2

85°K

E_3

Liquid Nitrogen

64°K

E_4

43°K

20.4°K

FIGURE 2.21. Schematic representation of a hydrogen liquefier.

T. Approximate values of temperature at various points in the cycle are shown in Figure 2.21.

The yield of this hydrogen liquefier can be computed in the same manner as was that of the Hampson air liquefier, using Equation 2.9 and substituting values for enthalpies of the high-pressure and low-pressure gas at the top of the final heat exchanger (J-T) and the enthalpy of the liquid. Enthalpies are given in the temperature-entropy diagram, Chapter 9. If the gaseous hydrogen is cooled to 64°K by the liquid nitrogen, the fraction of the flow that will be liquefied is

$$x = \frac{h_{lp64} - h_{hp64}}{h_{lp64} - h_{liquid}} \tag{2.37}$$

where h_{lp64} is the specific enthalpy of the low-pressure hydrogen, h_{hp64} is the specific enthalpy of the high-pressure hydrogen and h_{liquid} is the specific enthalpy of the liquid. For a high pressure of 100 atmospheres and a low pressure of 1 atmosphere the fraction liquefied is found to be 0.256.

2.19. Large Hydrogen Liquefier at NBS, Boulder. The large hydrogen liquefier of the National Bureau of Standards Cryogenic Engineering Laboratory at Boulder, Colorado, uses the circuit just described. The following description of this liquefaction system, including auxiliary components and major instrumentation, control, and safety equipment is presented here because it is one of the recent developments in this field and it is hoped that some of the information may be useful in future designs. It should be emphasized that there is no implication that the auxiliary equipment is recommended for all liquefiers. Extra precautions were taken and generous instrumentation was provided for this installation because (1) the large quantities of hydrogen handled involved increased hazards, (2) the urgency of the work was such that shutdown caused by malfunctioning could not be tolerated, and (3) it was thought that reliable data on performance would be useful for future designs.

General Description. Figure 2.22 is a block flow diagram showing all the major components. Where feasible, brief descriptions of the components are included in the legend.

To preserve clarity, only the simple circuit connecting those components

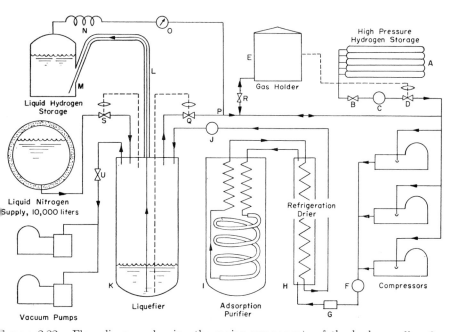

FIGURE 2.22. Flow diagram showing the major components of the hydrogen liquefier of the National Bureau of Standards Cryogenic Engineering Laboratory.

that are in use simultaneously during normal operation is shown. The complex piping and valve layout which allows the operator to select any desired high-pressure hydrogen storage bank, combination of compressors, purifier, and liquefier is omitted.

Hydrogen from the high-pressure storage A is reduced in pressure to 50 psig at B, passes through the catalyst chamber C (palladium on alumina) where oxygen is removed by causing it to combine with the hydrogen to form water. At the regulating valve D hydrogen is admitted to the compression system. The valve D is automatically controlled by the position of the gasholder E, and the control is normally adjusted so that the gasholder is kept half-full. Next the hydrogen is compressed to about 1800 psi, oil and water droplets are removed in the separator F, finer oil fog particles are trapped in the fog filter G, and the hydrogen enters the refrigeration purifier H, where the less volatile vapor impurities are condensed. Next the hydrogen passes through silica gel at 65°K in the purifier I, where more volatile impurities such as nitrogen and traces of oxygen which escaped the catalyst are removed by selective adsorption. Then the hydrogen passes through the high-pressure flowmeter J and enters the liquefier K. The liquid hydrogen is piped through the vacuum-insulated transfer line L to the large storage vessel M. Hydrogen evaporated during transfer returns through the warm-up coil N and the low-pressure flowmeter O, and joins the main stream of unliquefied low-pressure hydrogen from the liquefier at P. Finally the low-pressure stream returns to the intake of the compressors after being augmented by fresh hydrogen from storage to replace that removed from the system as liquid. The valve Q throttles the low-pressure exhaust from the liquefier so as to maintain the pressure over the liquid hydrogen required to effect the transfer to the storage vessel. This valve (butterfly type) is automatically controlled by a signal from the hydrogen liquid level gage in the liquefier receiver. Thus the pressure, and accordingly the rate of flow of liquid hydrogen, are maintained at the values required to keep the liquid level in the receiver constant.

There is another rather interesting device in this system which was installed because of the high elevation of the site, 5400 feet above sea level. At this level the average pressure of the atmosphere is about 12.2 psia so the hydrogen compressors, designed for sea-level operation, were not delivering their full capacity. This situation was remedied by installing in the line between the gasholder and the rest of the system a servo-valve which automatically maintains the pressure 2.5 psi higher on the liquefier side. The valve-operating mechanism is designed so that in the event of malfunctioning in the rest of the system which tends to lower or raise the pressure of the hydrogen in the low-pressure part of the cycle, the valve will open and allow the gasholder to perform its primary function of supplying or storing gas until the malfunction is corrected.

The liquid nitrogen for precooling is transferred through a vacuum-insulated

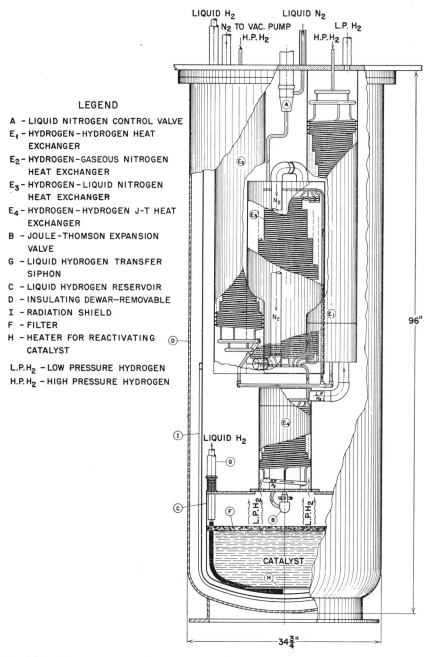

LEGEND

A – LIQUID NITROGEN CONTROL VALVE
E_1 – HYDROGEN–HYDROGEN HEAT EXCHANGER
E_2 – HYDROGEN–GASEOUS NITROGEN HEAT EXCHANGER
E_3 – HYDROGEN–LIQUID NITROGEN HEAT EXCHANGER
E_4 – HYDROGEN–HYDROGEN J-T HEAT EXCHANGER
B – JOULE-THOMSON EXPANSION VALVE
G – LIQUID HYDROGEN TRANSFER SIPHON
C – LIQUID HYDROGEN RESERVOIR
D – INSULATING DEWAR–REMOVABLE
I – RADIATION SHIELD
F – FILTER
H – HEATER FOR REACTIVATING CATALYST

L.P.H_2 – LOW PRESSURE HYDROGEN
H.P.H_2 – HIGH PRESSURE HYDROGEN

FIGURE 2.23. Cut-away assembly of the hydrogen liquefier proper, showing the arrangement of parts.

line and the rate controlled by the servo-valve R which is commanded by the signal from the liquid level gage in the nitrogen precooling bath. The pressure in the liquid nitrogen bath is lowered by the reciprocating vacuum pumps S. In this case also there is an automatic control valve, T, which prevents the pressure at the bath from reaching the triple point. The same types of valves are used to control the level and pressure of the liquid nitrogen surrounding the adsorption purifier. The pressure over the liquid nitrogen must not be allowed to go below the triple point of nitrogen because solid nitrogen would not make good thermal contact with the surfaces it is required to cool.

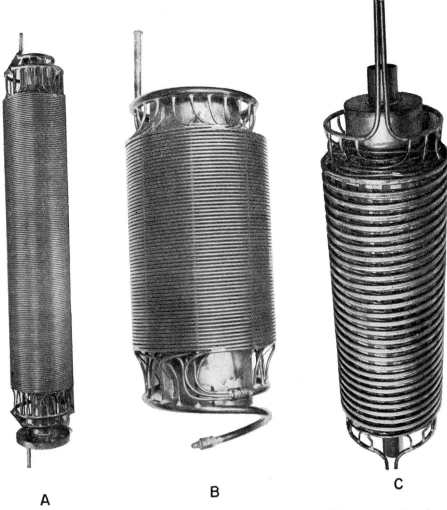

A   B   C

FIGURE 2.24. Three types of heat exchangers used in the NBS hydrogen liquefier.

FIGURE 2.25.   Giauque's spacer strips, used in maintaining uniform spacing between the tubes of a heat exchanger.

The Liquefier Proper. Figure **2.23** is a sectional drawing showing the actual arrangement of the liquefier heat exchangers indicated in the flow diagram, Figure **2.21**. These heat exchangers are shown in the photographs of Figure **2.24**. Referring again to Figure **2.23**, it may be noted that the heat exchanger designated E_2 (hydrogen to nitrogen vapor) actually consists of two type-A units in parallel. This was necessary to provide sufficiently low resistance to flow for the pumped nitrogen vapor so that a low nitrogen vapor pressure could be maintained in the precooling chamber. Heat exchangers E_1, the two units composing E_2, and the liquid nitrogen exchanger E_3 are grouped in the upper part of the assembly in order to minimize the space requirement. From thermal considerations, it would be better to place the exchanger E_3 below E_1 and E_2 to avoid heat leak from E_1 and E_2 to the colder exchanger E_3. However, such a distribution would have made the assembly unduly long. The arrangement shown has been quite satisfactory.

Heat exchangers type A and B, Figure **2.24**, are of the Giauque-Hampson design. They are constructed of multiple lengths of copper tubing $\frac{3}{16}$ inch O.D., 0.035 inch wall. The axial and radial spacing between the tubes is **0.030** inch, maintained by the use of Giauque's punched brass spacer strips (**pat-**ented), Figure **2.25**. Also in winding these exchangers, additional radial spacers of 0.30 inch thick cellulose acetate were used between the Giauque brass spacers and were later removed by dissolving with acetone after competing the winding. This procedure produced a very accurately round coil with uniform spacing. It was found that the lengths of tubes on different layers of the heat exchanger could be maintained nearly equal by varying the number of tubes per layer. The $\frac{3}{16}$-inch tubes were soldered into $\frac{1}{2}$-inch manifolds at each end as shown in the photographs. Data on type A and B heat exchangers are given in Table 2.4 The completed coils were sheathed with closely fitting thin stainless steel jackets so that the low-pressure gas would be confined to the 0.030-inch interstices between the tubes. Another heat exchanger of this type, shown in Table 2.4 as type D, is used in the refrigeration drier.

TABLE 2.4.   HEAT EXCHANGER DESIGN

Feature	Type A	Type B	Type D
Designation	E_1 and E_2	E_4(J-T)	Drier
Number of tubes	37	23	45
Number of layers	12	8	9
Average tube length, ft	77.0	43.6	86.4
Exchanger length	3 ft	$13\frac{1}{2}$ in.	6 ft
External diameter of exchanger, in.	$8\frac{3}{16}$	$9\frac{1}{2}$	$6\frac{15}{16}$
Internal diameter of exchanger, in.	3	6	3

Type C heat exchanger, used to cool the high-pressure hydrogen to the temperature of liquid nitrogen in the adsorption purifier, is of a quite different design. It consists of 16 copper tubes, $\frac{5}{8}$ inch O.D., 0.065 inch wall, soldered together in pairs. One tube of each pair carries the high-pressure hydrogen being cooled; the other tube carries the returning H_2 stream, also at high pressure. The layers and turns are spaced so that the cold nitrogen vapor, from the bath in which the adsorption purifier is immersed, can make contact with the tubes and thus help with the cooling. This, then, is a three-channel heat exchanger. The entering stream of high-pressure hydrogen is cooled by the leaving streams of returning hydrogen and nitrogen vapor. The nitrogen vapor cannot contribute much refrigeration because if the heat exchange between the two hydrogen streams is good there is very little excess heat to be absorbed by the cold nitrogen.

The expansion valve B, Figure 2.23, is made of stainless steel. The orifice size was chosen so that for normal flow the needle would have to be considerably withdrawn from its closed position. This has two advantages: (1) The annular opening is wider, so there is less tendency for clogging, and (2) the adjustment is less critical. An attempt was made both in the manifold and in the expansion valve to avoid traps which might accumulate solid oxygen. The valve stem extends through the top plate of the liquefier and is operated manually from the main control panel through a system of pulleys and a wire belt.

The liquid-gas mixture leaving the expansion valve is given a circular motion in a horizontal plane by four short curved outlet tubes. This provides an opportunity for suspended liquid droplets to settle out or be centrifuged so that they will not be carried up into the heat exchanger by the returning vapor.

The dewar vessel D, Figure 2.23, which surrounds the liquefier and provides the necessary thermal insulation, is 30 inches I.D. and 96 inches internal depth. The inner wall is 0.040-inch stainless steel and the outer wall ⅜-inch stainless. The vacuum is maintained at about 5×10^{-6} mm Hg by continuous pumping with a 100-liter-per-sec oil diffusion pump.

Producing Liquid Parahydrogen. Ordinary hydrogen at room temperature consists of two molecular varieties, orthohydrogen and parahydrogen, distinguished by the relative orientations of the two nuclear spins in the diatomic molecule. The room-temperature equilibrium composition is 75 percent orthohydrogen and 25 percent parahydrogen. When liquefied by the regular process, this composition is little changed, fresh liquid hydrogen having approximately the same ortho-para composition as the room temperature gas. However, the equilibrium concentration of the liquid at its boiling point, 20.3°K, is almost pure parahydrogen, so that the freshly made liquid normal hydrogen tends to change to parahydrogen. The spontaneous conversion is exothermic and the energy released is greater than the heat of vaporization of liquid hydrogen.

In the uncatalyzed reaction, heat is evolved at a rate sufficient to evaporate about 1 percent of the liquid per hour. This is a serious loss compared to the heat-leak loss in a good liquid-hydrogen storage vessel which may be considerably less than 1 percent per day. For this reason the NBS hydrogen liquefier was provided with means for producing almost pure parahydrogen, which, being already in the low-temperature equilibrium state, has very good keeping qualities. This modification was made by introducing the conversion catalyst into the liquid receiver. As the hydrogen is liquefied, it trickles through the catalyst particles and is converted to the para form. Of course, the heat of conversion is emitted and one may well wonder why any liquid remains after conversion, since the heat of conversion is greater than the latent heat of vaporization of the liquid. As a matter of fact, the liquefier output is reduced only to about 66 percent of its output of liquid normal hydrogen. This circumstance is explained by the fact that although much of the liquid formed is vaporized by the heat of conversion, this cold vapor is returned through the low-pressure channels of the Joule-Thomson heat exchanger, cooling the incoming high-pressure hydrogen to a lower temperature than it would have when liquid normal hydrogen is being produced. Since this hydrogen is colder before expansion, a greater fraction of it is liquefied by the expansion. Thus, although a large quantity of liquid hydrogen is evaporated by the heat of conversion, it is partially replaced by an increased liquefaction fraction, so the net result is a loss of capacity of about 34 percent.

Since the unliquefied hydrogen that is returned to the compressor is partially or totally converted to the para form and does not quickly revert to the high-temperature equilibrium composition during its traverse of the compressors and other warm components, a steady condition is soon reached wherein the hydrogen reaching the expansion valve already has higher-than-normal para concentration.

The fraction liquefied can be computed by considering the over-all process and ignoring the details of exact para composition at each part of the cycle. Thus gaseous normal hydrogen is admitted to the system and liquid parahydrogen is withdrawn, so Equation 2.37 is applicable, if we make sure that

$$x = \frac{h_{\text{lp64}} - h_{\text{hp64}}}{h_{\text{lp64}} - h_{\text{liquid}}} \tag{2.37}$$

the denominator represents the difference between the specific enthalpy of low-pressure gaseous normal hydrogen at the temperature of the top of the final heat exchanger, and the specific enthalpy of liquid parahydrogen being withdrawn. This follows because, for steady state operation, hydrogen is being liquefied, and converted to the para form, at the same rate fresh normal gas is added and liquid parahydrogen withdrawn. Thus, for the production of liquid parahydrogen, $h_{\text{lp64}} - h_{\text{liquid}}$ must include the heat of conversion from normal to parahydrogen.

Several different catalysts have been used for producing parahydrogen. The one currently employed at the National Bureau of Standards is hydrous ferric oxide [19] [20]. It is very active, so that a relatively small amount is all that is required, and it is sufficiently stable and rugged to last indefinitely in service. Its effectiveness is reduced in contact with moist air, but it is readily reactivated by heating to 120°C under vacuum (10^{-1} mm Hg). The catalyst shown in Figure 2.23 was the first catalyst used in this liquefier. It is a commercial material consisting of chromic oxide deposited upon small pellets of alumina. About 50 liters were required. The hydrous ferric oxide is so active that only about 1 liter is needed. Recent modifications of the hydrogen liquefier have included a catalyst for gas phase conversion at the temperature of liquid nitrogen boiling at reduced pressure. The early tests show substantial increases in liquefaction rate. This, of course, is to be expected, because part of the heat of conversion is removed with liquid nitrogen; so the fraction of the total flow that condenses is increased because the Joule-Thomson refrigeration by hydrogen is not called upon to cancel so much heat of conversion.

Purifiers and Gas Analyzers. The purification of the hydrogen before it enters the liquefier is a highly important process as may be inferred from the number of components designated for this purpose. It is considered preferable, however, to discuss this subject in Chapter 3, Separation and Purification of Gases, where the material can be treated more methodically.

n the same chapter, instruments for analyzing the gas are discussed. These
lso are quite important for reliable operation of the hydrogen liquefier.

Process Instrumentation. In addition to the gas-analysis equipment to be
lescribed later, there are numerous other instruments which aid in controlling
he operation and provide performance data which are of value in choosing
orrect operating procedures and deciding on modifications to improve the
erformance.

Temperatures at various points are measured with copper-constantan ther-
ocouples. Table 2.5 lists the locations and functions of the thermocouples.

TABLE 2.5. THERMOCOUPLES IN THE HYDROGEN LIQUEFIER

Designation	Location	Reference Junction
igh-pressure H₂ to liquefier	Surface of high-pressure hydrogen line to liquefier[a]	Ambient
ow-pressure H₂ from liquefier	Surface of hydrogen return line at top of liquefier[a]	Same
ow-pressure N₂ from liquefier	Surface of nitrogen exchanger exhaust lines[a]	Same
quid N₂ precooling bath	Inserted in liquid nitrogen precooling bath	Liquid N₂ at 76°K
igh-pressure H₂ from exchanger E₁	Surface of high-pressure line[a]	Liquid N₂ precooling bath
igh-pressure H₂ from precooler	Surface of high-pressure line from liquid N₂ bath[a]	Same
igh-pressure H₂ before J-T valve	Inserted in high-pressure line[a]	Same
quid hydrogen pot	In bottom of pot	Same
ow-pressure H₂ top of J-T exchanger	Inserted in low-pressure pipe	Same

[a] Pipe and thermocouple insulated from surrounding environment.

Table 2.6 shows the function of the principal pressure and vacuum gages
the liquefier circuit.

TABLE 2.6. PRESSURE GAGES

Designation	Type	Range
pply manifold (tube-bank pressure)	Bourdon tube	0 to 3000 psig
oxo pressure (outlet of PRV)	Same	30-in. vac. to 60 psig
pply to low-pressure system	Hg manometer	−30 to +30 in. Hg
mpressor discharge pressure	Bourdon tube	0 to 3000 psig

TABLE 2.6. PRESSURE GAGES (*continued*)

Designation	Type	Range
High-pressure hydrogen to liquefier panel	Same	Same
High-pressure to drier	Same	Same
High-pressure from drier	Same	Same
Differential pressure through coil spaces of drier	Bellows	0 to 50 psi
High pressure to liquefier	Bourdon tube	0 to 3000 psig
High pressure before J-T exchanger	Same	Same
High pressure before J-T valve	Same	Same
Differential through high-pressure side of J-T exchanger	Bellows	0 to 50 psi
Liquid hydrogen pot pressure	Bourdon tube	30-in. vac. to 15 psig
Dewar pressure (low pressure top of J-T exchanger)	Same	Same
Liquid nitrogen supply pressure	Same	30-in. vac. to 60 psig
Liquid nitrogen pressure in purifier	Same	30-in. vac. to 15 psig
Liquid nitrogen pressure in liquefier	Same	Same
Differential N_2 pressure across exchanger E_2	Bellows	25 in. Hg
Good vacuum line for reactivating catalyst and purifiers	Bourdon tube	30-in. vac. to 15 psig
Rough vacuum line for pumping nitrogen	Same	Same

An instrument which is a great help in operating the liquefier is the capaci-
tive liquid-level indicator-controller developed by Williams and Maxwell [21].
The level-sensitive element is a special coaxial-tube condenser whose capacity
is increased as liquid rises in the annular space between the tubes. This
condenser is one arm of an AC bridge whose unbalance is fed to a commercial
indicator-recorder-controller. There are three of these level devices used
during operation; one indicates the level in, and controls the admission of liquid
nitrogen to, the precooling chamber of the liquefier, another controls the filling
of the liquid nitrogen chamber of the adsorption purifier, and a third indicates
and controls the level of liquid hydrogen in the receiver at the bottom of
the liquefier.

Safety Measures. In addition to the purifiers which remove dangerous
contaminants from the hydrogen, and instruments which will detect such
materials if the purifiers fail (equipment to be described in Chapter 3), a
number of other precautionary measures were incorporated into the design of
the NBS hydrogen liquefaction plant.

All the available evidence indicates that the most effective safety measure are those which prevent a dangerous accumulation of hydrogen in the atmosphere. Although it is obviously desirable to eliminate sources of ignition, this precaution does not guarantee complete safety. Hydrogen has been known to ignite with seeming spontaneity. For example, tiny leaks in high-pressure hydrogen lines sometimes ignite from no apparent cause. The complete elimination of tribo-electric sparks is problematical. For this reason generous ventilation can hardly be overemphasized. In the CEL installation the air in the liquefaction plant is changed once every two minutes by powerful ventilating fans distributed along the ridge of the roof. The installation is also served by a combustible gas detection system which samples the air at eight different points throughout the building. If the concentration of hydrogen exceeds 15 percent of the lower explosive limit, an alarm sounds and the ventilating fans automatically double their speed. Also the compressors are stopped and the supply of hydrogen is shut off.

In order to avoid possible sources of ignition, all the electrical wiring and fixtures are of the totally enclosed "explosion-proof" type. Electrical instruments which have switching gear or other spark sources are totally enclosed and purged with fresh air at a pressure slightly above the ambient. The concrete floor of the building is finished with a surface layer of conducting material to reduce the chance of static electrical charges.

Performance of Large Hydrogen Liquefier. A critical summary of the performance of the hydrogen liquefier is contained in Table 2.7, which lists the principal operational data. The pressure differences across the heat exchangers and the temperature differences between the entering and leaving currents of hydrogen at the tops of the exchangers are measures of imperfection. These are given for the benefit of those who may wish to consider using this type of heat exchanger. It will be noted that the pressure drops in the high-pressure stream are of little consequence.

TABLE 2.7. OPERATIONAL DATA ON NBS-CEL HYDROGEN LIQUEFIER

Hydrogen supply rate (with 15.0 psia pressure at compressor suction)...	750 scfm

The following temperatures and pressures through liquefier heat exchangers are for production of 95 percent liquid parahydrogen with the compressor intake supercharged to 15.0 psia

Heat exchanger E_1, high-pressure to low-pressure H_2 (see Figure 2.21)	
High-pressure inlet (top)............................	1740 psig
Temperature.....................................	65°F
High-pressure outlet (bottom).......................	1715 psig[a]
Temperature.....................................	80°K[b]
Low-pressure ΔP.......................................	1.8 psi
Temperature difference (top)........................	20°F

TABLE 2.7 (*continued*)

Heat exchanger E_2, high-pressure H_2 to low-pressure N_2
Low-pressure ΔP, N_2 vapor, (3.9 in. Hg)............... 1.9 psi
Temperature difference (top)........................ 15°F
Heat exchanger E_3, precooler
Temperature H_2 in................................ 85°K[b]
Temperature H_2 out............................... 66°K
Temperature, liquid N_2........................... 66°K
Pressure, liquid N_2.............................. 15 cm Hg
Heat exchanger E_4, Joule-Thomson
High pressure ΔP................................ 10.5 psi
High-pressure outlet, to J-T valve.................. 1700 psig
Low-pressure ΔP................................ .25 psi
Low-pressure inlet (liquid H_2 reservoir pressure)........ 6 psig
Temperature difference (top)........................ 2°K

Liquefaction Rates in Liters per Hour

Normal hydrogen (66°K precooling temperature and 2°K ΔT)
at 640 SCFM[c] { Observed (24.5% yield)............... 320
{ Ideal, computed at 66°K (26.1% yield)... 340
Liquid nitrogen required for precooling................ 360
Computed production of liquid normal hydrogen with a
compressor supply of 750 scfm..................... 395
Production of 95 percent parahydrogen
at 750 scfm[c] { Observed (15% yield).................. 230
{ Ideal, computed (17%)................. 260
Liquid nitrogen required for precooling................ 340

[a] Pressure is not accurately measured relative to inlet pressure or J-T pressure.
[b] Heat balance calculations indicate that this temperature should be 87°K.
Thermocouple measurements show about the values listed.
[c] The installation of a supercharger to increase the flow from 640 scfm to
750 scfm was made at about the same time the liquefier was equipped with a
catalyst which resulted in the production of 95 percent liquid parahydrogen.
Thus operating data for producing liquid normal hydrogen at a compressor
delivery of 750 scfm were not obtained.

2.20. Small Hydrogen Liquefier. Figure 2.26 is the circuit diagram of
a small hydrogen liquefier designed and constructed by Macinko, Bjorklund,
and Jensen [22] at NBS-CEL. It will be noted that this liquefier employs
two liquid nitrogen precooling baths, one in which the liquid nitrogen boils
at slightly above atmospheric pressure and discharges the vapor to the atmosphere through one channel of a three-channel heat exchanger. The nitrogen
in the other precooling bath boils at reduced pressure and the vapor, on its
way to the pump, circulates through a coil soldered to a radiation shield
which gives added protection to the parts below liquid nitrogen temperature.
Since the nitrogen bath at atmospheric pressure provides most of the precooling refrigeration, a much smaller amount of vapor leaves the pumped
bath; accordingly a smaller pump is adequate to reach the triple point pressure.

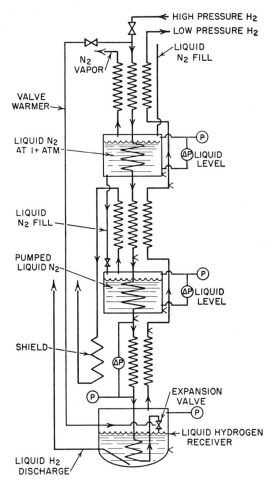

FIGURE 2.26. Flow diagram of a small hydrogen liquefier using the Collins' heat exchangers illustrated in Figure 2.9. P indicates a pressure gage on the liquefier panel, ΔP a differential pressure gage. The symbols, $<$, show the locations of thermocouple junctions.

A feature of this liquefier, which has also been used by others, is the section of heat exchanger immersed in the liquid hydrogen. This causes complete condensation of the high-pressure hydrogen before it reaches the expansion valve; as a result little vapor is produced as the hydrogen goes through the expansion valve. The advantage of this is that high gas velocities in the receiver are avoided and there is less danger of entrainment of liquid droplets. Of course the net fraction liquefied is unchanged; the condensation of the high-pressure stream is accomplished by evaporating some of the liquid already collected.

Figure 2.27 is a photograph of the liquefier with the insulating jacket and the hydrogen reservoir removed. The two large cylinders are the liquid nitrogen reservoirs. The heat exchangers are the small-diameter cylinders. These are the special Collins-type, finned, coaxial-tube heat exchangers described earlier and illustrated in Figure 2.9, p. 19. The assembly shown (after attaching the liquid hydrogen receiver) is suspended in a vacuum enclosure which is sealed with an O-ring to the top plate. Also the colder parts are given extra protection by the nitrogen-cooled shield (not shown) also suspended in the vacuum. This construction results in a very low heat leak, but of course the multitude of soldered connections inside the vacuum space must be absolutely tight. This puts a high premium on the skill of the assembler.

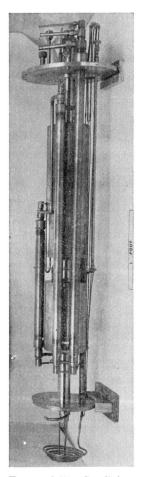

FIGURE 2.27. Small hydrogen liquefier with insulating vacuum shell and hydrogen receiver removed.

With 26.7 scfm of hydrogen at 1530 psi supplied by the compressor, this liquefier delivers 12.5 liters per hour of liquid normal hydrogen.

2.21. Liquefier with Isolated Refrigerative Circuit. Blanchard and Bittner [23] designed a hydrogen liquefier having two circuits, a closed refrigerating circuit in which very pure hydrogen was circulated, quite similar to the Joule-Thomson liquefiers which have been described, and a separate circuit in which hydrogen of moderate purity was cooled and condensed by evaporating the liquid produced in the closed circuit. The advantage of this process is that only the hydrogen in the closed circuit need be very pure; the gas condensed and withdrawn as a liquid can deposit its impurities on a rather large surface of heat exchanger and a considerable amount of impurity can be thus collected before the flow is seriously obstructed. In the actual design, the two circuits were isolated only at the warm end. At the cold ends where liquid hydrogen is being produced no condensable impurities exist, so there is no advantage in keeping the circulation paths separate here.

2.22. Hydrogen Liquefiers with Expansion Engines. Devices which utilize the expansion engine to produce refrigeration for the liquefaction of hydrogen are the Collins Helium Cryostat, the Collins helium liquefier, and the rather similar helium refrigerator used on the refrigerated transport dewars developed by Arthur D. Little and the Cambridge Corporation. A Collins helium liquefier will be described later. Arthur D. Little, Inc., has also developed a liquefier specifically designed for the condensation of hydrogen in which the refrigeration is produced by a helium cycle employing expansion engines. This system has the advantage of avoiding a high-pressure hydrogen circuit.

V. Liquefaction of Helium

2.23. Helium is the most difficult of all gases to liquefy because of its very low boiling point, 4.2°K, and its low inversion temperature for the Joule-Thomson effect, about 40°K. Helium was first liquefied in 1908 by H. Kamerlingh Onnes of the University of Leiden. He used the Joule-Thomson process, first precooling the gas to about 14°K with liquid hydrogen boiling at reduced pressure. Onnes' method is still extensively used and, for laboratories which have an adequate supply of liquid hydrogen, it is one of the most convenient and economical processes for helium liquefaction. When liquefying helium for laboratory use, economy of power is seldom a consideration. The major expenses are for the complex machinery and for the human effort needed to operate it.

The two most noteworthy advances in the liquefaction of helium since it was first accomplished by Onnes are (1) the Simon expansion process and (2) the liquefier utilizing expansion engines, first introduced by Kapitza and later greatly improved and developed by Collins.

2.24. **Joule-Thomson Helium Liquefier.** A circuit diagram of a Joule-Thomson helium liquefier is shown in Figure 2.28. It will be noted that this circuit is almost identical with that of the hydrogen liquefier, Figure 2.21. Helium enters the liquefier at room temperature and a pressure of 20 atmospheres. (The choice of the optimum operating pressure will be discussed later.) The flow divides, the fraction y passing through the heat exchanger E_1 where it is cooled by the unliquefied helium being returned to the compressor. The rest of the helium $(1 - y)$ is sent through the heat exchanger E_2, where it is cooled by hydrogen vapor, and then through E_3, where it is cooled by liquid hydrogen boiling at reduced pressure, 55 mm Hg, 14°K. The two high-pressure streams can be united either above or below heat exchanger E_3. It will be useful to consider both alternatives. First assume that the upper connection is used, joining the two high-pressure streams at T_3. In this case the total flow of helium is cooled by exchanger E_3. Then the high-pressure helium stream traverses exchanger E_4, expanding through valve V_2, where the fraction x is liquefied. The remainder $(1 - x)$ returns to the compressor through the low-pressure passages of E_4 and E_1.

Liquid hydrogen for precooling is introduced at atmospheric pressure and 20.4°K and is throttled at the valve V_1 entering the heat exchanger E_3 at a pressure slightly higher than that of the triple point. This reduction of pressure causes the evaporation of the fraction $1 - z$ of the hydrogen, the frac-

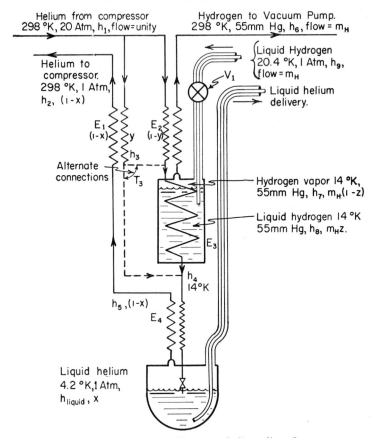

FIGURE 2.28.   Joule-Thomson helium liquefier.

tion z remaining liquid.   In the steady state, a mass m_H of liquid hydrogen is consumed for each unit mass of gaseous helium delivered to the liquefier by the compressor.   The temperatures, pressures, enthalpies (h), and rates of flow (m_H, x, y, z) are indicated at various points of Figure 2.28.

Analysis by Enthalpy Balances.   The operation of the liquefier can be analyzed by setting up enthalpy balances, assuming no heat leak and perfect heat exchange.   First the yield of the liquefier is

$$x = \frac{h_5 - h_4}{h_5 - h_{\text{liquid}}} \qquad (2.38)$$

Since the throttling of liquid hydrogen which takes place at V_1 causes no change in enthalpy,

$$h_9 = zh_8 + (1 - z)h_7 \qquad (2.39)$$

The cooling of the helium in heat exchanger E_3 is effected by the evaporation of a quantity $m_H z$ of liquid hydrogen having a heat of vaporization L; so

$$h_3 - h_4 = m_H z \, L \qquad (2.40)$$

The enthalpy balance for heat exchanger E_1 is

$$(1 - x)(h_2 - h_5) = y(h_1 - h_3) \tag{2.41}$$

and for exchanger E_2

$$m_H(h_6 - h_7) = (1 - y)(h_1 - h_3) \tag{2.42}$$

Upon substituting into Equations 2.38 and 2.42 the appropriate values of enthalpy and heat of vaporization for helium and hydrogen shown in the temperature-entropy diagrams of the chapter on cryogenic fluids, and evaluating the unknowns, it is found that

$$x = 0.195,$$

$$z = 0.87,$$

$$h_3 = 24.7 \text{ cal g}^{-1},$$

$$T_3 = 18.8°\text{K},$$

$$(1 - y) = 0.184,$$

$m_H = 0.0772$ g H_2 per g of He from compressor, or 0.70 liter of liquid hydrogen per liter of liquid helium.

More Detailed Analysis of Heat Exchange in E_2. At this point it is instructive to apply Equation 2.14 to heat exchanger E_2 and obtain a more complete picture of the temperature relation to be expected. It will be seen that some of the conclusions just obtained are untenable. In the analysis immediately preceding, only the over-all behavior has been considered; that is, the total enthalpy change in one stream has been equated to the change of enthalpy in the counterflowing stream. This is quite correct as far as it goes. However, in order for a heat exchanger to transfer heat, there must, of course, be a temperature difference of the proper sign between the two fluid streams. In applying the gross analysis of heat-exchanger operation, there is no assurance that there will be, at all parts of the heat exchanger, the temperature difference needed to transfer the heat. Therefore, for a reliable evaluation of a counterflow heat exchanger, it is necessary to determine in detail the temperature differences to be expected all along the exchanger. This can be done by applying Equation 2.14 and utilizing values of enthalpy obtained from the temperature-entropy diagrams of Chapter 9.

The conditions at the bottom of this exchanger are, according to the preceding analysis:

HELIUM: $T'_i = 18.8°\text{K}$, $m' = (1 - y) = 0.184$ g, $h'_i = 24.7$ cal g^{-1}

HYDROGEN: $T''_i = 14°\text{K}$, $m'' = m_H = 0.0772$ g, $h''_i = 160$ cal g^{-1}

The subscript i denotes the initial value of the variable at the bottom of the heat exchanger. Then from Equation 2.14, $d = -7.8$.

Table 2.8 shows how the temperature differences are computed. The temperature-enthalpy relations for helium and hydrogen used in this computation are given in the T-S diagram of Chapter 9. Curve A, Figure 2.29, is a graph of the temperature differences, $T' - T''$.

TABLE 2.8. COMPUTATION OF TEMPERATURE ALONG A PERFECT HEAT EXCHANGER IN WHICH HELIUM IS COOLED AND HYDROGEN WARMED

(*This is an impossible case because it requires that heat flow from a lower to a higher temperature.*)

T', °K	h', Cal g^{-1}	$m'h'$ ($m' = 0.184$), Cal deg^{-1} deg^{-1}	$m''h'' =$ $m'h' + 7.8$, Cal deg^{-1}	$h'' =$ $m''h''/0.0772$, Cal g^{-1} deg^{-1}	T'', °K	$T' - T''$, deg
18.8	24.7	4.53	12.3	160	14	4.8
30	40	7.36	15.2	196	28	2.0
50	67	12.3	20.1	260	54	−4
80	105	19.3	27.1	351	90	−10
100	130	23.9	31.7	411	113	−13
150	192	35.3	43.1	559	163	−13
200	253	46.9	54.7	710	211	−11
230	289	53.2	61.0	790	235	−5
250	312	57.4	65.2	845	252	−2
270	340	62.5	70.3	911	271	−1
300	380	69.9	77.7	1008	300	0

It is seen that except for a small temperature interval near the cold end of the exchanger, the temperature differences are all in the wrong direction to permit the transfer of heat from the incoming high-pressure helium to the outgoing hydrogen. Therefore the exchanger certainly will not work with this small temperature difference at the cold end, computed by the simple gross analysis of heat-exchanger behavior.

This difficulty arises when exchanging heat between hydrogen and helium because the specific heat of hydrogen changes in this temperature region from a value very nearly $\frac{5}{2} R$ to a value approaching $\frac{7}{2} R$, where R is the universal gas constant, while the specific heat of 20-atmosphere helium increases only slightly at the lower temperatures and then remains essentially constant. If the specific heats of the two streams were temperature-independent, the temperature difference would diminish uniformly from the bottom to the top of the heat exchanger.

For the helium-hydrogen exchanger to operate, the temperature difference at the cold end must be increased until nowhere along the exchanger will $T' - T''$ become negative. Since the minimum practical usable temperature of the hydrogen is limited by the triple point, 14°K, the temperature differences at the cold end can be increased only by increasing the temperature of the helium. This of course will increase the amount of liquid hydrogen evaporated in E_3, because the helium will be cooled more by evaporating hydrogen and thus change m''. Therefore, the exact analysis is not a straightforward one. By trial and error one could adjust $T_3 = T'_i$ to a higher value, determine a corresponding new value for m'', and arrive at a value of T_3 which would result in positive values of $(T' - T'')$. Some adjustment of y might be useful, but y can no longer be uniquely determined. A consequence will be a consumption of liquid hydrogen greater than that computed and wasted refrigeration resulting from the hydrogen vapor leaving the liquefier at a considerably lower temperature.

However, instead of pursuing this scheme further, let us consider the behavior of a liquefier using the alternative connection which unites the high-pressure streams below exchanger E_3. The enthalpy balance equations 2.36 to 2.42, will be the same except for 2.40 and 2.41; these become:

$$(1 - y)(h_3 - h_4) = m_H zL \tag{2.40a}$$

$$(1 - x)(h_2 - h_5) = y(h_1 - h_4) \tag{2.41a}$$

and upon substituting the known values it is found that

$x = 0.195,$

$y = 0.800,$

$m_H = 0.0772,$

$h_3 = 54$ cal g^{-1} deg^{-1},

$T_3 = 41°$K.

It will be noted that the consumption of liquid hydrogen is the same as that computed for the first circuit, but the value of T_3 is much larger and therefore more suitable for adequate heat exchange in E_3. Curve B of Figure 2.29 represents the temperature differences to be expected in this case. There

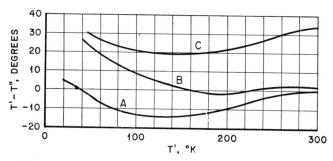

FIGURE 2.29. Calculated temperature differences in a counterflow heat exchanger in which helium at 20 atmospheres is being cooled with hydrogen at 0.07 atmosphere. T' is the temperature of the helium; T'' is the temperature of the hydrogen. Curves A and B represent impossible cases because there are regions in which the temperature difference is of the wrong sign to transfer heat from the helium to the hydrogen.

is now only a small region where $T' - T''$ becomes slightly negative. Curve C is for the same flow circuit, but T_3 has been raised from 41° to 45°K. In this case the minimum value of $T' - T''$ is about 18 degrees. This should be more than adequate for heat transfer in a good exchanger. The consumption of liquid hydrogen is increased to 0.79 liter of liquid hydrogen per liter of liquid helium. This ratio of liquid hydrogen to liquid helium should be realizable in a practical liquefier. It is seen that the behavior of the heat exchanger is very sensitive to change of the initial temperature difference; an increase in ΔT of only 4 degrees at the cold end resulted in the large spread between curves B and C at higher temperatures.

We may then conclude that (1) there is a substantial advantage in uniting the two high-pressure helium streams below the liquid hydrogen precooler, (2) it should be possible in a practical liquefier to achieve a consumption of liquid hydrogen of less than 0.8 liter of liquid hydrogen per liter of liquid helium, and (3) the temperature T_3 of the helium entering the exchangers where it is precooled with liquid hydrogen is quite critical; a change of only 4 degrees in T_3 produces a temperature difference for heat exchange of more than 18 degrees at the most unfavorable region.

In some designs of Joule-Thomson helium liquefiers it is very awkward to arrange to have two separate heat exchangers above the liquid hydrogen precooling bath. It is often desirable to utilize a three-channel exchanger in this temperature region. The analysis just presented shows that this will be wasteful of liquid hydrogen. The unfavorable heat-exchange characteristics make it impossible to satisfactorily utilize the refrigeration in the hydrogen vapor, hence the vapor will always emerge cold. However, the consumption of liquid hydrogen can be greatly reduced by introducing a liquid-nitrogen precooling bath ahead of the liquid-hydrogen bath. Some liquefiers now in use have such auxiliary liquid nitrogen baths.

Mann [25] has made a detailed analysis of a helium liquefier with a three-channel "warm" heat exchanger (ingoing high-pressure helium, outgoing low-pressure helium and outgoing precooling vapor) and concludes that the liquid nitrogen bath will greatly reduce the consumption of liquid hydrogen. His recommended design comprises a pumped liquid nitrogen bath utilizing the cold nitrogen vapor in the third channel of the top heat exchanger, an intermediate helium-helium-hydrogen heat exchanger between the liquid-nitrogen and liquid-hydrogen baths and finally a pumped liquid hydrogen bath. The cooling effect of the hydrogen vapor above 63°K is not used to refrigerate helium.

Optimum Pressure for Joule-Thomson Helium Liquefier. A pressure of 20 atmospheres was chosen in the liquefier analysis given above. However, an examination of the T-S diagram for helium shows that the isenthalpic has a maximum at about 30 atmospheres in the region of 14°K. Thus one would expect that the optimum operating pressure would be 30 atmospheres rather than 20. Nevertheless it has been found in some actual liquefiers that the yield is a maximum when the high pressure is from 17 to 20 atmospheres. Zelmanov [24] explained this anomaly, pointing out that at the bottom of the final heat exchanger E_4, Figure 2.28, there would be little difference of temperature to transfer heat from the 30-atmosphere helium just above the expansion valve to the 1-atmosphere, 4.2 degree helium vapor. This may be seen by reference to the T-S diagram of helium shown in Chapter 9 (p. 310).

The isenthalpic corresponding to a liquefaction fraction of 0.20 passes through the 30-atmosphere isobar at about 5°K, so there is a temperature difference of less than one degree to effect heat transfer to the 4.2°K helium vapor entering the bottom of the heat exchanger. This situation can be improved by having a distributed flow resistance in the high-pressure passages of exchanger E_4 so that the pressure falls from 30 atmospheres at the top to about 10 or 12 atmospheres just above the expansion valve. This will furnish a temperature difference of about 2.5 degrees for heat transfer at the bottom of E_4. Even this is a rather meagre ΔT; therefore heat exchanger E_4 must be very effective if the liquefier is to approach the ideal yield.

Zelmanov [27] devised a modified liquefier which permitted the use of higher pressures.

NBS Cryogenic Engineering Laboratory Helium Liquefier. Figure 2.30 is the flow diagram of a helium liquefier which employs some of the methods just discussed. This liquefier, designed by Mann, Bjorklund, and Macinko [26] utilizes the same basic structural design as that of the hydrogen liquefier illustrated in the photograph, Figure 2.27. Some additional Collins-type heat exchangers were needed, but it was found that these also could be accommodated in the evacuated space surrounding the precooling baths. The over-all size of the helium liquefier is the same as that of the hydrogen liquefier. It is seen that the helium liquefier indicated in Figure 2.30 avoids the difficult helium-to-hydrogen heat exchange by using a nitrogen precooling bath. Also an intermediate expansion valve was provided to increase the temperature difference available for heat exchange at the bottom of the final heat exchanger.

Early experience with this liquefier gives the following performance characteristics:

Helium supply . . . . 52 scfm at 30 atm
Rate of liquefaction . . . . 15 liters per hour
Fraction liquefied . . . . 12 percent
Liquid hydrogen consumption . . . . 24 liters per hour

It was learned, however, that the intermediate expansion valve did not increase the yield even when the pressure was as high as 30 atmospheres. This means that the heat exchanger below the liquid hydrogen bath is very effective even with a small temperature difference at the bottom. This was not entirely unexpected, because during the design it was seen that there was

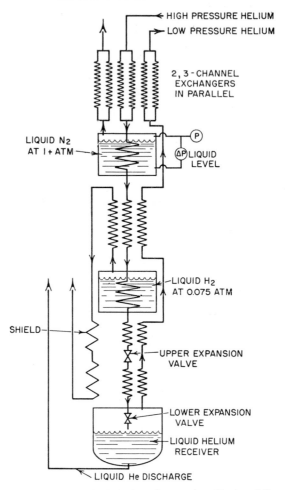

FIGURE 2.30.   Flow diagram of a helium liquefier used at National Bureau of Standards
Cryogenic Engineering Laboratory.

extra space available, and so this very critical heat exchanger was deliberately
overdesigned, the two sections together consisting of 9 feet of two-channel
Collins-type heat exchanger (see Figure 2.9, p. 19).

2.25. Simon Helium Liquefier. The Simon [28] process for liquefying
helium also uses liquid hydrogen for precooling, but employs a very different
refrigerative process to achieve further cooling. Figure 2.31 is a schematic
cross section of a Simon liquefier. The operation is as follows: Helium at
about 150 atmospheres is admitted to the strong container A. This container
is first cooled with liquid nitrogen and then with liquid hydrogen introduced
into the reservoir B. Finally, the pressure over the hydrogen is lowered by

pumping and the temperature of A and B is thereby reduced to about 10°K. At this temperature the hydrogen is a solid with a vapor pressure of 1.7 mm Hg, so sufficient time must be allowed to approach thermal equilibrium between the solid hydrogen and the container B. It saves time to close valve V_1 and stop further admission of warm helium when the minimum temperature is approached. Finally valve V_2 is opened, releasing the helium; and when the pressure reaches atmospheric, the vessel A is found to be almost full of liquid helium. The refrigeration which liquefies the helium results from the isentropic expansion of the helium which remains in A. This helium has done work in pushing out the helium which escaped, just as though it were pushing against a piston which does external work. The lack of significant friction makes this process almost truly isentropic.

One reason such a large amount of liquid is produced is the fact that the density of gaseous helium at 10°K and 150 Atm is about 1.6 times the density of the liquid at its boiling point. Unfortunately currently available T-S di-

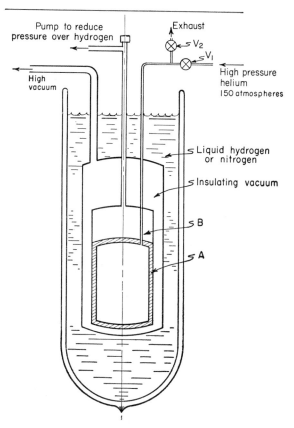

FIGURE 2.31. Schematic diagram of a Simon-type helium liquefier.

agrams of helium do not extend to the pressure of 150 atmospheres at 10°K, so yields cannot be computed from data given in Chapter 9. However, Pickard and Simon [29] have made a quantitative study of the liquefaction process and have determined the yields for different starting conditions as shown in Figure 2.32.

As a rule the Simon-type liquefier serves also as the experimental cryostat, the experimental chamber being inside or in good thermal contact with the high-pressure reservoir A. Cooke, Rollin, and Simon [30] described a liquefier from which the liquid was withdrawn by puncturing a diaphragm. The writer [31] designed a liquefier from which liquid was removed through a vacuum-insulated transfer tube having a valve at its exit. This design was later greatly enlarged and considerably simplified by W. E. Gifford. Gifford's design is shown in Figure 2.33. One of the objectives of this design was to keep the liquid hydrogen consumption low, so liquid nitrogen was used as the environment In operation the internal parts are cooled to liquid nitrogen temperature before introducing liquid hydrogen. Then, during most of the remaining cool-down, the ingoing helium is cooled by the hydrogen vapor in the counterflow exchanger, effecting further saving of

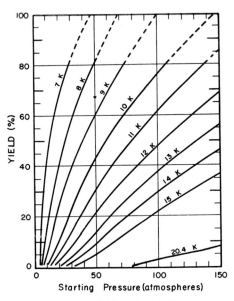

FIGURE 2.32. Yield of the Simon-type helium liquefier (percent of volume of chamber filled with liquid after expansion).

liquid hydrogen. In order to reach the lowest possible pressure(and temperature) of the solid hydrogen, the final pumping is done with the upper valve open, bypassing the flow resistance of the heat exchanger.

With this liquefier, almost all the helium liquefied can be utilized in the experimental cryostat to which it is transferred. Little or no liquid is evaporated in cooling down equipment because the very cold vapor which precedes the liquid from the transfer tube cools the experimental apparatus almost to the temperature of liquid helium before liquid appears. This is an important consideration because of the small heat of vaporization of liquid helium. The refrigerative effect of evaporating 1 gram of helium is approximately the same as that realized in warming 1 gram of gas only 4 degrees. Theoretically, the yield of this liquefier is somewhat greater than that of the original Simon liquefier (according to the data of Figure 2.32) because Joule-

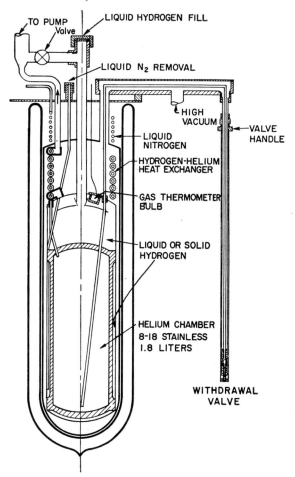

FIGURE 2.33. Simon-type helium liquefier with withdrawal siphon.

Thomson cooling causes some liquid to appear in the receiver before the pressure in the expansion chamber reaches atmospheric. About 1.5 liters of liquid helium is delivered in one expansion with a total hydrogen consumption of 3 liters.

2.26. Helium Liquefiers with Expansion Engines. Instead of depending on the Joule-Thomson effect to produce the refrigeration needed in the liquefaction of helium, one can employ the much greater refrigeration produced by having the expanding helium do work in an engine which delivers its energy to the exterior, the Claude principle. One of the advantages of the expansion-engine helium liquefier is the fact that liquid hydrogen precooling can be dispensed with, thus eliminating a quite expensive and somewhat hazardous refrigerant. When using expansion engines, the only refrigerant needed in liquefying helium is helium itself; liquid helium can be produced with no heat sink cooler than the temperature of the room in which the liquefier operates. As a matter of practical economy and expediency expansion-engine helium liquefiers usually employ liquid air or liquid nitrogen for precooling, since these liquids are cheap and safe and their use will more than double the output of such a helium liquefier.

The first Claude-type (or expansion engine) helium liquefier was designed by Kapitza [32]. Collins developed the principle into a very well-engineered, complete liquid helium facility, the Collins Cryostat (manufactured by Arthur D. Little, Inc., Cambridge, Massachusetts).

More recently Collins [33] constructed a much larger liquefier of more advanced design. His excellent description—reproduced verbatim here*— clearly sets forth the basic theory and practical utilization of modern techniques of cryogenic engineering:

A plant for the liquefaction of helium on a large scale has recently been completed in the Cryogenic Engineering Laboratory of the Massachusetts Institute of Technology. The chief characteristics are:

Rate of liquefaction	25-32 l/hr
Power required	45 kw
Helium circulated	215 g mols/min (185 cfm)
Operating pressure	12.5 atm
Refrigeration	Expansion engine plus liquid nitrogen
Liquid nitrogen consumed	(If no liquid nitrogen is used, rate of helium liquefaction is 10 l/hr)
Heat exchanger	Hampson type
Actual work expended (N₂ plant included)	3.1 kwhr/l
Computed requirement (actual liquefier but with N₂ plant and helium compressor assumed reversible)	0.87 kwhr/l
Computed requirement (entire process reversible)	0.24 kwhr/l

Because of the extremely low boiling point of helium, 4.22°K or −452°F, special techniques are required to create and maintain the necessary environment for the production of the liquid phase. The quantity of heat that must be removed from a given amount of gaseous helium originally at room temperature in order to bring about its liquefaction is not unusually large, but the work required to extract heat from condensing helium and to discard it at room temperature is about 800 times greater than that necessary if the refrigeration level were the freezing point of water. Furthermore, the problem of adequate insulation against the leakage of heat is acute.

The minimum work required to convert one gram of gaseous helium at one atmosphere and room temperature into liquid helium at 4.22°K can be con-

---

* Dr. Collins has kindly permitted this reproduction from his article in *Science* which contains further data on heat-exchanger design and details of actual performance.

veniently determined by considering the change in entropy which the helium undergoes. If we assume that waste heat can be rejected to cooling water at 300°K (80.3°F), for instance, the gain of entropy by the cooling water is exactly equal to the loss of entropy by the helium, the liquefaction being accomplished reversibly. This is shown graphically [in Figure 2.34]. By virtue of the definition of entropy the area of the field ABCDE represents the heat removed from one gram of helium when it is cooled from 300°K to 4.2°K and condensed at one atmosphere. The area of the rectangle AEDF is a measure of the heat discarded to the surroundings. The difference between the two must be the work put into the system to bring about the liquefaction. It will be observed that the minimum expenditure of work exceeds by fourfold, and more, the heat taken from the helium. Expressed as kilowatt hours per liter of liquid helium (125 g), the result is 0.24.

In the design of apparatus for the attainment of high efficiency in the liquefaction of helium it is necessary to consider the nature of the refrigerative load. A process such as the manufacture of ice, for example, is concerned mostly with latent heat. The refrigeration requirement can be met efficiently by the evaporation of a liquid refrigerant at the proper temperature level. If provision is made for reasonably effective transfer of heat, the entropy gained by the refrigerant in the evaporator does not greatly exceed that lost by the water being frozen, thus fulfilling a condition for high efficiency.

The reduction of warm gaseous helium to the liquid state at 4.2°K is a different problem. From one gram of helium at 300°K and one atmosphere, 367 calories of heat must be taken to reduce its temperature to the boiling point, 4.22°K. To effect condensation, only 4.8 calories more must be withdrawn. The refrigerative load is, therefore, distributed over an enormous temperature range. The ordinary refrigeration cycle that employs a liquid refrigerant is unsuitable for this type of service. No single refrigerant exists that can span so great a range of temperature. Even if such a refrigerant could be found, the cycle would be quite inefficient, because all the heat would have to be pumped from the lowest temperature level instead of a descending series of levels as the stream of helium is progressively cooled. The entropy gained by the refrigerant would greatly exceed that lost by the helium.

The only practicable way, probably, to cool a stream of fluid substantially, reversibly utilizes a second stream of the same or other fluid in an adiabatic counterflow heat exchanger. This principle is employed in the liquefying cycle described below. The second stream of cold gas is provided by the adiabatic expansion in an engine of a part of the first stream. In its idealized form the cycle is shown [in Figure 2.35]. A large stream of helium circulates in the direction of the arrows. A small fraction of the stream is removed as liquid at 6, an equivalent amount of gaseous helium being added to the stream at 1. Isothermal compression (1 to 2) occurs in the compressor. Cooling of the compressed gas (2 to 5) is accomplished in the counterflow heat exchanger by the transfer of heat to the colder outgoing stream of low-pressure gas (5′ to 1). A fraction of the stream of compressed helium at 2 is expanded in an engine to 2′, where it joins the main stream of low-pressure gas. The drop in temperature is a result of the external work done. Since helium is an almost perfect gas at higher temperatures, the preferred rate of flow through the first engine (2 to 2′) exactly equals the rate of liquefaction. Under this condition the mass rate of flow in the high-pressure channel of the heat exchanger (2 to 3) equals that in the low-pressure channel (2′ to 1), and, consequently, the temperature drop from 2 to 3 equals the

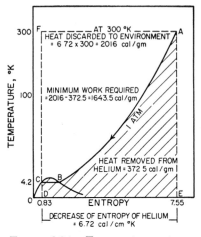

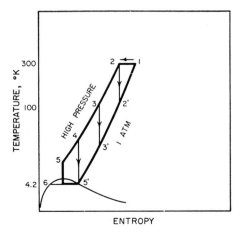

FIGURE 2.34. Temperature-entropy diagram of cooling process.

FIGURE 2.35. Idealized cycle for cooling a helium stream.

temperature rise from 2′ to 1. Assuming the heat exchanger to be perfect, no net gain of entropy occurs in this part of the heat exchanger, and thus far the process is reversible. For the next stage of cooling, a second fraction of the stream of compressed helium is split off at 3 and expanded in a second engine to 3′. At lower temperatures the effect of pressure upon the specific heat of helium is not negligible. If the temperature drop from 3 to 4 is to equal the temperature rise from 3′ to 2′, the mass rate of flow through the second engine (3 to 3″) must exceed slightly the rate of liquefaction. By so doing, complete reversibility in this section of the heat exchanger can be closely approached. A third engine is indicated by the path 4 to 5′. Finally, the remainder of the stream is expanded in a fourth engine. Even with a perfect heat exchanger and a perfect engine, however, this stage of the process is quite irreversible. Because of the rapidly rising specific heat of the high pressure stream, the unliquefied portion of the flow through the final engine plus the flow from the third engine (5′) must exchange heat with a fluid that is considerably warmer. There is, therefore, a large net increase in entropy in this section of the heat exchanger. The number of engines required in the cooling cycle just described depends upon the magnitude of the ratio of the pressure involved—the greater the pressure ratio, the smaller the number of engines. With high and low pressures of 12 atmospheres and one atmosphere, respectively, 5 engines would be indicated, and the work required would be 0.30 kwhr/l of liquid helium as compared to 0.24 kwhr/l for a reversible process.

DESCRIPTION OF LIQUEFIER

A flow diagram of the actual cycle chosen is given [in Figure 2.36]. It differs from the idealized cycle [of Figure 2.35], not only because the heat exchangers and expansion engines are necessarily imperfect, but also because practical considerations have influenced the choice of apparatus and procedures. For the sake of compactness of the liquefier and greater production of liquid from available compressed helium, liquid nitrogen is employed to the extent of its utility. The transfer of heat from gaseous helium to liquid nitrogen evaporating at a constant temperature is irreversible, of course, and a net increase of entropy is incurred. A final difference lies in the substitution of a throttle valve for the fourth engine of the cycle [of Figure 2.35].

In the flow diagram shown [in Figure 2.36], compressed helium (about 12 atm) from the compressor is treated for entrained oil in an oil trap and for vaporized oil in a refrigerated heat exchanger 3. Thereafter the stream divides, about 8 percent going to heat exchanger 4, in which it is cooled to 80°K by means of liquid nitrogen and then expanded in engine E_1, the remainder going to the principal heat exchanger 5. The temperature of the gas in heat exchanger 5 ranges from room temperature at the upper end to 15°K at the bottom. At the zone of exchanger 5 where the temperature is 40°–45°K, a second fraction (about 15 percent of the whole) of the compressed helium is led off for expansion in the second engine, E_2. At the lower end of exchanger 5 a final division of the stream occurs. About 52 percent is used in expansion engine E_3 and 25 per cent flows through the small exchangers 6 and 7 to the expansion valve D.

All the helium that enters exchanger 4 passes through engine E_1, the pressure falling to substantially one atmosphere and the temperature falling from 80°K to about 45°K. The expanded helium joins the low pressure stream in exchanger 5. All three engines are served by a single crankshaft and are identical in size. The bore is 2 inches, and the stroke is 2 inches. Each engine is comprised of a single cylinder. Although the three engines receive compressed helium from the same supply line and discharge their spent gas into the same low-pressure conduit, they operate at different temperature levels and embrace different sections of the heat-exchange system. Helium enters E_2 at about 45°K and is discharged at about

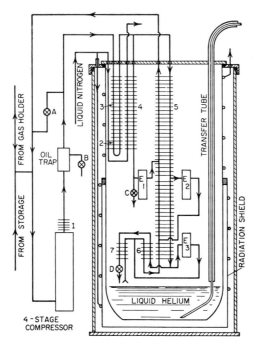

FIGURE 2.36. Flow diagram of helium liquefier.

25°K. The inlet temperature of E_3 is about 15°K, and the outlet temperature is estimated to be about 9°K.

Liquid helium forming at the throttle valve D drops into the bottom of the Dewar vessel in which the heat exchangers and engines are suspended. Space for 30 liters is provided.

Certain features of the earlier helium cryostat [12] have been retained. The heat exchangers and engines, which hang from a steel plate, are surrounded by an atmosphere of helium rather than by the insulating vacuum. Minor leaks from the high-pressure stream can be tolerated. The helium atmosphere is contained by a large metal Dewar vessel, the vacuum jacket of which is continuously pumped. The lower half of the inner wall of the vacuum jacket is enclosed by a nitrogen-cooled radiation shield.

The engine cylinders and pistons are made of nitrided nitralloy and are so closely fitted that piston rings are unnecessary. The piston rods are relatively long and slender, and are made to operate in tension to promote perfection of alignment of the piston within the cylinder. There exists a thermal gradient in the helium atmosphere surrounding the heat exchangers and engines, the temperature being approximately 295°K at the top and 4.2°K at the bottom. As far as practicable, the cylinders of the engines are located at the proper elevation for matching temperatures inside with outside in order to reduce convection to a minimum. The stuffing boxes for the piston rods and valve pull rods and the running gear of the engines are placed on top of the lid of the Dewar so that heat generated in these parts can be kept out of the cold region.

The piston rods and valve pull rods are attached to the ends of horizontal walking beams, as in ancient steam engines. The beams are 2 feet in length, are pivoted at one end, and at the point immediately above the crankshaft are fitted with ball bearings to act as cam followers. With a stroke of only 2 inches the end of the piston rod travelling in an arc of 2-foot radius is not pulled away from the vertical by an appreciable angle. Speed control is achieved by centrifugal action of a split flywheel within a brake drum. The two halves of the flywheel are fitted with brake shoes. Speed is adjusted by changing the compression of a spring. This adjustment may be made while the engine is running.*

2.27. Combination Liquefiers. Occasionally, it is advantageous to combine hydrogen and helium liquefiers. Rollin [34] designed a combination liquefier which produced liquid hydrogen by the Joule-Thomson method and used this hydrogen inside the same insulated system to cool a Simon-type helium liquefier. Spoendlin [35] designed a combined hydrogen and helium liquefier in which Joule-Thomson refrigeration was used for condensing both gases.

It is not necessary to build separate Joule-Thomson liquefiers for hydrogen and helium. Since the circuits are identical, the same liquefier can be used for either gas. Thus the large hydrogen liquefier of the NBS Cryogenic Engineering Laboratory was used experimentally to liquefy helium, by employing liquid hydrogen for precooling instead of the liquid nitrogen that is used to precool hydrogen. A liquefaction rate of 120 liters per hour was achieved when circulating helium at a rate of approximately 500 cubic feet per minute.

* Pages 68-72 are reproduced verbatim from an article in *Science* by Dr. Collins with the permission of the author. See footnote to page 68.

Of course a liquefier designed specifically for liquefying hydrogen cannot be expected to be quite so efficient for helium liquefaction. In the test mentioned above the precooling temperature was about 16°K. If the heat exchange were perfect the fraction liquefied would have been about 16.5 percent. The measured liquefaction fraction was 10 percent.

2.28. Metal Bellows Expansion Engines for Helium Liquefaction. Long and Simon [36] devised a helium liquefier with an expansion engine which avoided the problems of piston friction and leakage by utilizing an elastic metal bellows instead of the piston and cylinder previously used. The bellows had an internal diameter of 4 cm, the engine stroke was 2.7 cm, and the speed 2 to 3 revolutions per second. With precooling to 80°K this lique-fier produced 0.6 liters of liquid helium per hour.

It is to be expected that under this strenuous service there is danger that the bellows may fail from fatigue. Fortunately, resistance of metals to fa-tigue increases markedly at low temperatures. A type of bellows which failed after 5×10^3 cycles at room temperature was found to withstand about 5×10^5 cycles at liquid hydrogen temperature.

Another bellows expansion engine for helium liquefaction has been described by Eder [37]. This liquefier produced 0.4 liters per hour.

REFERENCES FOR CHAPTER 2

[1] J. G. Daunt, *Encyclopedia of Physics,* **14,** 1 (1956).
[2] S. C. Collins, *Encyclopedia of Physics,* **14,** 112 (1956).
[3] P. Kapitza, *J. Physics, U.S.S.R.,* **1,** 7 (1939).
[4] W. H. Keesom, *Leiden Comm.,* Suppl. No. **76a.**
[5] M. Ruhemann, "The Separation of Gases," 2nd ed., Oxford University Press, N.Y., 1949.
[6] William Ball, *Refrig. Eng.,* **62,** 54 (April 1954).
[7] D. H. Parkinson, *Conférence de Physique de basses températures,* Paris, 2-8 September (1955).
[8] William H. McAdams, "Heat Transmission," 3rd ed., McGraw-Hill Book Com-pany, Inc., N.Y., 1954.
[9] M. Jakob, "Heat Transfer," John Wiley & Sons, Inc., N.Y., 1949, Vol. I.
[10] S. C. Collins, *Chem. Eng.,* **53,** 106 (1946); also *Rev. Sci. Instr., 26,* 671 (1955).
[11] S. C. Collins, *Rev. Sci. Instr.,* **26,** 671 (1955).
[12] S. C. Collins, *Rev. Sci. Instr.,* **18,** 157 (1947).
[13] R. Linde, *Zt. gesamte Kalte-Industrie,* **41,** 183 (1934).
[14] P. Kapitza, *J. Physics, U.S.S.R.,* **1,** 7 (1939).
[15] Judson S. Swearingen, *Trans. Amer. Inst. Chem. Eng.,* **43,** 85 (1947).
[16] J. R. Roebuck, A novel form of refrigerator, *J. Appl. Physics,* **16,** 285 (1945).
[17] G. J. Ranque, United States Patent No. 1,952,281 (1934).
[18] Rudolf Hilsch, *Rev. Sci. Instr.,* **18,** 18 (1947). English translation by I. Ester-mann.
[19] D. H. Weitzel and O. E. Park, *Rev. Sci. Instr.,* **27,** 57 (1956).
[20] D. H. Weitzel, W. V. Lobenstein, J. W. Draper, and O. E. Park, *J. Research NBS,* **60,** 221 (1958) RP 2840.
[21] W. E. Williams, Jr., and E. Maxwell, *Rev. Sci. Instr.,* **25,** 111 (1954).

[22] John Macinko, W. R. Bjorklund, and J. E. Jensen. Manuscript in preparation (1959).

[23] E. R. Blanchard and H. W. Bittner, *Rev. Sci. Instr.,* **13,** 394 (1942).

[24] I. L. Zelmanov, *Comptes rendus (Doklady) Acad. Sci. URSS,* **19,** 469 (1938); *ibid.* **20,** 537 (1938).

[25] D. B. Mann. Unpublished results NBS-CEL (1957).

[26] D. B. Mann, W. R. Bjorklund, and John Macinko, NBS. Manuscript in preparation (1959).

[27] I. L. Zelmanov, *Comptes rendus (Doklady) Acad. Sci. URSS,* **22,** 25 (1939).

[28] F. Simon, *Zt. gesamte Kalte-Industrie,* **39,** 89 (1932); and *Proc. 7th Int. Cong. Refrig.,* **1,** 367 (1936).

[29] G. L. Pickard and F. E. Simon, *Proc. Phys. Soc.,* **60,** 405 (1948).

[30] A. H. Cooke, B. V. Rollin, and F. Simon, *Rev. Sci. Instr.,* **10,** 251 (1939).

[31] R. B. Scott and J. W. Cook, *Rev. Sci. Instr.,* **19,** 889 (1948).

[32] P. Kapitza, *Proc. Roy. Soc.,* **147A,** 189 (1934).

[33] S. C. Collins, *Science,* **116,** 289 (1952).

[34] B. V. Rollin, *Proc. Phys. Soc.,* **48,** 18 (1936).

[35] R. Spoendlin, *J. Rech. CNRS,* **28,** 1 (1954).

[36] H. M. Long and F. E. Simon, *Appl. Sci. Res.,* **4,** 237 (1954).

[37] F. X. Eder, *Conférence de Physique de basses temperatures,* Paris, Sept. 2-8 (1955).

Chapter III

SEPARATION OF GASES

3.1. The separation and purification of gases constitute the major industrial application of low-temperature processes. Almost all commercial oxygen and nitrogen, and all neon, argon, krypton, and xenon, are obtained by the distillation of liquid air. When a rectifying column is designed to concentrate the rare gas constituents of air, the helium present also can be concentrated, but this is a very minor source of helium. The bulk of commercial helium is obtained from helium-bearing natural gas. However, here also the separation is effected by a low-temperature process. Low temperatures have been used commercially to separate hydrogen from coke-oven gas and other sources of impure hydrogen. The low-boiling components of natural gas, methane, ethane, ethylene, etc., are separated and purified by low-temperature distillations. Finally a start has been made in the commercial production of deuterium by distilling liquid hydrogen.

Because of the economic importance of this application of cryogenics, extensive experimental and theoretical studies of the processes have been carried out and there has been a continuous development leading to better and more efficient equipment and methods. As a result, there is a quantity of literature on the subject, one of the most complete and modern treatises being "The Separation of Gases" by Ruhemann [1].

It is the intention here only to illustrate in a qualitative way the methods and principles employed in some commercial low-temperature gas-separation plants, since detailed treatments are available elsewhere. More detail will be given about less-known processes, particularly those employing temperatures lower than are normally encountered in commercial gas-separation plants.

3.2. At the outset it is well to consider briefly the theoretical ideal process for separating gases. This is the well-known idealized process, described in thermodynamics texts, using the fictitious "semipermeable membranes" (see Figure 3.1).

Assume that the cylinder contains n moles of a gaseous mixture of which xn are nitrogen and $(1 - x)n$ are oxygen, at a moderate pressure, for example 1 atmosphere, such that we can without serious error assume that the ideal gas laws are applicable. The partial pressures of the two components will be xP and $(1 - x)P$ respectively, where P is the total pressure. The problem is to determine the least amount of work required to separate the mixture into two parts, one pure nitrogen and the other pure oxygen, still at atmospheric pressure.

Suppose the container to be fitted with two frictionless pistons as shown in Figure 3.1, A. Piston I is permeable to nitrogen only and piston 2 is permeable to oxygen only. Now if the pistons are slowly moved as shown at B at relative speeds that will everywhere maintain the initial pressure, the end result will be C, wherein all the nitrogen is in the left part of the cylinder and all the oxygen at the right, both still at atmospheric pressure. This result was attained at the expense of a certain amount of energy. The energy required is least if we further assume that heat can flow out of the container and thus render the process isothermal. In this case the energy expended is simply that required to compress isothermally the two gaseous components from the partial pressures they exerted as constituents of the mixture to their final pressure, one atmosphere. This energy is, for the oxygen,

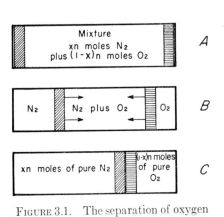

FIGURE 3.1. The separation of oxygen and nitrogen using the fictitious "semipermeable" membranes. This process removes the "entropy of mixing" and requires the least work.

$$W_{O_2} = (1 - x)n \int_{(1-x)P}^{P} p \, dv = (1 - x)n \left[-RT \ln p \right]_{(1-x)P}^{P}$$
$$= nRT(1 - x) \ln (1 - x)$$

since for an ideal gas $pv = RT$.

For the nitrogen

$$W_{N_2} = xn \int_{xP}^{P} p \, dv = xn \left[-RT \ln p \right]_{xP}^{P} = nRT \, x \ln x$$

Then the total work of isothermal separation is

$$W = W_{N_2} + W_{O_2} = nRT[(1 - x) \ln (1 - x) + x \ln x].$$

Thus to separate 1 mole of air into pure oxygen and nitrogen at 25°C, 298.15°K, would require

$$W = 1.986 \times 298.15[0.21 \ln 0.21 + 0.79 \ln 0.79]$$
$$W = -304.3 \text{ cal per mole}$$

The negative sign indicates that work is done upon the gas.

One mole of air weighs $0.21 \times 32 + 0.79 \times 28.016 = 28.82$ g.

$$1 \text{ cal} = 4.183 \text{ Joules} = \frac{4.183}{3600} \text{ watt hours}$$

Therefore the separation of air will require an energy expenditure of

$$304.3 \times \frac{453.6}{28.82} \times \frac{4.183}{3600} = 5.56 \text{ watt hours per lb}$$

Or,

$$\frac{5.56}{0.21} = 26.5 \text{ watt hours per lb of oxygen.}$$

Needless to say, the practical methods of gas separation do not approach this figure. However, it is of interest to compare practical results with the theoretical minimum. Ruhemann [1] reports a power consumption of 550 watt hours per cubic meter of 98 percent oxygen for the Linde-Fränkl low-pressure oxygen plant. This is 175 watt hours per lb, or about 6.6 the theoretical minimum.

Even though this appears to be a very feeble approach to the ideal, the low-temperature process still is the most efficient so far discovered for separating the components of air. The process consists of cooling the air until it is partially liquefied and then processing the mixture of oxygen and nitrogen in a rectifying column which separates the low-boiling nitrogen from the high-boiling oxygen.

I. The Rectifying Column

3.3. The operation of a rectifying column depends upon the different vapor pressures of the components of the mixture being treated. Thus when there is equilibrium between the liquid and vapor phases of a mixture, the lower-boiling component tends to concentrate in the vapor phase. Figure

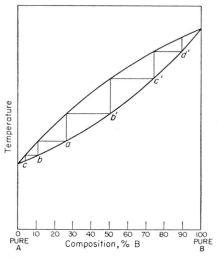

Figure 3.2. Two-component liquid-vapor phase equilibrium diagram.

3.2 is a phase equilibrium diagram showing the relations between the liquid and vapor phases of such a mixture. The upper curve is the curve of the "dew points," the temperature at which vapor of a given composition starts to condense. The lower curve shows the temperature at which liquid of the indicated composition will boil. Thus for a given temperature of equilibrium between liquid and vapor, the corresponding point on the upper curve gives the composition of the vapor and the point at the same ordinate on the lower curve gives the composition of the liquid. It is evident that a simple evaporation will effect a partial separation; the vapor will be richer in the lower-boiling component (since its vapor pressure is higher) and the remaining liquid will become richer in the higher-boiling component.

The rectifying column is a device for cascading the effects of a large number of evaporations. A typical rectifying column consists of a boiler at the bottom, a number of trays or plates, each holding a layer of liquid through which the ascending vapor is caused to percolate, and a condenser at the top where a large fraction of the vapor is condensed, and the liquid thus formed is returned to trickle down the column. Figure 3.3 illustrates a rectifying column which uses perforated plates. The perforations are so small, about $\frac{1}{40}$ inch, that the vapor rising through them prevents the liquid from running down through, so the liquid level on each plate rises until the excess spills over the weir into the standpipe which carries it down to the next lower plate. A "theoretical plate" would achieve the complete equilibrium indicated by the phase diagram, Figure 3.2. It is customary to indicate a figure of merit of a

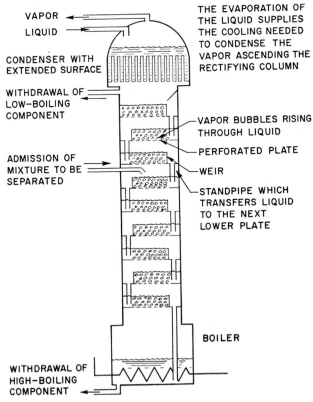

FIGURE 3.3. Rectifying column using perforated plates.

rectifying column in terms of the number of equivalent "theoretical plates." In the ideal case the vapor leaving a given plate is in equilibrium with the liquid on the plate according to the phase equilibrium shown in Figure 3.2. Also, the liquid on the plate next above will have the same composition as the vapor below. This also implies that there is a definite temperature difference between the two, a difference just sufficient to maintain equal vapor pressure above the trays of liquids of different composition. (For this analysis it can be assumed that the pressure throughout the column is constant.) This critical temperature difference (and difference in composition) between the liquids on adjacent "theoretical plates" may be explained as follows: If the upper of the two plates being considered should tend to get cooler, extra condensation of the rising vapor will warm it. Conversely, if the plate should tend to get warmer, because of an excess concentration of the higher-boiling component, the lower-boiling component in the rising vapor will dilute the mixture, increase its vapor pressure, and accordingly lower its temperature.

The lines forming steps between the equilibrium curves of Figure 3.2 illustrate the behavior of an ideal multiple-plate rectifying column when referred to the phase equilibrium diagram. Assume that saturated vapor of composition a is admitted at an appropriate intermediate level as indicated. After steady operating conditions have been reached, the liquid on the plate above will have the same composition. The vapor above this next plate, however, will have the composition indicated by b. Likewise, an additional plate will bring the composition to c; so by adding more and more plates we can approach as closely as desired to the completely pure low-boiling components. The same argument applies to the lower part of the column, stepping from the inlet composition a to b' to c', etc. This discussion is strictly applicable only to a column operating at *total reflux*, that is complete condensation of the vapor which reaches the condenser. This simple analysis will serve to illustrate the principle of operation; of course, the behavior of a column with partial reflux is more complex. Thorough treatments of distillation theory and practice may be found in references [2], [3], [4], [5].

II. Separation of Air

3.4. Since the production of oxygen from air was the first and is still economically the most important low-temperature industrial process, the separation of air will be considered first. For simplicity air will be considered to be a binary mixture of 21 percent oxygen and 79 percent nitrogen. The air introduced into the low-temperature cycle of a separation plant is usually free of carbon dioxide and water vapor, but it does contain 0.93 percent argon. In practice the argon cannot really be ignored, but the fundamentals of air separation can best be described without this added complication. The other rare gas constituents of air—helium, neon, krypton and xenon—are present in such small quantities and have boiling points so far removed from those of oxygen and nitrogen that they introduce no important complications.

The simplest form of air separation plant is shown in Figure 3.4, the original single-column Linde cycle first operated in 1902. Compressed air, introduced through the heat exchanger, traverses a coil in the liquid reservoir (evaporator) at the bottom of a rectifying column, is expanded to atmospheric pressure at the valve V, and the resultant mixture, mostly liquid with a little vapor, is delivered to the top of the column. The liquid filters down the column and is enriched in oxygen by intimate contact with the rising vapors. Finally, it is partially or wholly evaporated in the boiler by thermal contact with the compressed air passing through the condensing coil. In the state of dynamic equilibrium, oxygen, either as a liquid or as a gas, is continuously withdrawn from the bottom of the column and impure nitrogen vapor from the top. If the oxygen is withdrawn as a gas, both the nitrogen and oxygen return through the heat exchanger, precooling the incoming compressed air. If liquid oxygen is withdrawn, only cold nitrogen vapor returns through the exchanger.

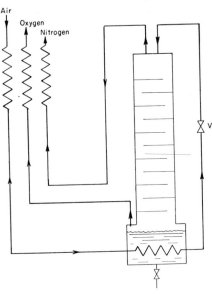

For the production of gaseous oxygen, pressures of 30 to 60 atmospheres are needed. If the plant is to yield liquid oxygen, the greater demand for refrigeration requires initial pressures up to 200 atmospheres.

FIGURE 3.4.   Simple Linde air separation column.

Figure 3.5 shows a series of isobaric curves giving phase equilibria for mixtures of oxygen and nitrogen. If we turn our attention to the pair of curves marked $P = 1.000$ (1 atmosphere), it is noted that for a liquid mixture of 79 percent nitrogen and 21 percent oxygen the composition of the equilibrium vapor will be about 7 percent oxygen. Thus the waste gas that is discharged through the heat exchanger in the single Linde column carries with it a great deal of the oxygen originally present in the air. This is a serious shortcoming of the simple single column. It can be remedied by providing a double column as shown in Figure 3.6. Here the liquid air is introduced at an intermediate point B along the lower column, and a condenser-evaporator at the top of the lower column makes the arrangement a complete reflux distillation

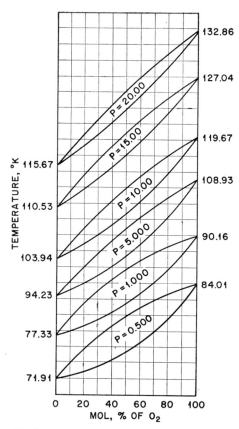

FIGURE 3.5. Phase equilibria of oxygen-nitrogen mixtures [Dodge and Dunbar, Circulation Method, *J. Amer. Chem. Soc.*, **49**, 591 (1927)].

column, which delivers pure nitrogen at E. In order for the column simultaneously to deliver pure oxygen, the oxygen-rich liquid (about 38 percent O_2) from the bottom boiler is introduced at an intermediate level C along the upper column. The reflux and rectification in the upper column produce pure oxygen at the bottom and pure nitrogen at the top. Since the condenser must condense nitrogen vapor by evaporating liquid oxygen, it is necessary to operate the lower column at a higher pressure, about 5 atmospheres, while the upper column is operated at approximately atmospheric pressure. This requires regulating valves to reduce the pressure of fluids from the lower column as they are admitted to the upper column.

In the circuit shown, gaseous oxygen and nitrogen are withdrawn at room temperature. This is the same result that was accomplished by the ideal process described earlier. Of course liquid oxygen could be withdrawn from

D and liquid nitrogen from E, but in this case more refrigeration would be needed.

As has been stated before, even the best modern low-temperature air separation plant has an efficiency only a small fraction of the theoretical optimum. The principal sources of inefficiency are threefold: (1) the non-ideality of the refrigerating process, (2) the imperfection of the heat exchangers, and (3) losses of refrigeration through imperfect insulation. When the product of the separation is delivered as liquid, the efficiency of the refrigeration process is usually of the most importance, since the refrigeration required to cool and condense the gas is much greater than that wasted through imperfect heat exchange or heat leak through insulation. When the pure gaseous product is delivered at atmospheric temperature, nearly all the refrigeration supplied is consumed by losses through insulation and by imperfect heat exchange, so in this case the over-all efficiency of the process is just as dependent on good heat exchange and good insulation as it is on efficient refrigeration.

3.5. Removal of Argon from Air. Since atmospheric air contains 0.93 percent of argon, which has a boiling point intermediate between those of nitrogen and oxygen, argon will appear as an impurity in either or both the nitrogen or the oxygen delivered from an air separation column such as that shown in Figure 3.6. If the argon is collected with the oxygen, the latter will contain about 5 percent argon. If the argon is extracted together with the nitrogen, the nitrogen will have 1.3 percent argon as an impurity. Thus if really pure oxygen and nitrogen are needed, it is necessary to remove the argon. Moreover, there is an extensive commercial demand for argon, so there is an economic incentive to obtain the argon as a third pure constituent in an air-separation plant. Argon is widely used as the inert gas for shielded-arc welding and to provide the inert atmosphere to retard filament evaporation in incandescent lamps.

Figure 3.7 illustrates an air separation column having an auxiliary column in which argon is concentrated. The main column is tapped at the level where the argon concentration is highest and gas from this level is fed to the argon column where the argon is separated and the O_2 and N_2 mixture returned to the appropriate level of the principal column. The yield of this plant is said to be 50 percent of the atmospheric argon, and the mixture delivered contains 45 percent argon, 50 percent oxygen and 5 percent nitrogen. The oxygen is readily removed by chemical reduction. The remaining nitrogen impurity is not undesirable if the argon is to be used for filling incandescent lamps. However, for shielded-arc welding, the argon must be nitrogen-free. This requirement has led to some modifications in equipment for concentrating argon. Detailed information is not presently available, although it is logical to assume that the effort has been directed toward a complete elimination of nitrogen even at the expense of a higher oxygen

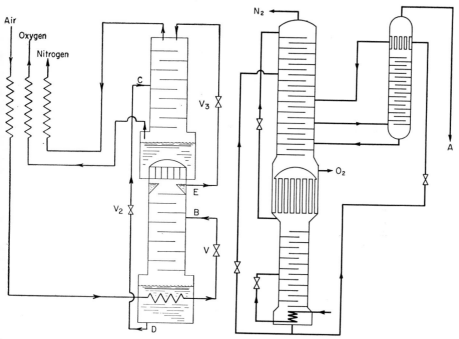

FIGURE 3.6. Linde double-column air separator.

FIGURE 3.7. Air separation plant with
auxiliary column for separating argon.

concentration in the argon, since it is relatively easy to remove the last traces
of oxygen.

3.6. Separation of Neon and Helium.

When a double column for air
separation is operated continuously for long periods, it is found that the effectiveness of the condenser-evaporator begins to decrease. It seems that the
heat transfer between condensing vapor in the tubes and evaporating liquid
around them suffers deterioration. This is caused by a gradual accumulation
of helium and neon in the nitrogen, lowering the partial pressure of the
nitrogen so that it will not condense at the existing temperature. This blocking can be easily overcome by providing a purge line through which the accumulation of helium and neon in the nitrogen is discharged at regular intervals.

However, instead of throwing the neon away, it can be collected by directing
the mixture being withdrawn into a condenser cooled with liquid nitrogen.
Since the mixture is at a pressure of 5 atmospheres and a temperature of about
93°K, cooling to 77°K at the same pressure will condense a great deal of the
nitrogen, which then is admitted to the top of the upper column. The remaining gas will be considerably richer in the helium-neon mixture; Ruhemann
gives the figures shown in Table 3.1 as a rough average.

TABLE 3.1. COMPOSITION OF THE NEON-HELIUM
FRACTION REMOVED FROM AN AIR SEPARATION
PLANT, PERCENT BY VOLUME

Gas	Concentration
N_2	70 percent
Ne	23 percent
He	7 percent

The neon is the valuable constituent of this product; helium can be obtained much more cheaply from helium-bearing natural gas. The nitrogen is removed first by further condensation accomplished by compressing the mixture to 50 atmospheres and cooling it with liquid nitrogen. The last traces of nitrogen are removed chemically by reaction with hot calcium or magnesium. The principal use of the neon in gaseous discharge tubes used for advertising signs requires the complete removal of nitrogen, but the helium contamination is not objectionable; so "technical neon" containing about 30 percent helium is often used in such tubes. The neon could be readily separated from the helium by the use of liquid hydrogen as a refrigerant (as was done by Meissner [6]) but since liquid hydrogen is not at this time usually available in industrial processes, this method of separation is not extensively used. Selective adsorption on extended surface material such as charcoal or silica gel can be used to separate helium from neon, since neon is much more strongly adsorbed and retained.

3.7. Concentration of Krypton and Xenon. Krypton and xenon, being the heaviest of the inert gases, are most suitable for filling incandescent lamps to reduce filament evaporation. In the usual air separation plant they appear as slight impurities in the oxygen and are generally ignored because of their extremely low concentration. Small amounts have been separated from the oxygen in an industrial plant, but the process is quite laborious and costly. Because of the need, a number of firms began to design plants specifically for the production of a krypton-xenon mixture, and not as by-products of a plant producing oxygen or nitrogen. The essential feature of this process is the scrubbing of a large quantity of gaseous air by a countercurrent of a small amount of liquid air. In this process nearly all the krypton and xenon are removed from the gaseous air and dissolved in the liquid air. The result is a manageable quantity of liquid air, rich in krypton and xenon, from which the rare gases can be removed by partial evaporation and rectification.

Other developments have combined air separation with the production of krypton. One of the large krypton plants was built by the Linde Company in Hungary. It treats 25,000 cubic meters of air per hour, extracting a mixture of 93.5 percent krypton and 6.5 percent xenon. The rare gas recovery is said to be more than 90 percent. The power consumption amounts to 34-36 kilowatt hours per liter of gaseous product (STP).

III. Separating Helium from Natural Gas

3.8. The large-scale separation of helium from natural gas has been described by Mullins [7]. His description specifically refers to the Otis, Kansas, plant of the United States Bureau of Mines, where the natural gas contains approximately 1.4 percent helium, 12.7 percent nitrogen, 78.2 percent methane and 7.7 percent ethane and other heavier hydrocarbons. However, the description is representative of other Bureau of Mines plants which process natural gas of different composition. The helium content at the various plants ranges from 1 to 8 percent and the nitrogen from 12 to 80 percent.

Figure 3.8 is a schematic diagram of the helium separation plant. Natural gas, compressed to 600 psi and treated to remove carbon dioxide, hydrogen sulfide, and water vapor, enters the heat exchanger A, where it is almost totally condensed by the cold outgoing gas. The pressure is then reduced to 250 psi and the gas is admitted to the heat exchanger-separator B, where it is further cooled with nitrogen vapor. In the separator about 98 percent of the gas is liquefied, and the part remaining in the vapor phase consists of about 60 percent helium and 40 percent nitrogen with a very small amount of methane. The cold nitrogen vapor from a separate refrigeration cycle passes down cooling tubes of exchanger B and, in addition to its cooling function,

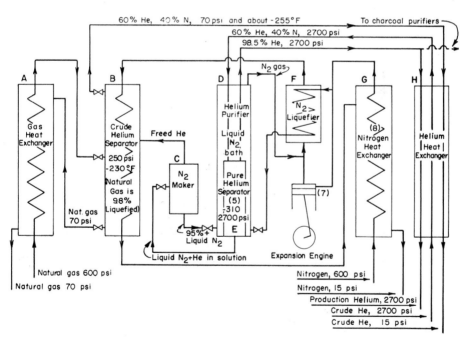

Figure 3.8. Schematic diagram of a helium separation plant of the United States Bureau of Mines.

causes some rectification of the gas phase which increases the helium content. Both liquid and gas are continuously withdrawn from the separator. The gas phase, called *crude helium* is warmed to near room temperature in heat exchanger H and sent to temporary storage pending further purification. The liquid phase, which has been depleted of helium, passes through heat exchanger A and furnishes the refrigeration to cool and condense the incoming gas. Finally the processed gas is recompressed and returned to the natural gas pipeline. The process improves the value of the natural gas as a fuel, since only non-combustible constituents have been removed.

The purification of the crude helium is accomplished by compressing it to 2700 psi, cooling it first by passage through heat exchanger H and then in the separator pot E, which is immersed in a bath of liquid nitrogen. In the separator pot nearly all the nitrogen in the crude helium is condensed and removed as liquid. This liquid contains some dissolved helium which is largely removed and returned to the process gas by reducing the pressure to 250 psi and separating the resultant liquid and vapor phases in the nitrogen-maker C. Helium from the separator E has a purity of about 98.5 percent. The final purification is accomplished by passing this cold helium through charcoal adsorption purifiers to remove the 1.5 percent of nitrogen. One of the principal industrial uses of helium, shielded-arc welding, requires the very complete elimination of nitrogen and hydrogen, so nearly all the helium produced today is subjected to the purification by charcoal adsorption purifiers. The nitrogen liquefier F, with its heat exchanger G, supplies the liquid nitrogen for the pure-helium separator D and the cold gaseous nitrogen for the crude-helium separator B.

IV. Separating Deuterium from Natural Hydrogen by Distilling Liquid Hydrogen

3.9. The separation of deuterium from natural hydrogen by distillation has been under consideration for many years. Some economic and technical studies have been made which indicate that where there is an abundant supply of natural hydrogen, deuterium can be produced at low cost by this method. The economics will not be discussed here, but since inquiries are frequently made concerning the process, a brief outline of some of the technical aspects seems advisable.

Natural hydrogen contains about 1 part in 6400 of deuterium. The deuterium atoms are in combination with hydrogen in the form of diatomic HD. Thus if deuterium is to be concentrated by distillation the first step is to concentrate HD. The technical feasibility of this concentration seems quite attractive when it is noted that at the boiling point of normal hydrogen, $20.38°K$, where H_2 has a vapor pressure of 760 mm Hg, the vapor pressure of HD is only 438 mm Hg. Of course the low concentration is a drawback; and if 3200 cubic feet of hydrogen had to be liquefied from scratch to produce 1 cubic foot of HD, the scheme would be very unattractive. However, distillation equipment can be arranged so that refrigeration required by the condenser is largely supplied by the evaporation taking place in the boiler and the cooling required by the incoming feed gas is mostly supplied by the outgoing streams of enriched and depleted hydrogen.

A circuit of this kind is illustrated in Figure 3.9. Cold vapor from the top of the column is compressed slightly by the pump and condensed in the heat exchanger immersed in the boiler, causing the surrounding liquid to boil. The liquid thus formed is returned to the top of the column through a throttling valve where its pressure is reduced to that of the column. The multichannel heat exchanger cools the feed stream by exchanging its heat to the three exit streams. It is seen that if the equipment is well insulated and the pump and heat exchangers are efficient, the amount of liquid hydrogen supplied by the liquefier need be only a small fraction of that treated in the column.

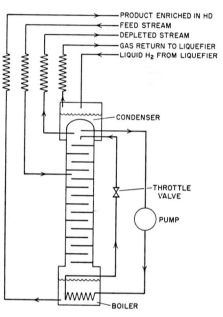

Timmerhaus, Weitzel, Flynn, and Draper [8] have made some laboratory studies to determine the behavior of liquid hydrogen being distilled and to investigate the effect of varying certain characteristics of the distillation column. Their objective was to obtain the data needed by those who may be interested in using low-temperature distillation for large-scale separation of deuterium. They studied packed columns, perforated plates, and plates made of screen wire. A packed column $\frac{1}{2}$ inch in diameter was found to have a height equivalent to a theoretical plate of about $\frac{1}{2}$ inch. Since packed columns of large diameter are subject to channeling, they are seldom used in large-scale separation columns.

FIGURE 3.9. Flow diagram illustrating a column for separating HD from natural hydrogen.

The most useful measurements were those made on screen plates. To observe the behavior, a single-plate still with an observation window was first constructed (Figure 3.10). The column was made of $1\frac{1}{2}$ inches O.D., thin-wall stainless steel tubing. With this apparatus it was found that the cross-sectional area of the liquid downcomer had to be unusually large (about 10 percent of the column cross section) in order to achieve maximum throughput. Also it was found that a $\frac{3}{16}$-inch weir height was almost as effective as a 2-inch height. Accordingly low weirs with their consequent small liquid holdup can be used. This also permits a closer plate spacing. Screen plates from 40 to 100 mesh were tried, and there was no significant difference in their performance. The liquid stayed on top of the plate with no tendency to run through.

Following these single-plate experiments, a multiplate still of the same diameter was studied. This still was constructed so that the types of plates, plate spacing, and downcomer areas could be changed. The still was operated with several mixtures of H_2 and D_2. The results are summarized as follows:

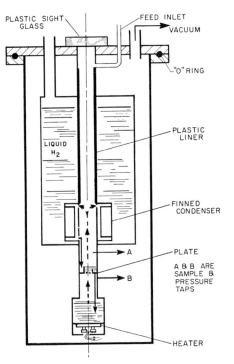

FIGURE 3.10. One-plate still.

(1) The conclusions reached by observing the single plate were confirmed.

(2) A large plate spacing is not required. A separation of $2\frac{1}{2}$ inches was found to be as good as a 5-inch separation.

(3) Vapor velocities as high as 7 inches per second are permissible for the 40-mesh screen plates without causing unstable operation of the column.

(4) The over-all plate efficiencies are encouraging.

The information obtained from these experiments was used to design a pilot plant for studies of the actual separation of HD from natural hydrogen. This column contains thirty 40-mesh-screen plates 6 inches in diameter and has a maximum feed rate of 14.2 scfm. The column has been operated with vapor velocities ranging from 0.2 to 2.0 inches per second, and reflux ratios ranging from total reflux to an L/D of 2.0, where L is the mass rate at which liquid is being returned to the top of the column by the condenser and D is the mass rate at which vapor is being withdrawn from the top of the column. Over-all plate efficiences were found to be between 45 and 55 percent, depending upon the vapor velocity. These values are lower than those found previously in $1\frac{1}{2}$-inch diameter columns employing the same type of plate. However they are higher than values reported for bubble-cap plates.

No dependence of the over-all plate efficiencies on either composition or reflux ratio was found. It was noted, however, that at very low vapor velocities (0.1 to 0.5 inch per second) the plate efficiency dropped sharply. This effect is not uncommon, since at low vapor velocities the vapor tends to jet up through the liquid wherever irregularities may appear in the plate surface. This poor mixing of liquid and vapor on the plate naturally tends to lower the plate efficiency.

Two hydrogen distillation plants have been constructed and operated in Europe. One at Toulouse, France, has a deuterium production rate equivalent to 2.5 tons of heavy water per year. Another in Germany has an equivalent rate of 6 tons of heavy water per year.

V. PURIFICATION

3.10. The term *purification* is used here to denote the removal of small amounts of objectionable contaminants from a gas being processed; for example, the removal of water vapor and carbon dioxide from air prior to liquefaction. It is useful to treat such purification processes separately because they are in a somewhat different category from the purification effected by the gas separation columns described earlier. Just to be precise about the use of the terms in this discussion, the following admittedly artificial distinction is made: *Purification* removes and discards unwanted contaminants; *separation* concentrates and preserves desirable constituents.

3.11. Chemical Purification. Although chemical methods of purification do not themselves involve low temperatures, they are often used in purifying gases for liquefaction. Water can be removed by passing the gas over a desiccant, which takes up the water as water of crystallization. This method of drying is little used in large plants at the present time, however, having been replaced by methods utilizing physical adsorption or refrigeration. The standard process for removing carbon dioxide from air has been to pass the air through a tower in which it is scrubbed with a countercurrent of a caustic solution such as sodium hydroxide. It is necessary to renew the caustic solution from time to time as the reaction with CO_2 forms sodium carbonate and accordingly weakens the solution. This method is still extensively used, although many modern plants are adopting refrigerative purifiers which have the advantage that there is no requirement for renewing chemicals.

The removal of oxygen from hydrogen being liquefied is accomplished by causing it to react with the hydrogen to form water. There are several catalysts which will promote this reaction. Metallic nickel chemically deposited on an extended surface support such as alumina is a good catalyst when heated to about 300°C. A very effective catalyst, available commercially, consists of palladium which has been chemically deposited upon an extended surface support. This catalyst is operative at ordinary room temperatures. Its principal disadvantage is the fact that it is rendered temporarily ineffective (poisoned) by some impurities such as certain hydrocarbons or carbon monoxide, and it is permanently deteriorated by chlorine. The hot nickel catalyst is less subject to these objections.

3.12. Purification by Refrigeration. The refrigeration purifier developed by W. F. Giauque is a very successful device for removing readily condensable impurities such as water and oil vapor from a gas before liquefaction. A purifier of this type used in the NBS hydrogen liquefaction system is shown in Figure 3.11. In this application the refrigeration purifier is combined with a silica-gel adsorption purifier so that the liquid nitrogen which cools the silica-gel also provides the cooling for the refrigeration purifier. Hydrogen at high pressure, containing water and oil vapor, enters the bottom of the strong insulated tube and passes through the interstices between the tubes of a heat exchanger E_1 of the Giauque-Hampson type. As it rises, the water and oil condense on the surfaces of the progressively colder heat-exchanger tubes. The velocity of the gas is kept low enough that these liquids can drain by gravity and be removed.

At a certain level the freezing temperature is reached (the "frost line") and from here up the water is deposited as ice. Of course, the thickest deposit of ice is at the level where the freezing temperature is just reached, because the

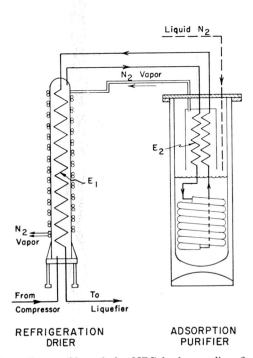

FIGURE 3.11. Refrigeration purifier of the NBS hydrogen liquefier. The illustration includes an associated adsorption purifier to show the source of refrigeration.

amount of water vapor in equilibrium with the hydrogen decreases rapidly at lower temperatures. From the top of the purifier (about $-110°C$) the hydrogen goes to heat exchanger E_2, where it is further cooled, and finally flows through the silica-gel adsorption purifier, where nitrogen and possibly other volatile impurities are removed. The returning pure hydrogen, still at high pressure, flows up through heat exchanger E_2, cooling the incoming stream, and then returns through the small tubes of heat exchanger E_1, providing the cooling to condense the moisture on the outside of the tubes. The cold nitrogen vapor is routed through a third passage of heat exchanger E_2 and through tubes wound on the outside of the refrigeration purifier. It should be pointed out that the refrigeration purifier could be served by a refrigerator which cools the gas at the top instead of sending it through the exchanger E_2 and the adsorption purifier.

After some time of operation, usually a few hours, the accumulation of ice begins to seriously restrict the passages and causes the pressure difference across the purifier to increase. At this time the hydrogen can be diverted to a second purifier and the first warmed until the ice all melts and drains out. However, it has been found that a simple expedient will greatly prolong the time of continuous operation of a single purifier. When it is noted that the pressure drop across the purifier has increased markedly, some of the returning cold hydrogen is allowed to bypass the purifier. This results in less cooling and consequently the "frost line" will rise, and a great deal of the ice formerly deposited will melt and can be removed as liquid water. Care should be taken that the water is given sufficient time to drain, because the refreezing of the water can exert sufficient pressure to collapse the copper tubes.

Alternating regenerators and reversing heat exchangers were discussed in Chapter 2 in relation to the liquefaction of air. It was necessary to include them at that time because of their function of conserving refrigeration. Because it would have been awkward to do otherwise, their purifying function in this application was also discussed at that time. However, no consideration was given to their possible use in purifying gases other than air. It is natural to assume that this purification process is generally applicable to the problem of purification of gases being liquefied. However, upon closer examination it is seen that for air liquefaction there is a unique circumstance which favors the process. That is the fact that the atmosphere provides an essentially infinite reservoir of raw material; returning the impurities to the atmosphere has no appreciable effect upon its composition. On the other hand, if the process were applied without modification to the purification of hydrogen, and the impurities were returned to the feed gas, the concentration of impurity would increase without limit as pure hydrogen is withdrawn from the system. Thus it is obvious that one must provide a mechanism whereby impurities are completely removed from the system if the process is to be used to purify a gas from a finite supply.

Figure 3.12 is a flow diagram illustrating how a reversing heat exchanger may be utilized to remove from a gas being liquefied the final traces of impurities of the type which in higher concentrations are removable by chemical methods. For simplicity the ordinary Joule-Thomson liquefier is used for illustration. Figure 3-12A shows the first phase of the operation wherein the high-pressure impure gas is being cooled and is depositing its impurities on the surfaces of channel I of the reversing heat exchanger. Figure 3.12B shows the other phase during which the high-pressure gas is traversing channel II, depositing its impurities while the impurities previously deposited in channel I are being evaporated and carried out by the low-pressure return stream. Concentration of the impurities at the warm end of the heat exchanger is defeated by the chemical purifier which removes the excess impurity resulting from the return of the impurities to the compressor.

It is apparent that this scheme will work if the impurity being dealt with is one which can be readily removed by chemical means. For some impurities (for example, nitrogen in hydrogen) chemical removal is rather difficult.

3.13. Enhancement of Vapor Pressure of Impurity Caused by High Pressure of Principal Constituent. In the design of equipment utilizing refrigerative processes for removing condensable impurities it should be noted that one cannot assume that the vapor pressure of an impurity will be that given by the measurements on the pure material. If the principal constituent

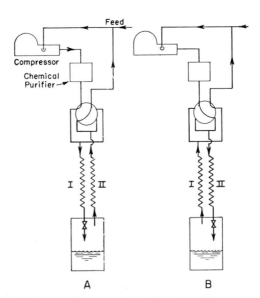

FIGURE 3.12. Reversing heat-exchanger purifier being used in combination with a chemical purifier.

is at a high pressure, the vapor pressure of the impurity may be greatly enhanced. For example, Dokoupil, van Soest, and Swenker [9] have computed and made extensive measurements of the equilibrium of small amounts of nitrogen and carbon monoxide in hydrogen at various pressures and at relatively low temperatures. They found that the vapor pressure of solid nitrogen in high-pressure hydrogen could be many times that computed from the equilibrium, single-component vapor-pressure-temperature relation.

3.14. Purification by Physical Adsorption. In the process known as adsorption, a layer of gas (having a thickness of one or more molecules) is condensed on the surface of a solid. The mechanism which causes this phenomenon is believed to be the attraction (van der Waals forces) between the molecules of the solid and those of the gas. Thus the molecules of the first layer are attracted most strongly and those in additional layers have diminishing affinity. Also, the amount adsorbed increases greatly as the temperature is lowered toward that at which the gas will normally condense. The heat of adsorption of the first layer is usually much greater than the ordinary heat of condensation of the gases and becomes of the same order of magnitude as the heat of condensation when the number of adsorbed layers becomes large. The amount of gas that can be adsorbed onto materials having smooth surfaces, such as ordinary glass or metals is quite small; however, there are certain substances, notably silica gel, alumina gel, and charcoal prepared from dense organic materials, that have a very porous structure, the pores being generally submicroscopic in size. As a result, their effective surface areas are enormous, as much as several hundred square meters per gram, and they will adsorb large quantities of gas. Both the pore size and the total area of the pore surfaces play a part in determining the amount of a given gas that will be adsorbed at a certain temperature and pressure.

Adsorbents of this type are very useful in purifying gases because of the preferential behavior; a gas near its condensation temperature is adsorbed very strongly, while one far removed from condensation is only slightly adsorbed. Thus charcoal at $77°K$ will adsorb and remove nitrogen from helium or hydrogen. The amount of gas adsorbed is a function of both temperature and pressure. Adsorption isotherms may be determined by measuring the variation of the amount adsorbed as a function of the pressure, while keeping the temperature constant. Figure 3.13 shows two such isotherms each for argon and nitrogen on an iron catalyst. It will be noted that as the pressure is increased there is an initial rapid rise in the amount adsorbed, followed by a slower rise. It is postulated that the initial steep part of the curve corresponds to the deposition of the first layer of adsorbed molecules, and the less steep part corresponds to the building up of additional layers. The further increase in slope at still higher pressure results from the near approach to saturation pressure at which condition the gas would condense as a bulk liquid. Bru-

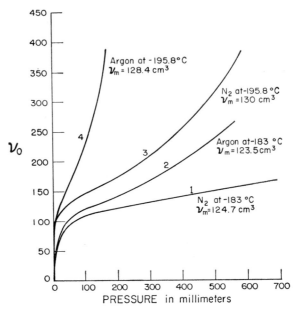

FIGURE 3.13. Adsorption isotherms for nitrogen and argon on a promoted iron catalyst. The isotherms for −195.8°C (shown by solid lines) were calculated from those
for −183°C by means of the BET equation. From Brunauer [11].

nauer, Emmett, and Teller [10] developed for such multimolecular adsorption
isotherms the equation,

$$\frac{P}{v_o(P_o - P)} = \frac{1}{v_m c} + \frac{(c-1)}{v_m c} \times \frac{P}{P_o} \tag{3.1}$$

where P and P_o are the actual pressure and the saturation pressure, respectively, v_o is the volume of gas adsorbed on a unit mass of adsorbent, v_m is the
volume required to furnish a monomolecular layer, and c is a constant. This
equation assumes that there is no limit to the number of adsorbed layers.
However, since the pores in good adsorbents are only a few molecular diameters wide, they will soon fill up, and deviations from Equation 3.1 would
be expected at higher pressures. This effect is taken into consideration in
the BET* equation

$$v_o = \frac{v_m c x}{1 - x} \cdot \frac{1 - (n+1)x^n + nx^{n+1}}{1 + (c-1)x - cx^{n+1}} \tag{3.2}$$

where $x = P/P_o$ and n is the number of layers that can be adsorbed on the
walls. Figure 3.14 is a plot of isotherms according to Equation 3.2 for several
values of n.

The effective surface of the adsorbent can be calculated from the experi-

* BET = Brunauer-Emmett-Teller.

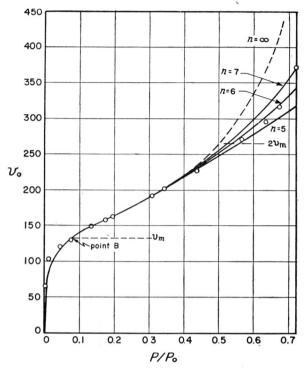

FIGURE 3.14. Adsorption isotherm for nitrogen on an iron catalyst at −195.8°C, plotted according to the BET Equation 3.2 for a series of values of n.

mental value of v_m, the volume of gas required to furnish one molecular layer of absorbed gas on a unit mass of adsorbent. This is done by assuming that the adsorbed molecules are packed side by side with the same intermolecular spacing as they would have in the solid or liquid state. The area of an adsorbent is usually given in square centimeters per gram. It is in general a good measure of the effectiveness.

This discussion of the Brunauer-Emmett-Teller equation has been presented because it seems to best describe and correlate the phenomena observed in physical adsorption at relatively high pressures. The discussion here has necessarily been very brief. For a better understanding of the subject, there is a wealth of literature; in particular there are several books which treat the subject systematically [11], [12], [13].

For an understanding of the utilization of physical adsorption in purifying a gas, it may be instructive to consider a specific case, the removal of nitrogen from hydrogen, prior to liquefaction. To be even more specific, the adsorption purifier of the hydrogen liquefier at the NBS Cryogenic Engineering Laboratory will be studied. This purifier consists of a stainless steel tube 3.36 inch I.D., $\frac{1}{8}$-inch wall, 50 feet long, wound in a compact coil 28 inches in outer diameter,

Figure 3.11. It contains 140 pounds, 3.1 cubic feet of high-surface silica gel. Silica gel was chosen in preference to charcoal because the available information at the time indicated that the adsorptive capacity *per unit volume* of "high surface" silica gel was greater than that of charcoal, even though the charcoal rated better on a mass basis. The adsorber is immersed in liquid nitrogen at approximately 65°K. The isotherms of Figure 3.13 show the advantage of lower temperature.

The large ratio of length to diameter of the purifier coil was chosen because it was believed that this would promote the saturation of the upstream region of the adsorbent while the downstream part was still essentially unsullied and therefore was still capable of removing very minute traces of nitrogen. Also, a tube of moderately small diameter allows the heat of adsorption to be transferred more readily to the surrounding bath of liquid nitrogen.

The question naturally arises about the effect of the presence of a large quantity of hydrogen on the adsorption of nitrogen. The fact that the process works is proof that the hydrogen does not blanket the surface of the adsorber and prevent the adsorption of nitrogen. The cause of this is probably the much greater heat of adsorption of the nitrogen. When nitrogen replaces previously adsorbed hydrogen, there is a substantial decrease in total potential energy of the system.

Figure 3.15 is a hypothetical representation of the condition of the adsorption purifier after being used for some time with hydrogen containing a definite concentration of nitrogen. A substantial part of the purifier near the inlet end will be saturated at the prevailing pressure and will accept no more nitrogen. Then there will be a region of transition to relatively unused adsorbent. The sharpness of the transition will depend upon the rate of flow of hydrogen, the rate at which the adsorbent can absorb the nitrogen, and the relation between the partial pressure of the nitrogen and the amount adsorbed. It is probable that the rate of adsorption will also depend upon

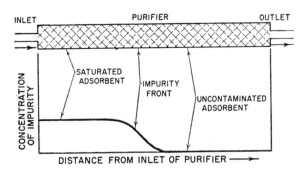

FIGURE 3.15. Qualitative representation of the concentration of nitrogen in the hydrogen passing through an adsorption purifier.

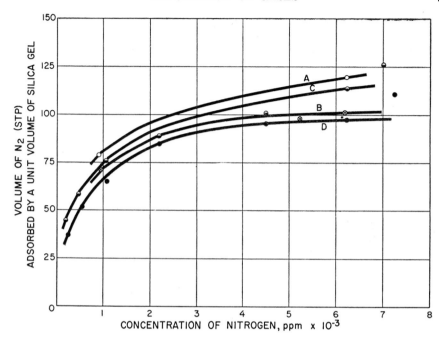

FIGURE 3.16. Observed adsorptive capacity of silica gel for nitrogen in high-pressure hydrogen. A, 900 psi, 70°K; B, 900 psi, 77.4°K; C, 1800 psi, 70°K; D, 1800 psi, 77.4°K.

the dimensions of the adsorbent particles because of the time required for the gas to penetrate to the interior of a particle. (In experiments on catalysts for the ortho-para conversion of hydrogen, it was found that decreasing the size from 10 mesh to 30 mesh caused a very substantial improvement in activity. Going to still smaller particle size was of little value.)

Some data reported by Johnson [14] accumulated in experiments with the adsorption purifier may be useful in designing other purifiers of this type. It is recognized that these measurements are not of the quantity or quality required as the basis of an empirical formula, although they are in qualitative agreement with the a priori reasoning given above.

The measurements were made by circulating hydrogen through the purifier at a known rate and maintaining a constant concentration of nitrogen at the inlet of the purifier by injecting a small flow of nitrogen into the low-pressure hydrogen near the intake of the compressors. The concentration of nitrogen was measured at the inlet to the purifier, at three taps equally spaced along the purifier, and at the exit. The total amount of nitrogen required for satura-tion was determined for several different sets of conditions. The data ob-tained are presented as isotherms for a given total pressure, showing the observed adsorptive capacities as functions of the concentration of the nitrogen in the hydrogen, Figure 3.16. It is seen that the adsorptive capacity increases with both decreasing temperature and decreasing pressure. The capacities shown are about half what would have been obtained for pure nitrogen at the same partial pressure. That is, the "enhancement factor" resulting from the presence of the high-pressure hydrogen is about 2. Thus it is seen that the presence of high-pressure hydrogen increases the apparent vapor pressure of adsorbed nitrogen just as it increases that of the pure condensed phase.

REFERENCES FOR CHAPTER 3

[1] M. Ruhemann, "The Separation of Gases," 2nd ed., Oxford University Press, N.Y., 1949.
[2] C. S. Robinson and E. R. Gilliland, "Elements of Fractional Distillation," 4th ed., McGraw-Hill Book Company, Inc., N.Y., 1950.
[3] E. Kirschbaum, "Distillation and Rectification," Chemical Publishing Company, Inc., N.Y., 1948.
[4] J. H. Perry, "Chemical Engineers' Handbook," 3rd ed., McGraw-Hill Book Company, Inc., N.Y., 1950.
[5] B. F. Dodge, "Chemical Engineering Thermodynamics," McGraw-Hill Book Company, Inc., N.Y., 1944.
[6] W. Meissner and K. Steiner, *Zt. gesamte Kalte-Industrie*, **39**, 49 (1932).
[7] P. V. Mullins, *Chem. Eng. Prog.*, **44**, 567 (1948).
[8] K. D. Timmerhaus, D. H. Weitzel, T. M. Flynn, and J. W. Draper, NBS. Unpublished results (1957).
[9] Z. Dokoupil, G. van Soest, and M. D. P. Swenker, Leiden, Comm. No. 297, *Appl. Sci. Res.*, (A)**5**, 182 (1955).
[10] S. Brunauer, P. H. Emmett, and E. Teller, *J. Amer. Chem. Soc.*, **60**, 309 (1938).
[11] S. Brunauer, "The Adsorption of Gases and Vapors:" Vol. I, Physical Adsorption, Princeton University Press, Princeton, N.J., 1943.
[12] J. W. McBain, "The Sorption of Gases and Vapors by Solids," George Routledge & Sons, London, 1932.
[13] N. K. Adam, "The Physics and Chemistry of Surfaces," 3rd ed., Oxford University Press, N.Y., 1941.
[14] V. J. Johnson, *Proc. 1957 Cryogenic Engineering Conf.*, Boulder, Colorado.

Chapter IV

COOLING BY ADIABATIC DEMAGNETIZATION

4.1. Low temperatures are usually produced by means of a liquefied gas. Temperatures below that of the normal boiling point of the liquid can be attained by lowering the pressure over the liquid surface and accordingly producing a lower vapor-liquid equilibrium temperature. For example, a temperature of about 63°K is readily obtained by pumping away the vapor from an insulated bath of liquid nitrogen and reaching the triple point condition. Of course, additional lowering of the pressure over the solid will further decrease the temperature; but since heat transfer from a solid is poor, most equipment refrigerated with pumped nitrogen is not usually cooled below the triple point. The Simon-type helium liquefiers described in Chapter 2 (pp. 64-67) were cooled with pumped solid hydrogen to temperatures as low as 10°K.

In 1932 Keesom [1] performed an experiment to attain the lowest possible temperature by lowering the pressure over liquid helium. By surrounding the silvered glass dewar containing the pumped helium with a larger dewar containing liquid helium boiling at atmospheric pressure, the radiation and conduction of heat into the pumped vessel were reduced to very small values. The inner vessel was connected by an exhaust tube of low flow resistance to a battery of diffusion pumps with an aggregate pumping speed of 675 liters per second. With this system the pressure over the liquid helium was reduced to 3.6 microns of mercury. The temperature corresponding to this vapor pressure is a little above 0.7°K. Because of the rapidly decreasing vapor pressure of helium, it appeared that this was very near the minimum temperature that could ever be produced by this means.

However, a method of producing even lower temperatures had already been suggested. In 1926 Giauque [2] and Debye [3] independently pointed out that the magneto-caloric effect would be expected to be large for paramagnetic substances at very low temperatures and could probably be used to produce lower temperatures. The experiment was first performed by Giauque and MacDougall [4] in 1933. A temperature of 0.25°K was reached.

I. The Process of Adiabatic Demagnetization

4.2. Figure 4.1 is a representation of an experimental arrangement for producing very low temperatures by adiabatic demagnetization. The paramagnetic salt is suspended by a thread in a tube containing a low pressure of gaseous helium to provide thermal communication with the surrounding bath of pumped helium. In operation the liquid helium bath is cooled by pumping to the lowest practical pressure, usually achieving a temperature in the neighborhood of 1°K. The temperature of the paramagnetic salt approaches that of the helium bath by conduction through the exchange gas.

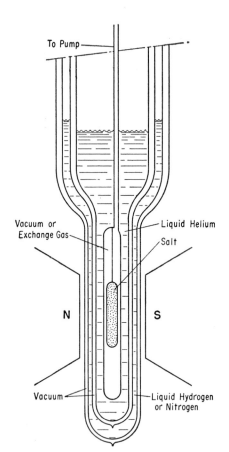

To Pump

Vacuum or
Exchange Gas

Liquid Helium

Salt

N   S

Vacuum

Liquid Hydrogen
or Nitrogen

FIGURE 4.1. Apparatus for attaining very low temperatures by the isentropic demagnetization of a paramagnetic salt.

Next the magnetic field is turned on, causing heating of the salt and a decrease in entropy of the magnetic ions by virtue of their partial alignment in the direction of the applied field. The heat produced is conducted to the surrounding bath of liquid helium so that the temperature again approaches 1°K. If the magnetic field is increased slowly the heat can flow out as it is generated—the magnetization being almost isothermal. Next the exchange gas surrounding the sample is removed by pumping, and now, with the salt thermally isolated, the magnetic field is turned off. The temperature of the sample decreases markedly as a consequence of the adiabatic demagnetization, which allows the magnetic ions to regain some of their entropy (and energy) at the expense of the lattice energy of the salt.

Some of the straightforward thermodynamic aspects of the process can be indicated by reference to the entropy-temperature diagram shown in Figure 4.2. This is an approximate representation of the data of de Klerk [5] for chromium potassium alum. The salt, originally in zero field ($H = 0$, $S = S_1$), is magnetized isothermally at the temperature T_1 by increasing the magnetic field to $H = H_1$. This magnetization, by orienting the magnetic ions of the salt and thus decreasing their disorder, causes a reduction in entropy from S_1 to S_2. Now the salt is thermally isolated from its surroundings and thus

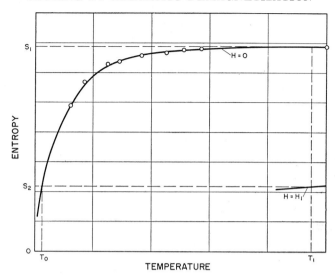

FIGURE 4.2. Temperature-entropy diagram of a paramagnetic salt, illustrating the process of magnetic cooling.

when the magnetic field is reduced to zero the process follows the horizontal isentropic line and the temperature falls to T_0.

The great decrease in temperature and the close approach to absolute zero is a consequence of the peculiar shape of the entropy-temperature relation. It is apparent that this shape corresponds to a specific heat which is greater at low temperatures. The scale of Figure 4.2 does not allow a good representation of the unusual character of the thermal properties of the salt near absolute zero. Figure 4.3 shows how the specific heat of chromium potassium

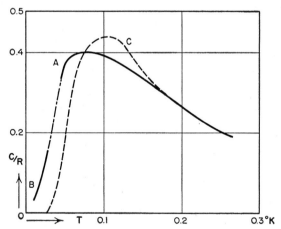

FIGURE 4.3. Specific heat of chromium potassium alum near absolute zero. Curves A and B experimental, C calculated.

alum behaves in this temperature region. The theoretical curve comes from a statistical mechanical calculation of the effect of the interaction between the magnetic chromium ions and the electric field of the crystal, which results in two energy levels differing in energy by an amount δ. This is believed to be the basic mechanism responsible for the specific heat anomaly. The resultant equation is

$$\frac{C}{R} = \frac{\delta^2}{k^2 T^2} \frac{e^{-\delta/kT^2}}{1 + e^{-\delta/kT^2}}$$

where C is the specific heat in zero magnetic field, R is the universal gas constant, δ is the energy difference between the two levels, k is Boltzmann's constant, and T is the absolute temperature. At these temperatures the ordinary lattice specific heat of the crystal is so small as to be negligible in comparison with the anomalous specific heat resulting from the paramagnetic ions.

It should be pointed out that the paramagnetic salts most suitable for producing very low temperatures are the dilute salts in which the paramagnetic ions are separated from each other by non-magnetic atoms so that there is little interaction between neighboring magnetic ions. For example, in the chromium potassium alum just discussed each magnetic chromium atom is surrounded by 47 non-magnetic neighbors.

An excellent review article on magnetic cooling has been published by Ambler and Hudson [6].

II. The Low Temperature Records

4.3. The lowest temperature thus far produced by adiabatic demagnetization of paramagnetic salts is approximately 0.001°K. De Klerk, Steenland, and Gorter [7], using mixed crystals of chromium alum and aluminum alum, reached a temperature computed to be 0.0014°K. This record has been equaled or perhaps surpassed in an experiment which used two-stage demagnetization [8], but this temperature appears to be near the minimum attainable by the method. This is a consequence of the thermal properties of the paramagnetic salts at very low temperatures. The same basic properties which are responsible for the phenomenon of adiabatic cooling interpose a barrier which limits the lowest attainable temperature.

However, quite recently much lower temperatures have been achieved by nuclear adiabatic demagnetization. The possibility was pointed out by Simon in 1937, and the experiment was first performed by Kurti, Robinson, Simon, and Spohr [9] in 1956. In this experiment the nuclear spins of copper atoms were aligned by a powerful magnetic field after the copper had been cooled to about 0.01°K by the adiabatic demagnetization of a paramagnetic material. The paramagnetic salt was chromium potassium alum in the form of a slurry with glycerin and water. The copper specimen was made up of

1540 enameled wires of No. 40 S.W.G. These wires formed the thermal link to the paramagnetic salt and the copper "specimen" consisted of the same wires folded four times in a length of about 7 cm to form a compact mass of about 0.75 gram atom of copper. It was necessary to use finely divided insulated copper to minimize the eddy-current heating which, in a solid specimen, would be about one hundred times as great as the energy removed by the adiabatic cooling.

In the experiment the paramagnetic salt was first cooled to approximately $1.0°K$ in the presence of a magnetic field of 20 kilogauss. The demagnetization of the salt reduced the temperature of the salt and the nuclear specimen to about $0.01°K$. Next the nuclear specimen (copper) was slowly magnetized to fields as high as 28 kilogauss. The heat so produced was absorbed by the paramagnetic salt without causing a significant increase of temperature. Then, upon demagnetization, the temperature of the copper nuclei fell to approximately 20 microdegrees. Thus at this writing the low temperature record is 20 millionths of a degree above absolute zero. Kurti, et al., point out, however, that the importance of this type of experiment is not the record low temperature but the information that it may yield about the behavior of nuclear spins in solids and their interaction with their environment.

There are two known procedures that may be expected to contribute to the further production of very low temperatures. The first is the employment of more intense magnetic fields. Many laboratories have, or are in the process of acquiring, equipment capable of producing fields of 100 kilogauss or greater. The second method is the further use of the cascade principle to produce lower temperatures. A lower starting temperature for nuclear demagnetization could be achieved by employing two or more adiabatic precooling stages. Of course there is always the practical problem of designing so that the magnetic field of one stage does not enter those regions in which the field should be zero. Also the provision of thermal paths when and where they are needed and the necessary thermal insulation may pose difficult problems.

The method of measuring temperatures produced by adiabatic demagnetization is discussed in Chapter 5.

III. A MAGNETIC REFRIGERATOR

4.4. In most experiments using the adiabatic demagnetization process as described above, the experimental region is initially cooled and measurements are made as the temperature rises. Since the thermal isolation is exceptionally good, the undisturbed temperature rise is usually very slow. However, some measurements introduce energy and increase the rate of temperature rise.

An apparatus capable of extracting heat continuously and thus maintaining a constant low temperature indefinitely would be of considerable value in

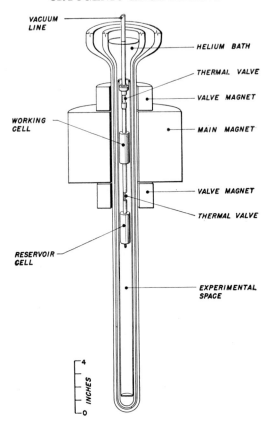

FIGURE 4.4.   Magnetic refrigerator.

many investigations. Such an apparatus, called a magnetic refrigerator, has
been developed by Heer, Barnes, Daunt, McMahon, Reitzel, and Simon [10,
11, 12] and is now manufactured by the Arthur D. Little Company. Although the apparatus is intended solely for basic research at extremely low
temperatures its development constitutes an excellent example of modern
cryogenic engineering, utilizing many of the unusual properties of materials
at very low temperatures and extending cryogenic engineering to a new temperature region.

4.5. Principle of the Refrigerator.   The use of a paramagnetic salt for
the continuous removal of heat from an experimental space below 1°K is
made possible by thermal "valves" which may be opened or closed as required. Figure 4.4 illustrates the process. The thermal valves consist of
links of metal which are superconducting in the absence of a magnetic field
and have normal electrical resistance in a field of a few hundred oersteds.
Daunt and his collaborators used strips of lead for the thermal valves.

The thermal conductivity of lead in its normal and superconducting states

is shown in Figure 4.5. It has been postulated that the low thermal conductivity of a
metal at very low temperature in the superconducting state stems from the macroscopic
"quantum state" of the material. The electrons responsible for the phenomenon of
superconductivity are withdrawn from their
ordinary functions (conduction of heat in
this case) and remain in a state that is
analogous to that of the electrons in the
shells of stable atoms. These electrons only
accept or donate external energy when they
are caused to deviate from their routine
orbits. In a similar way the electrons which
take part in the phenomenon of superconductivity are not available to participate in the
heat transfer. It is apparent that these thermal valves are not perfect; they offer some
resistance to the flow of heat when they are
open and they allow a small heat leakage
when they are closed because of the lattice

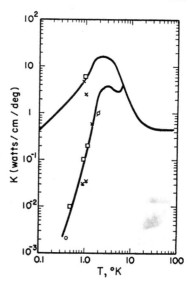

FIGURE 4.5. Thermal conductivity of lead in superconducting
and normal states.

conductivity of the metal and the contributions of the free electrons that are not
in the superconducting state. However, in spite of these deficiencies the apparatus illustrated enjoys the distinction of having practical proof of success. The cycle of operation is as follows: (1) with valve 1 open and valve

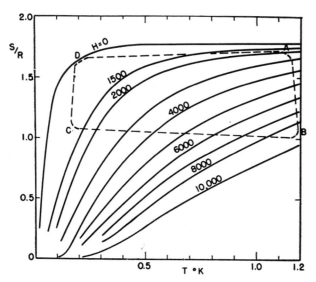

FIGURE 4.6. Entropy-temperature diagram of iron ammonium alum at various magnetic fields with the magnetic refrigerator cycle.

2 closed, the working salt is magnetized and the heat of magnetization flows into the bath of liquid helium at a temperature of about $1.15°K$; (2) with both valves closed the magnetic field is reduced (not to zero) and the working salt has its temperature greatly reduced as a result of the adiabatic demagnetization: (3) with valve 1 closed and valve 2 open, the magnetic field is further reduced and heat flows almost isothermally from the experimental space into the working salt; (4) with both valves closed the working salt is remagnetized until the starting temperature is reached.

Figure 4.6 is an entropy-temperature diagram for iron ammonium alum for various magnetic fields; on it is superposed the refrigeration cycle ABCDA, just described. From A to B the working salt is magnetized isothermally and the heat is absorbed by the liquid helium bath. From B to C the salt is demagnetized isentropically, causing a substantial decrease of temperature. From C to D the work-

FIGURE 4.7. Magnetic refrigerator. (Courtesy Arthur D. Little, Inc.)

ing salt is demagnetized isothermally, extracting heat from the experimental region. From D to A the working salt is remagnetized to its starting condition. Of course an ideal cycle is not fully realized because of unavoidable heat leaks, eddy-current heating and thermal resistances. Figure 4.7 is a photograph of the refrigerator.

4.6. Performance of the Refrigerator. Figure 4.8 illustrates the chronological sequence of operation, which is programed for automatic cycling. Table 4.1 shows the performance of the refrigerator at several temperatures.

4.7. Thermal Valves. Since thermal valves are a critical part of the magnetic refrigerator, it should be pointed out that superconducting valves are not the only possible solution. Thermal switches, making and breaking metallic contact, have been proposed. These would have the advantage of perfect isolation when open. Their disadvantage is that energy is dissipated when contact is made or broken, and in this region where extremely small amounts of energy are significant, appreciable mechanical energy of this type cannot be tolerated.

TABLE 4.1. THE PERFORMANCE OF THE MAGNETIC
REFRIGERATOR AT VARIOUS TEMPERATURES

T, in °K	dT/dt, in °K sec^{-1}	dq/dt, in erg sec^{-1}
.6	3.5×10^{-3}	490
.5	2.1×10^{-3}	400
.4	1.1×10^{-3}	275
.35	0.5×10^{-3}	162
.30	0.35×10^{-3}	143
.25	0.13×10^{-3}	83
.20	0.00	0.0

The very high magneto-resistance of cadmium has been proposed for use as a thermal valve. Also Fulton and others [13] described a thermal rectifier of mixtures of liquid helium of atomic weight 3 and ordinary helium of atomic weight 4.

IV. VAPOR PRESSURE OF HELIUM AT VERY LOW TEMPERATURES

4.8. It is of academic interest to estimate the vapor pressure of helium, the most volatile of all materials, at the temperatures reached by adiabatic demagnetization. It has been remarked elsewhere that the vapor pressure of helium at these temperatures is so small that the vapor density would be less than that represented by a single atom of helium vapor in the entire known physical universe. Although this is a dramatic way of emphasizing the low

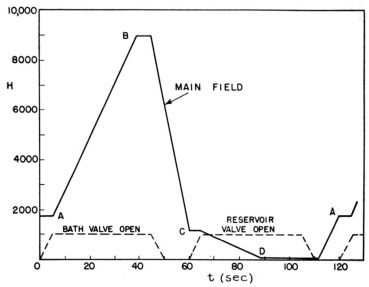

FIGURE 4.8. Cycles of the three magnets of the magnetic refrigerator.

vapor pressure, it still falls far short of the mark. Below 1.4°K the vapor pressure of helium is well represented by the relation

$$\log_{10} p_{cm} = -\frac{3.117}{T} + 2.5 \log_{10} T + 1.196$$

Thus at 0.01°K the vapor pressure is approximately 0.3×10^{-315} cm Hg. One mole of gas, 22,400 cm^3 at standard conditions contains 6.025×10^{23} molecules (Avogadro's number); so 1 cm^3 at STP will contain 2.7×10^{19} molecules. At 0.01°K, 1 cm^3 at 0.3×10^{-315} cm Hg will contain

$$2.7 \times 10^{19} \times \frac{0.3 \times 10^{-315}}{76} \times \frac{273}{0.01} = 3 \times 10^{-294} \text{ molecule.}$$

One molecule will then be found in a space of approximately 3×10^{293} cm^3. One light year is approximately 9.46×10^{17} cm. To determine the radius of the sphere, in light years, that will contain one atom of helium vapor in equilibrium with liquid at 0.01°K, let r be the radius in light years,

$$\text{Volume} = \tfrac{4}{3}\pi r^3 \times (9.46 \times 10^{173}) = 3 \times 10^{293} \text{ cm}^3$$

$$r = 4.4 \times 10^{79} \text{ light years}$$

The largest present-day telescope can detect galaxies somewhere between 10^9 and 10^{10} light years away; so the atom of helium vapor would almost never find itself in a space so greatly restricted as our observable universe.

Many experimenters take advantage of the extremely low vapor pressure of helium at the temperatures reached by isentropic demagnetization and do not remove the exchange gas as indicated in Figure 4.1. The salt is demagnetized rapidly and the helium exchange gas condenses on the cold salt.

REFERENCES FOR CHAPTER 4

[1] W. H. Keesom, *Leiden Comm.*, No. **219a**, *Proc. Roy. Acad. Amsterdam*, **35**, 136 (1932).
[2] W. F. Giauque, *J. Amer. Chem. Soc.*, **49**, 1870 (1927).
[3] P. Debye, *Ann. Physik*, **81**, 1154 (1926).
[4] W. F. Giauque and D. P. MacDougall, *Phys. Rev.*, **43**, 768 (1933).
[5] D. de Klerk, in "Temperature, Its Measurement and Control in Science and Industry," Reinhold Publishing Corp., N.Y., 1955, Vol. 2, p. 251.
[6] E. Ambler and R. P. Hudson, *Reports on Progress in Physics*, **18**, 251 (1955).
[7] D. de Klerk, M. J. Steenland, and C. J. Gorter, *Leiden Comm.* No. **282a**, *Physica*, **16**, 571 (1950).
[8] J. Darby, J. Hatton, B. V. Rollin, E. F. W. Seymour, and H. B. Silsbee, *Proc. Phys. Soc.*, **A64**, 861 (1951).
[9] N. Kurti, F. N. H. Robinson, Sir Francis Simon, and D. A. Spohr, *Nature*, **178**, 450 (1956).
[10] C. V. Heer, C. B. Barnes, and J. G. Daunt, *Rev. Sci. Instr.*, **25**, 1088 (1954).
[11] J. G. Daunt, C. V. Heer, H. O. McMahon, J. Reitzel, and I. Simon, *Conférence de Physique des basses températures*, Paris, 2-8 September 1955, p. 362.
[12] J. G. Daunt, *Proc. Phys. Soc.*, **B70**, 641 (1957).
[13] C. D. Fulton, C. F. Hwang, W. M. Fairbank and J. M. Vilas, *Proc. 1956 Cryogenic Engineering Conf.*, 1956.

Chapter V

LOW-TEMPERATURE THERMOMETRY

5.1. The accurate measurement of temperature is often the most difficult aspect of a cryogenic project. It sometimes appears that very exacting demands have to be met with inadequate thermometers and an unsatisfactory temperature scale. However, although methods and apparatus usable at low temperatures are far from being standardized, there is available a great deal of information. Several types of thermometers have been investigated and developed to a stage of usefulness, and as a rule, it is possible to choose a method which will yield acceptable results even though it is recognized that improvement is urgently needed. This chapter is concerned primarily with practical thermometry; the peculiarities, advantages and limitations of the various instruments and techniques that have been applied successfully to the measurement of very low temperatures. It is hoped that the information presented here will help the investigator to choose the method of temperature measurement most suited to his particular application.

The importance of choosing the thermometer or method which best fits the need is not always recognized. In some instances there is little or no freedom of choice. For example, the magnetic thermometer is the only device that has proved suitable thus far for the absolute measurement of temperature below 1°K, and the semiconducting resistance thermometer is the only secondary thermometer found to be useful at such temperatures. However, in most cases there is latitude in the selection of the method of temperature measurement, and the requirements should be carefully considered when a method is selected. The many possible methods vary greatly in respect to the following characteristics:

(1) Absolute accuracy on the thermodynamic scale
(2) Reproducibility—maintenance of calibration from day to day or year to year
(3) Sensitivity—ability to detect a small change of temperature
(4) Stability at constant temperature (required of thermostats and thermometers used to determine a change of temperature)
(5) Ability to measure small temperature differences

(6) Simplicity of operation
(7) Heating effect
(8) Heat conduction
(9) Heat capacity
(10) Cost
(11) Convenience

Other characteristics may be of importance in some applications. It is necessary for the user to decide which qualities are of the greatest importance in his particular application and choose the most suitable thermometer accordingly.

I. TEMPERATURE SCALES AND FIXED POINTS

5.2. International Temperature Scale of 1948. The International Temperature Scale [1] was established so that laboratories throughout the world would have a common basis for temperature measurement. It consists of a set of definitions, formulas, values of physical constants, and experimental procedures adopted by international agreement. It is a centigrade scale, although in its adoption it was recognized that the Kelvin scale is the fundamental thermodynamic scale to which all temperature measurements should ultimately be referable. The first International Temperature Scale was adopted in 1927, and in 1948 was superseded by an improved scale. Unfortunately for workers at low temperatures, the International Temperature Scale extends only down to $-183°C$. In the temperature region below $630.5°C$ it is defined by four fixed temperatures and a formula which gives the temperature resistance relation of a standard strain-free platinum resistance thermometer calibrated at these fixed temperatures. The fixed temperatures are: (1) the normal boiling point of oxygen, having the assigned value $-182.97°C$; the melting point of ice, $0°C$; the normal boiling point of water, $100°C$; and the normal boiling point of sulfur, $444.600°C$. The temperature-resistance relation of the platinum resistance thermometer below $0°C$ is

$$R_t = R_0[1 + At + Bt^2 + C(t - 100)t^3]$$

where R_t is the resistance at the temperature $t°C$, R_0 is the resistance at the ice point, and A, B, and C are constants determined by calibration conforming to specified procedures at the fixed points. Details of these procedures are given in reference [1].

5.3. National Bureau of Standards Scale Below 90°K. In 1939, Hoge and Brickwedde [2] calibrated a number of platinum resistance thermometers by means of a gas thermometer in the temperature region 11° to 90°K. The resulting temperature scale has been the basis of NBS calibrations below 90°K since that time. In establishing this scale the authors used the oxygen boiling point as the known temperature to which all their measurements were referred. They assigned the value 90.19°K to this point as being consistent with the centigrade value given by the International Temperature Scale and the then "best" value of the thermodynamic temperature of the ice point, 273.16°K. They estimated the accuracy as ±0.02 degree. This scale has been used to determine the vapor pressures and triple points of normal and parahydrogen [3] and the vapor pressure, triple point, and solid-solid transition temperature of oxygen [4]; thus in these regions the scale can be reproduced without resort to direct comparisons with the thermometers calibrated at NBS.

5.4. Low-Temperature Scale of Pennsylvania State University. The fundamental gas-thermometer measurements of Moessen, Aston, and Ascah [5] constitute an important contribution to thermometry at low temperatures. Their work was more precise than that of NBS [2]; it was estimated that their determinations agree with thermodynamic scale within 0.005°K. They determined the temperature of the normal boiling point of oxygen to be 90.154°K and that of normal hydrogen 20.365°K. They also calibrated some platinum resistance thermometers, including one that had been calibrated on the NBS scale below 90°K. It was found that when proper allowance was made for the difference in oxygen points, the two scales agreed to within 0.02 degree, the accuracy claimed by Hoge and Brickwedde.

5.5. Helium Vapor-Pressure Scale. Practical temperature measurements in the range 1° to 4.2°K are nearly always referred to the temperature scale based on the vapor pressure of helium. In July 1948, a specific vapor-pressure temperature relationship was adopted by agreement at an informal meeting held in Amsterdam between representatives of cryogenic laboratories in Holland, the United States, and Great Britain. Since the adoption of this scale, errors and irregularities have been found, and efforts have been made to obtain a more accurate relation. At the Conference on Low Temperature Physics at Paris in September 1955 [6], several papers on this subject were presented and a special session of conference delegates was convened to consider the adoption of an improved scale, based on a theoretical treatment of Van Dijk and Durieux [7]. Their scale had been found to be in much better agreement with later experiments than the 1948 scale. The result of the special session was that the delegates voted to recommend the use of the new scale. The vapor pressures of helium given in Chapter 9 conform with the 1955 scale.

5.6. Fixed Points. The triple point of a pure material constitutes an excellent fixed point for thermometry. The only additional requirement for accuracy is the establishment of thermal equilibrium. A very elegant and precise way of insuring thermal equilibrium is to perform the measurements in an adiabatic calorimeter like that mentioned later in this chapter, Figure 5.6. However, such elaboration is unnecessary if a sufficient amount of the pure material is available. For example, the triple point temperatures of hydrogen, nitrogen, or oxygen are easily realized by lowering the pressure over the boiling liquid. Some solid-solid transition temperatures are suitable as fixed points but these do not approach the perfection of the solid-liquid-vapor triple points; calorimetric studies show that the solid-solid transition usually takes place over a narrow range of temperatures rather than at a precise single temperature. One should be wary of using commercial liquid nitrogen to realize the nitrogen triple point. Since air contains almost 1 percent of argon, it is possible that the liquid nitrogen which is essentially oxygen-free may still contain enough argon to seriously affect the triple point. Nitrogen prepared by the decomposition of a pure crystalline nitrogen compound is much more likely to have the required purity.

TABLE 5.1. FIXED POINTS BELOW 90°K

Point	Temperature, °K	
Helium λ point	2.186	±0.010
Helium boiling point	4.211	±0.01
Parahydrogen triple point	13.81	±0.02
Parahydrogen boiling point	20.27	±0.02
Neon triple point	24.56	±0.02
Neon boiling point	27.07	±0.02
Oxygen transition point	43.70	±0.10
Oxygen triple point	54.33	±0.03
Nitrogen transition point	35.5	±0.10
Nitrogen triple point	63.14	±0.02
Nitrogen boiling point	77.35	±0.02

Table 5.1 lists some fixed points which are of value in low-temperature thermometry. Many of these were taken from the survey made by Hoge [8]. The variation noted with temperature is an estimate of accuracy based on the disagreement among recent measurements and an estimate of the probable accuracy of the temperature scale used. This is not a critical survey. The fixed points are listed here for the reader's convenience.

II. Gas Thermometry

5.7. Although most of the temperature scales in use today are realized by calibrating certain interpolation instruments at fixed points, they are based on measurements with a gas thermometer, since this instrument is the most accurate means yet devised for determining true thermodynamic temperature according to the definition of Lord Kelvin.

Before proceeding with the discussion of gas thermometry it will be necessary to describe a recent important innovation in the definition of absolute or thermodynamic temperatures. The thermodynamic scale originally proposed by Lord Kelvin was based on two fixed points, the temperature of melting ice and that of boiling water, more commonly designated the ice and steam points. The interval between these two temperatures was assigned the same value that it has on the centigrade scale, 100 degrees. Thus the temperature of absolute zero on the centigrade scale, or, conversely, the absolute temperature of the ice point, was left to be determined by experiment. Lord Kelvin noted the possibility of modifying the definition of the absolute scale of temperatures by assigning a definite value to the absolute temperature of the ice point and allowing the interval between ice and steam to be different from precisely 100 degrees. In fact Kelvin recommended that this new definition be adopted as soon as the thermodynamic temperature of the ice point had been determined with sufficient accuracy. In 1939 W. F. Giauque urged that Lord Kelvin's recommendation be adopted. Finally, in 1954, by international agreement, the triple point of water was assigned the temperature 273.16°K. The melting point of ice in equilibrium with air-saturated water is very nearly 0.010 degree lower, 273.15°K. The triple point was chosen in preference to the ice point because the former is an invariant temperature, characteristic of the pure substance and not requiring control of pressure or realization of a precise degree of contamination by dissolved air.

5.8. Constant-Volume Gas Thermometer. Figure 5.1 is a diagram of a relatively simple constant-volume helium gas thermometer which was used in calibrating a group of platinum resistance thermometers in the temperature interval 12° to 90°K [2]. The gas-thermometer bulb, a short cylinder

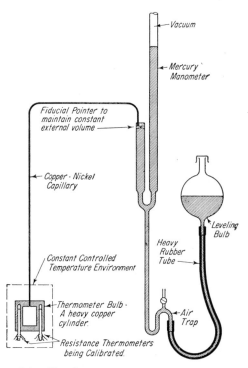

FIGURE 5.1. Simple constant-volume gas thermometer.

made of thick copper to promote uniformity and constancy of temperature, is connected by the poorly conducting copper-nickel alloy capillary to the mercury manometer which measures the pressure. Before a pressure measurement is made, the level of the mercury in the manometer is adjusted by means of the leveling bulb so that the apex of the mercury meniscus just touches the fiducial pointer on the pressure side of the manometer. In this way the external volume containing gas is kept at a constant, small value. The air trap below the manometer intercepts traces of air which might otherwise be carried with the mercury when it flows from the leveling bulb into the manometer. Diffusion of air through the rubber tube is prevented by making the dimensions of the glass parts of the manometer such that the pressure inside the rubber tube is always greater than atmospheric.

If the gas thermometer contains n moles of gas which, for the moment, we will assume perfect, and we further assume that the mass of gas in the manometer and connecting capillary can be neglected, the pressure registered by the thermometer will be given by the ideal gas law

$$p = \frac{nRT}{v} \qquad (5.1)$$

where n is the number of moles of gas, R the universal gas constant, T the Kelvin temperature, and v the volume of the thermometer bulb. If, for bulb temperatures T_1 and T_2, the corresponding pressures are determined to be p_1 and p_2,

$$\frac{T_2}{T_1} = \frac{p_2}{p_1} \qquad (5.2)$$

Thus the gas thermometer determines ratios of absolute temperatures. If T_1 is chosen to be the defined ice point, 273.15°K, Equation 5.2 gives T_2, the temperature being determined, on the new Kelvin scale.

Of course, the above analysis is greatly oversimplified. In order to obtain accurate results it is necessary to correct for (1) the imperfection of the gas, (2) the effect of "nuisance volume" or the volume of gas which is not at the temperature being measured, (3) the change of volume of the bulb with changing temperature, and (4) variations in the amount of gas adsorbed on the walls of the gas-thermometer bulb. Moreover, the necessity for accurate pressure measurement is in itself a formidable requirement. These considerations make precision gas thermometry an arduous and exacting occupation. It is beyond the scope of this book to deal with the refinements of gas thermometry. There are several articles on the subject in references [8] and [9].

Although using the gas thermometer as an accurate primary standard is a major undertaking, it is often very convenient as a secondary thermometer. The gas thermometer just described may be calibrated at a few known temperatures, obtaining a pressure-temperature relation from which intermediate temperatures can be determined. As a rule the pressure-temperature relation obtained by calibration will deviate by only a small amount from the linear equation 5.2, so very widely separated calibration points are adequate. In some cases it is preferable to use a dial pressure gage rather than the manometer shown in Figure 5.1. This sacrifices some accuracy but makes the thermometer very convenient to read, comparable with a liquid-in-glass thermometer.

5.9. A Non-linear Gas Thermometer for Wide Temperature Ranges.

If a gas thermometer circuit includes a volume at room temperature which is large in comparison with the volume of the measuring bulb, the sensitivity of the thermometer will depend upon the temperature of the bulb so that the scale is compressed at high temperatures and magnified at low temperatures [10]. Consider the thermometer illustrated in Figure 5.2. When the temperature of the bulb B is high, most of the gas is in the auxiliary volume V, so that changing the temperature of B by a small amount has little effect on the pressure. However, when the temperature of B is very low, 15°K or below, most of the gas is in B, so that now the pressure in the system is almost proportional to the temperature of B. This device is obviously not very accurate. It is useful as a permanent installation in a helium liquefier to follow the initial cool-down and monitor the operation thereafter.

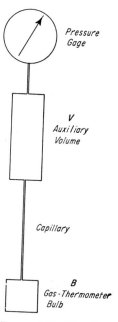

FIGURE 5.2. Non-linear gas thermometer for wide temperature ranges. Auxiliary volume, V, remaining at room temperature is about 10 times as large as gas-thermometer bulb, B.

III. VAPOR-PRESSURE THERMOMETRY

5.10. A vapor-pressure thermometer consists of a bulb filled partly with a liquid or solid and partly with vapor in equilibrium with the condensed phase, connected by a pressure-transmitting line to a pressure-measuring instrument. With an adequate pressure-measuring device, the vapor-pressure thermometer is an excellent secondary standard, since its indications are determined by a physical property of a chemical element or compound. However, if any part of the pressure-transmitting line reaches a temperature below the temperature of the bulb, liquid will condense there and the pressure will tend towards the value corresponding to the lowest temperature in the system. Thus it is necessary to make sure that the measuring bulb is the coldest part.

The vapor-pressure thermometer illustrated in Figure 5.3 [11] [8] was used for calibrating thermocouples and platinum resistance thermometers in the region of the oxygen boiling point. The bulb of the vapor-pressure thermometer is a small cavity in a heavy cylindrical copper block. This block

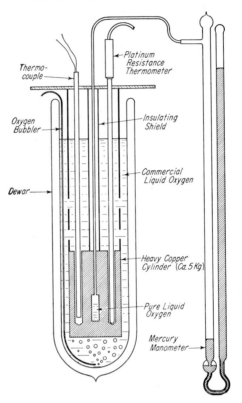

FIGURE 5.3. Oxygen vapor-pressure thermometer for calibrating working thermometers

constitutes the region of uniform temperature enclosing the vapor-pressure
bulb and the thermometers being calibrated. It will be noted that the vapor
pressure of pure oxygen is being measured while commercial liquid oxygen is
used to maintain the temperature. The oxygen bubbles prevent superheating
of the bath.

A vapor-pressure thermometer can be used over the entire range of measurable vapor pressure of the material with which it is filled, but this is seldom
done because of the extreme non-linearity of the pressure-temperature relationship. In the laboratory it is convenient to use a vapor-pressure thermometer with a mercury manometer and cover a pressure range from a few
centimeters of mercury to about 76 centimeters. In other cases a different
temperature range can be covered by operating at higher pressures, using a
Bourdon gage to measure the pressure.

Table 5.2 shows the temperature ranges readily covered by some vapor
pressure thermometers commonly used at low temperatures. The corresponding sensitivities are also shown.

TABLE 5.2. CHARACTERISTICS OF SOME VAPOR-PRESSURE THERMOMETERS

Material	Pressure = 50 mm Hg		Pressure = 760 mm Hg	
	T, °K	dP/dT (sensitivity), mm Hg/deg	T, °K	dP/dT (sensitivity), mm Hg/deg
Carbon dioxide	166.3	5	194.6	62
Oxygen	70.4	10	90.19	80
Hydrogen	14.0	34	20.4	223
Helium	2.30	110	4.2	720

The vapor-pressure thermometer can be an extremely precise instrument; this is especially true when the lower-boiling elements are used. For example, at the boiling point of helium, the helium vapor-pressure thermometer has a sensitivity of 720 mm per degree and, with reasonable care, a mercury manometer can be trusted to 0.1 mm Hg; so such a thermometer can be made reproducible to about 0.0001 degree. By using a more sensitive manometer, e.g., a differential oil manometer, it is possible to detect changes in temperature of the order of 10^{-5} degree.

For the most precise work with vapor-pressure thermometers it is necessary to take into account several small correction terms. Of course, precise manometry demands a temperature correction for the expansion of the mercury and the scale, meniscus corrections for the capillary depression of the mercury, and reduction to standard gravity. There is another correction that is sometimes significant—the pressure exerted by the column of pressure-transmitting gas.

Table 5.2 implies another limitation in the use of vapor-pressure thermometry—the fact that some temperature regions are inaccessible to this method because no material exists that has a useful vapor pressure in these temperature regions. For example, the region 40° to 50°K is above the critical temperature of neon, while oxygen and nitrogen have such low vapor pressures that accurate pressure determinations cannot be made. The use of vapor-pressure thermometers as working instruments is usually restricted to applications that require good sensitivity in a narrow temperature range.

There are a great many materials whose vapor pressures are suitable for low-temperature thermometry, but those most useful to cryogenic workers are carbon dioxide, oxygen, nitrogen, hydrogen, and helium, substances used to produce low temperatures. The vapor pressure-temperature relationships for the last four of these materials are given in Chapter 9.

Commercial solid carbon dioxide is very convenient to use to check a thermometer or make a calibration at or near the normal sublimation temperature. There is one important precaution regarding the use of solid CO_2; that is, make sure that the solid is in equilibrium with its own vapor. Solid CO_2 crushed in the presence of air becomes colder because the air reduces the partial pressure of the CO_2 in contact with the solid. The effect is the same as though the CO_2 were in a partial vacuum. It was found [11] that the equilibrium could be restored by placing the powdered solid CO_2 in a glass dewar jar and covering the top with a compact pad of cotton so that diffusion of air into the dewar was prevented while allowing the excess CO_2 vapor to escape. After standing overnight, temperature equilibrium was established. Equilibrium could be reached in a few minutes by adding energy with a 25-watt electric heater in the bottom of the dewar. Without these precautions errors of several degrees are probable. There is evidence also that some commercial solid CO_2 contains occluded air. The temperature of the solid CO_2 is given by the following equation [12]:

$$\log_{10} P_{\text{mm Hg}} = 9.81137 - \frac{1349}{T}$$

where T is in degrees Kelvin. This equation is valid in the neighborhood of the normal sublimation temperature of CO_2; if greatly different temperatures are produced (by pumping, for example), the necessary vapor pressure relations can be obtained from reference [12].

Although the oxygen vapor-pressure thermometer described earlier in this chapter was designed for calibrations at or near the normal boiling point of oxygen, it can, of course, be used to calibrate thermocouples and resistance thermometers over the entire usable range of vapor pressures. The principal reason that the oxygen vapor-pressure thermometer is rather elaborate is the fact that large quantities of liquid oxygen of sufficient purity for thermometry are not readily obtained. Therefore, it is necessary to prepare a small sample of pure oxygen and keep it sealed in the thermometer. On the other hand, when using helium, calibrations are made simply by immersing the thermometer in the liquid helium bath and measuring the pressure over the bath. As normally produced, helium is of a purity more than adequate for precise vapor-pressure thermometry, because the only impurity which could conceivably cause error is the very rare isotope, helium of atomic weight 3.

There is a troublesome phenomenon which is sometimes encountered in working with liquid helium. It is observed when a narrow tube, open at the cold end, communicates between a room-temperature region and one at the temperature of liquid helium. Under certain conditions spontaneous thermal-acoustical oscillations will occur in such a tube and the mean pressure at the warm end will be markedly higher than that at the cold end. The driving energy for the oscillations apparently comes from transfer of heat from the warm to the cold part of the tube. In some cases this transfer is so vigorous that liquid helium is rapidly evaporated. Clement and Gaffney of the Naval

Research Laboratory have investigated the phenomenon [13] and discovered that the oscillations can be suppressed by surrounding the tube by an insulating vacuum space. While a simple $\frac{1}{4}$-inch thin-wall, poorly conducting tube oscillated badly, it could not be made to oscillate when it was surrounded by a vacuum space enclosed by a $\frac{3}{8}$-inch tube. Tubes closed at the cold end could not be made to oscillate. A tube open at the warm end would not oscillate unless its diameter was less than 1 mm. Some workers have inserted knotted thread into capillary tubes to damp out the oscillations. Oscillations of this kind have also been observed when using liquid hydrogen.

When using a bath of liquid hydrogen to maintain a definite, known temperature it is very important to take into consideration the ortho-para composition if accuracy better than 0.1 degree is required. Equilibrium liquid hydrogen (99.8 percent parahydrogen) is greatly to be preferred for this work because its vapor pressure is known and its composition does not change with time. Some hydrogen liquefiers are equipped to produce parahydrogen, but as a rule the designer of a converter to produce liquid parahydrogen in a liquefier is satisfied with a composition somewhat less than the equilibrium concentration. Thus, one should use a catalyst in the temperature measuring bath to assure complete conversion. Hydrous ferric oxide [14] [15] has proved to be a very effective catalyst. It is suggested that 50 grams of the hydrous ferric oxide be placed in a 1- or 2-liter bath of liquid hydrogen, disposed so that the liquid hydrogen will circulate through the catalyst by convection. The heat of conversion will promote convection. If the liquid hydrogen originally has a low para concentration, a large fraction will be evaporated by the conversion. Another method of realizing vapor pressures of parahydrogen (practically indistinguishable from equilibrium H_2 at 20°K) is to use a vapor-pressure thermometer with a small amount of catalyst in the bulb where the liquid condenses. A typical vapor-pressure thermometer would have about $\frac{1}{2}$ cm^3 of catalyst in the bulb and enough liquid to cover the catalyst.

Because impurities which normally occur in electrolytic hydrogen do not affect the vapor pressure, there is no need to have a sealed vapor-pressure thermometer like that described for oxygen. A convenient method is to arrange to evacuate the thermometer and then introduce electrolytic hydrogen with a mercury displacement pump. Of course, contamination by helium should be carefully avoided when using hydrogen for vapor-pressure thermometry.

IV. Thermoelectric Thermometry

5.11. Two dissimilar wires, connected to each other at one end, constitute a thermocouple. A difference of temperature between the joined and unjoined ends of this pair of wires results in a difference of electrical potential between the unjoined ends. The potential difference can be a measure of temperature.

From this very brief description a number of favorable characteristics of thermocouples are immediately evident. They are simple, usually inexpensive, are easily installed in complex apparatus, can have low heat capacity, can respond quickly to temperature changes, and can be read at a convenient location.

There are, however, some other characteristics that present distinct difficulties. In the first place the emf produced is quite small, so that sensitive (and therefore expensive) equipment is required to measure it. The sensitivity of a thermocouple is expressed as the thermoelectric power of the combination of metals, and is defined as the change in emf produced by a unit change in temperature of the working junction. The sensitivity of the copper-constantan thermocouple, commonly used at low temperatures, is about 40 microvolts per degree at room temperature, 17 microvolts per degree at 90°K (oxygen boiling point), and 5 microvolts per degree at 20°K (hydrogen boiling point). (The thermoelectric power of all thermocouples approaches zero at absolute zero.) This considerable change in sensitivity is another undesirable quality. A less objectionable disadvantage is the requirement of a known reference temperature. The reference ends of the wire must be kept at an accurately known temperature. This is usually done by providing an ice bath to keep the ends of the wires at 0°C and completing the circuit to the measuring instruments with copper wires. When measuring very low temperatures it is often preferable to utilize a low-temperature reference such as that of liquid nitrogen or liquid hydrogen boiling at a known pressure. This technique will very often greatly improve the absolute accuracy of a thermocouple because it avoids the traverse of large temperature gradients by the thermocouple wires.

In spite of these shortcomings, copper-constantan thermocouples, made of carefully selected wire, have been used as laboratory standards. W. F. Giauque et al., [16] at the University of California calibrated a number of copper-constantan thermocouples with a gas thermometer as their primary standard, and used the thermocouples as secondary standards in the excellent work in low-temperature calorimetry, at temperatures as low as 12°K.

5.12. Quality of Thermocouples. Since a number of other combinations of metals exhibit much larger thermoelectric powers, the question naturally arises as to why copper-constantan thermocouples are so popular. The answer to this question emphasizes another ill that all thermocouples are heir to: inhomogeneities. The wires of which a thermocouple is made are not completely homogeneous; slight differences in chemical or phase composition, changes in crystal structure, mechanical strain, work-hardening and possibly other causes contribute to the inhomogeneities. These inhomogeneities behave like local thermocouples in series, parallel or series-parallel combinations with the main thermocouple, and if they occur where there is a temperature gradient in the wire, they produce parasitic emf's which change when the temperature gradient changes and may introduce a serious error into the reading of the thermocouple. Most copper wire and some carefully selected constantan wire suffer less from such defects than do other potential thermocouple materials. Some of the high-thermoelectric-power combinations are very bad actors. Even when using selected copper and constantan it is unusual to find a thermocouple which is free from this defect to better than 1 or 2 microvolts in 5000 (an emf corresponding to measuring a temperature of about 90°K with reference junctions in ice), so such a couple cannot be trusted for this measurement to better than about 0.1 degree.

5.13. Effects of Intermediate Metals. It was mentioned in the last paragraph that inhomogeneities give rise to spurious emf's *when there is a temperature gradient* in the region of the inhomogeneities. This brings up a principle of thermocouples and thermocouple circuits that should be well understood in order to maintain correct techniques. Consider Figure 5.4.

Figure 5.4A shows the ordinary thermocouple circuit that we have been discussing. L and M are two different metals joined at J_1 and connected to the instrument E which will measure the emf. The junction J_1 is in a region of uniform temperature T_1. The instrument and connections to the thermocouple are at a uniform temperature T_2. The emf registered in this case will depend only on the temperatures T_1 and T_2. Now consider Figure 5.4B. A piece of the metal M has been replaced by a third metal N, forming a new junction J_2. Notice, however, that J_2 is still in the region of uniform temperature T_1. Arrangement 5.4B will register the same emf as arrangement

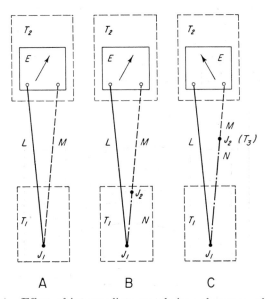

FIGURE 5.4.   Effect of intermediate metals in a thermocouple circuit.

5.4A. No difference of potential is introduced by an intermediate metal if the intermediate metal is in a constant temperature region. Finally consider Figure 5.4C. The same metal N has been introduced, but part of N lies in the region of changing temperature between T_1 and T_2 and the junction J_2 is now at an intermediate temperature T_3. In this case the emf registered will not be the same as in cases A and B; the intermediate metal present in a temperature gradient introduces an additional emf. This principle applies to all parts of the thermocouple circuits and to any electrical circuit in which small potentials are significant. It is best to maintain an all-copper circuit, but if another metal must be introduced, for example a soldered joint, one should be careful to avoid the possibility of a temperature difference across the joint. A solder with the same thermoelectric power as copper is now on the market. It should be useful in connecting thermocouple leads.

Thermocouple junctions are usually made by welding, silver solder or tin-lead solder. From the foregoing discussion it is obvious that all that is required is a good electrical connection; *the metal or method used in making the junction can have no effect on the emf of the thermocouple,* since the junction lies in a region of uniform temperature. Careful handling of the thermocouple wires to avoid strains, work-hardening, irregular annealing, etc., is very necessary in the parts which traverse temperature gradients; but at or near the junctions, where the temperature will always be uniform, no special precautions are required, only a good electrical connection, insulation from nearby emf's, and the avoidance of galvanic effects which can be caused by moisture.

5.14. Multiple-Junction Thermocouples. There is a way to improve two of the weaker points of thermocouples at the sacrifice of some of the simplicity and convenience; that is to connect a number of thermocouples in series as shown in Figure 5.5. This arrangement is sometimes called a thermopile, but White [17] coined the useful name "Thermel," a contraction

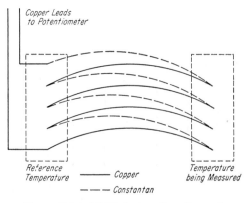

Figure 5.5. Multiple-junction thermel.

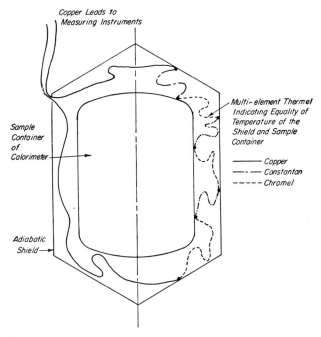

Copper Leads to
Measuring Instruments

Sample
Container
of
Calorimeter

Adiabatic
Shield

Multi-element Thermel
Indicating Equality of
Temperature of the
Shield and Sample
Container

———— Copper
—·—— Constantan
————— Chromel

FIGURE 5.6.   Difference thermel in an adiabatic calorimeter.

of thermoelectric thermometer. This term can be used for either a thermo-couple or multiple-element system.

It is apparent that a $2n$-element thermel produces n times the emf of a simple thermocouple. Moreover, since the emf's due to inhomogeneities in the leads of the various elements are just as likely to cancel each other as to add, the probable resultant emf error from this cause is only $\sqrt{n}$ times as large as with a simple thermocouple. Hence the temperature error from this cause will be reduced by the factor $1/\sqrt{n}$.

5.15 Difference Thermocouples. There is one application in which ther-mocouples are unexcelled; that is the measurement of small differences of temperature under circumstances that avoid substantial temperature gradients in the thermocouple. An example of such an application is the thermel in an adiabatic calorimeter (Figure 5.6) with one set of junctions on the radiation shield and the other set attached to the sample container. Such an arrange-ment will reliably indicate temperature differences as small as 0.01 degree. In this application the objective is to keep the two surfaces at the same tem-perature to prevent transfer of heat. The indications of the difference thermel can be used to actuate a servomechanism which will adjust the temperature of one surface. Such a difference thermel is relatively free from the spurious emf's caused by inhomogeneities, because the thermocouple wires traverse a region between the two surfaces that is nearly of uniform temperature. The leads which pass through a temperature gradient to the measuring instrument can be made of copper which is relatively free from inhomogeneities that give rise to emf's. It will be noted that the distribution of junctions shown in Figure 5.6 causes the thermel to respond to an average temperature difference rather than the temperature difference between two specific points.

5.16. Thermocouple Materials. As previously mentioned, copper-constantan thermocouples are more often used at low temperature than are couples of other metals, because of their relatively good homogeneity. For some work other combinations are preferable. Copper is a good thermal conductor and in apparatus concerned with heat measurements it is well to avoid good thermal paths through copper thermoelements. Chromel-P® versus constantan makes a couple having a somewhat higher thermoelectric power than copper-constantan, and both metals are alloys of low thermal conductivity. Such a combination of metals is very satisfactory as a difference instrument. Thus for the calorimeter illustrated in Figure 5.6, Chromel-P® and constantan were used as the thermel elements.

For use at very low temperatures there is an alloy developed by the Leiden Laboratory that has a much higher thermoelectric power than the couples mentioned. This alloy consists of gold with an admixture of 2.11 atomic percent cobalt. The other thermocouple element can be copper; but to keep thermal conductivity low it is better to use an alloy of silver with a small amount of gold. This thermocouple has a thermoelectric power of about 16 microvolts per degree at $20°K$, and in the range 0 to $20°K$ its thermoelectric power is approximately proportional to the temperature. Some of this wire was found to have inhomogeneities which resulted in spurious emf's as large as $\frac{1}{500}$ or the total emf of the couple. There is evidence that the gold-cobalt alloy is not strictly stable and that excess heating will change its thermoelectric power. Experiments are now in progress at the NBS Cryogenic Engineering Laboratory to study the stability and if possible improve it. Even though this thermocouple has larger spurious emf's than do the best copper-constantan thermocouples, there are applications where the larger thermoelectric power more than compensates for the disadvantage. Suppose we wish to measure a temperature difference of about 10 degrees, from $20°K$ to $30°K$, for example, the difference in temperature between the ends of a thermal-conductivity specimen. A (Au + Co) vs. (Ag + Au) difference thermocouple will develop about 200 microvolts under these conditions. The error due to inhomogeneities in the thermocouple will be about $\frac{20}{500}$ or 0.4 μv. The copper leads to the measuring equipment may add 1 μv, so the total error may be 1.4 μv or 0.07 degree.

A copper-constantan difference thermocouple under the same conditions will develop about $65\mu v$ and have a total error of about 1 part in 2000 for the difference measurement plus about 1 μv for inhomogeneities in the leads.

This corresponds to about 0.16 degree. Thus for this application the gold-cobalt thermocouple is superior. For smaller temperature differences the high-power thermocouple is even more favored. This reasoning can be applied to other thermocouple applications. It is admittedly crude, but should indicate a preference if there is much difference between the two systems under consideration.

5.17. Measuring Equipment for Thermocouples. It was stated earlier that the measuring equipment for thermocouples is rather expensive. As is usually the case, the expense is a function of the quality. The equipment consists of a potentiometer, standard cell, galvanometer, and ice bath for reference junctions. For high-precision work, where it is desired to get the ultimate accuracy from the best thermocouple obtainable, the potentiometer will cost in the neighborhood of $2000, the galvanometer about $150 or if we use the more modern chopper-type DC amplifier instead of a D'Arsonval galvanometer we may pay $800. An unsaturated Weston standard cell costing about $70 is satisfactory if frequently calibrated. This equipment is designed for high over-all accuracy and its ultimate capabilities are realized only when spurious thermal emf's are kept to a minimum.

Of intermediate quality, but quite adequate for a great proportion of thermocouple work, is a potentiometer exemplified by the Leeds & Northrup, Type K, and the Rubicon, Type B. These are capable of an accuracy of 1 or 2 μv if properly manipulated. In this connection it may be well to mention a technique that will greatly reduce errors caused by spurious thermal emf's in the measuring equipment. This technique consists of substituting for the thermocouple a thermal-emf-free resistor of the same resistance as the thermocouple. The emf indicated by the potentiometer when the substitution is made is subtracted (algebraically) from the thermocouple reading made just before or after the substitution. Care must be taken that the contacts made and broken during the substitution do not themselves introduce an emf. This check should be made rather frequently because "thermals" in a circuit change with time. Some potentiometers are equipped with a "zero adjuster," a potential divider that introduces a small compensating emf which cancels spurious emf's in the circuit. The zero setting is made by substituting a shorting link for the emf being measured.

There are less expensive potentiometers that are adequate for some work; these are usually self-contained units with a built-in galvanometer, such as are used with pyrometer-thermocouples; also quite accurate and sensitive portable instruments with built-in galvanometers are now available. Sometimes it is useful simply to connect the thermocouple to a millivoltmeter.

Another type of measuring equipment now widely used is the potentiometer-recorder. These are potentiometers equipped with servomechanisms which may select each of several different thermocouples in succession, determine the emf, and print a time record of the emf of each couple. They are available in many ranges and are self-contained, needing only a standard 115-volt 60-cycle AC power source and connections to the thermocouples. Of course the same principles apply in obtaining the best results from this automatic gear, reduction of spurious emf's, etc.

5.18. The Installation of Thermocouples. Since the thermocouple is a simple device, there is a tendency to assume that it will indicate the desired temperature whenever it is inserted into the region whose temperature is required. Such a technique is very likely to be disappointing; heat flowing along the thermocouple wires will influence the temperature of the junction. This brings up a principle, particularly pertinent to thermocouples but applicable in greater or less degree to all temperature measurements: *A thermometer always indicates a temperature intermediate between that of the region being investigated and any other environment with which the thermometer has thermal communication.* A well-known example of this is a weather thermometer placed in the sunshine; it registers a temperature intermediate between that of the surrounding air and that of the sun (fortunately somewhat nearer the air temperature). It is the responsibility of the investigator to make sure that the sensitive element of the thermometer assumes a temperature sufficiently close to that of the object or region whose temperature is being determined. When using a thermocouple this can sometimes be accomplished by soldering the thermojunction to the metal surface whose temperature is being measured. This procedure cannot always be absolutely depended on, however, because if the surface is of thin, poorly conducting metal, heat conduction along the thermocouple wires can still warm or cool the junction.

Another method, widely used, is to temper the thermocouple wires by bringing them approximately to the desired temperature at a little distance from the junction. This is frequently accomplished by winding a substantial length of the thermocouple wires on the surface to be measured. For example, when measuring the temperature of a pipe, the thermocouple junction is fastened in good thermal contact with the pipe and a foot or two of the wires are wound around the pipe near the spot whose temperature is being measured. As a rule it is unwise to solder thermel junctions to grounded surfaces because this increases danger that electrical leakage may spoil the readings. If thin electrical insulating material is used it is possible to achieve good thermal contact and still have the junction electrically insulated. Thin mica is very good.

It is particularly difficult to achieve good thermal contact between a thermocouple junction and a surface that is in a vacuum. In this case it is usually necessary to use a varnish or cement to improve the thermal contact with the insulated wires because there is no gas to carry heat. In the calorimeter illustrated in Figure 5.6, No. 32 AWG single-silk-enamel insulated copper wires entered the apparatus at room temperature and after an interven-

ing length of about 100 cm in vacuum they were cemented with Glyptal ®
lacquer to a metal surface at the temperature of liquid hydrogen. It was
found that a 15-cm length of wire, wound tightly in a single layer and cemented to the surface, did not approach within 1 degree of the temperature
of the surface. In the final assembly about 30 cm of the wires were applied
in this way and it was estimated that they reached a temperature less than $\frac{1}{2}$
degree above that of the metal surface.

Another difficult subject for temperature measurements is a liquefier. The
performance of a Joule-Thomson liquefier depends upon temperature differences between the high- and low-pressure streams at the warm ends of the
heat exchangers; therefore the measurement of such differences is very important in evaluating the performance of a liquefier. A thermojunction can
be brought to the temperature of the low-pressure gas by soldering the fine-
gage thermocouple to a copper vane of 5 or 10 cm² area and placing this so
that the gas passes over it. One method of measuring the temperature of the
high-pressure stream is to fasten a thermojunction of fine wires, ca. AWG
#30, to the outside of the tube carrying the gas. If this is done, extra care
must be taken to provide adequate tempering of the thermocouple wires by
winding a substantial length on the tube being measured and covering this
area with insulation to protect these wires and the junction from the low-
pressure gas flowing in countercurrent over the outside of the high-pressure
tube. Otherwise the flowing low-pressure gas would strongly influence the
temperature of the junction. Sometimes the thermocouple is inserted into a
well extending inside the high-pressure tube. This is a good technique provided good contact is made with the thermal junction and sufficient length of
wire is provided for adequate tempering. Fine wires having small heat
conduction should always be used. The heavy wires normally used for
pyrometers are quite unsuitable.

5.19. Spurious EMF's.   Before leaving the subject of thermocouples it
may be well to emphasize again the need to avoid sources of spurious emf's.
In the earlier discussion spurious thermal emf's were the main consideration.
They can be reduced by careful design, and by avoidance wherever possible
of connections of dissimilar metals, or where such connections cannot be
avoided, by enclosing the connections in a region of uniform temperature.
It should be pointed out that the resistance wire used for potentiometers is
usually manganin, an alloy of copper, manganese, and nickel. This has a
thermal emf against copper of about 1 μv per degree, a value that is quite
small but certainly cannot always be neglected. Large temperature differences
in different parts of the potentiometer can easily give rise to serious errors
from this source.

At the risk of dwelling on the obvious, it may be worthwhile to point out
another source of error that can be very serious in thermocouple work. That
is electrical leakage. A nearby DC circuit, if not carefully isolated from the

thermocouple circuit, can play havoc because the voltages and currents being handled in the thermocouple circuit are so small. Although DC is obviously more likely to cause trouble than AC, the latter source of error should not be dismissed. There may be present accidental rectifiers; in fact, the high-resistance electrical leak may itself be a partial rectifier. Sometimes the leakage responsible for error is in the potentiometer itself. A large error was once found to be caused by conducting dust which had accumulated on the terminal panel of a potentiometer and resulted in leakage from the energizing storage battery (6 volts) into the thermocouple-galvanometer circuit.

5.20. Thermocouple Tables. For thermocouple materials in common use it is customary to construct a temperature-emf table by calibrating a representative couple (for example, copper-constantan) at many temperatures properly distributed over the desired temperature range. By a combination of analytical and graphical methods a "best fit" smooth table is prepared. Such a table may not accurately represent the emf of another thermocouple made of materials having the same nominal composition, but by calibrating the new couple at very few temperatures the deviations from the table can be determined quite accurately. Then the standard table, together with the deviation curve, constitutes a very satisfactory calibration. Thus the laborious task of calibrating at many different temperatures needs to be done only once for a pair of thermocouple elements of nominal composition. With reasonable process control the manufacturer can reproduce the compositions and the temperature-emf characteristics closely enough that deviations from the standard table will be small. It may be worth mentioning that the deviation curve is often nearly a straight line, if the deviations in emf are plotted as ordinate against the emf of the table as abscissa. Tables of the emf's of several metals frequently used for low-temperature work are given in Chapter 10.

V. Resistance Thermometry

5.21. Pure Metals. The resistivity of a pure metal near room temperature is approximately proportional to its absolute temperature. This property is made use of in a very successful temperature measuring instrument, the *resistance thermometer.* The best-known, most reliable resistance thermometer is the standard, strain-free platinum resistance thermometer through which temperatures on the International Temperature Scale are realized in the range −183° to 630°C. Even at lower temperatures, the platinum resistance thermometer has served as a very satisfactory standard [2].

Some of the more general characteristics of resistance thermometers of pure metals can be seen by reference to the graph, Figure 5.7. At room temperature the resistance-temperature curve is very slightly concave downward and has a slope which would intersect the temperature axis at a positive absolute temper-

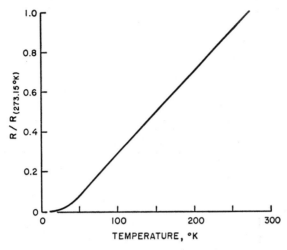

FIGURE 5.7. Resistance of platinum as a function of temperature.

ature. That is, if the resistance-temperature relation maintained this slope, the resistance would vanish at a finite temperature. It is seen, however, that the curve exhibits an inflection point and the resistance actually approaches a small finite value at the lowest temperature.

It is obvious that where the resistance is constant (temperature coefficient zero) the metal is not useful as a resistance thermometer. At 20°K the temperature coefficient of resistance of platinum is only about $\frac{1}{5}$ its room-temperature value. Some metals maintain a high temperature coefficient of resistivity to lower temperatures. The soft metals, those with low Debye characteristic temperatures, are best in this respect. Lead is quite good, but suffers from some other disadvantages. Lead anneals and flows at room temperature; therefore it is apt to change resistance upon standing. Moreover lead becomes superconducting at 7.2°K, so this is the lower limit of its usefulness. White and Woods [18] constructed thermometers of indium which had good sensitivity over the range 4° to 300°K.

Mechanical strain causes the resistance of a metal to increase; therefore it is important to mount the wire of which a resistance thermometer is made in in a way to avoid strain. In particular, expansion and contraction of the mounting, when the temperature is changed, should not strain the wire. A fairly good design is to wind the wire upon a support made of the same material; copper wire on a copper spool, or platinum wire on a platinum spool. This method has had some success, but the best method so far discovered is that used in constructing standard platinum resistance thermometers. In these instruments the platinum wire (about 0.1 mm diameter) is wound in notches cut in a mica cross. After winding, the assembly is carefully annealed, with the result that the wires are supported with a minimum of mechanical constraint; the annealing has relieved residual strains and the stresses encountered in use are only those sufficient to support the wire.

Figure 5.8 shows a design of a strain-free platinum resistance thermometer particularly suitable for use at low temperatures [19], [20]. This consists of a fine helix of platinum wire wound on a mica cross. The cross is housed in a platinum tube which is capped with a soft glass seal through which the platinum thermometer leads emerge. The thermometer is filled with helium at a pressure of 3 or 4 cm Hg at room temperature.

Resistance thermometers of nickel wire and of copper wire have had some use at low temperature. For example, a copper resistance thermometer was used as the sensitive element of a thermostat at NBS to control the temperature of a bath surrounding a gas flow-calorimeter [21]. This arrangement could be trusted to maintain a temperature constant to 0.01 degree. This thermometer was not used to determine a temperature, but only to indicate a change in temperature. The thermometer was made by winding about 140 ohms of No. 37 AWG insulated copper wire on a brass tube (single layer) and coating with glyptal lacquer. Apparently the coefficients of expansion of copper and brass are so nearly equal that no undue strain resulted. It seems that some care must be exercised in the construction of such resistance thermometers, because some commercial thermometers with copper resistors submitted to NBS for calibration were found to drift in resistance at liquid-oxygen temperature to such an extent that they were useless. The internal construction was not determined, but it seems likely that mechanical strain, caused by differential contraction, was responsible for the unsatisfactory behavior.

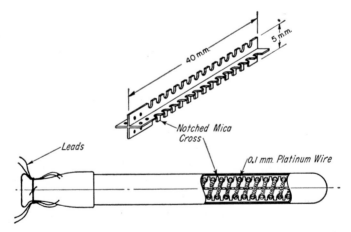

Figure 5.8. Capsule-type, strain-free platinum resistance thermometer. The 0.1mm wire is first coiled into a helix of 0.5 mm O.D. and then the helix is wound bifilarly on the notched mica cross.

5.22. Effect of Impurities. A small impurity increases the resistance of a metal by an amount that is almost independent of the temperature. It acts almost as though a temperature-independent resistance were placed in series. Thus the resistance-temperature curve of a thermometer made of an alloy of platinum plus 10 percent rhodium was found to be nearly parallel to that of a pure platinum thermometer of the same dimensions but displaced to considerably higher values of resistance. Many alloys have resistance that is almost independent of temperature; for example, the resistance of constantan at liquid-helium temperature is only about 5 percent lower than the room-temperature value. As a rule, the purer the metal the more sensitive the thermometer. This is particularly true if we define sensitivity as $(1/R)$ (dR/dT). According to this definition of sensitivity, a platinum resistance thermometer has a higher sensitivity at 20°K than at room temperature in spite of the fact that the value of dR/dT is much smaller. A platinum thermometer of 25 ohms at room temperature has a resistance less than 0.2 ohm at 20°K. In such a case the definition $(1/R)$ (dR/dT) for sensitivity is not truly practical, because most measuring equipment is not suited for measuring the very low resistances with high fractional precision. A more realistic expression for sensitivity of a particular thermometer and its associated measuring circuit would probably lie somewhere between $(1/R)$ (dR/dT) and $1/R_0$ dR/dT, where R_0 is the resistance at the ice-point. By providing equipment particularly suited to the precise measurement of very low resistance it is possible to extend the useful low-temperature limit of the platinum resistance thermometer.

Van Dijk of the University of Leiden (Netherlands) has used platinum thermometers at temperatures as low as 4.2°K. Of course, in theory one could construct a platinum thermometer having a resistance of many thousands of ohms at room temperature, so that its low-temperature resistance would be suitable for measurement by instruments commonly used. However, practical difficulties of size are apt to be encountered.

Although, as a rule, alloys are to be avoided when choosing a material for a resistance thermometer, constantan, an alloy of about 40 percent nickel and 60 percent copper, has been used as a thermometer in the region 2° to 20°K. It has a fairly uniform temperature coefficient of approximately 0.001 per degree in this temperature range.

5.23. Semiconducting Resistance Thermometers. A number of materials of the class known as semiconductors have useful thermometric properties. A semiconductor may be defined as a material whose electrical conductivity is much less than that of a metallic conductor but much greater than that of a typical insulator. Certain types of semiconducting resistance thermometers, made of metallic oxides and known as Thermistors® are now readily available as commercial items. The properties of Thermistors® have been described by Becker, Green, and Pearson [22].

Elemental semiconductors which are good thermometers down to very low temperatures include germanium, silicon, and carbon. Germanium and silicon, when very pure, have resistivities too high to be useful at the lower temperatures. Small amounts of impurity are required to provide electronic carriers. For example, germanium with about 0.0005 atomic percent indium was found to be a good thermometer below 20°K. Figure 5.9 shows the resistance-temperature relations of two semiconductors as contrasted with those of two pure metals.

Of all the semiconductors so far investigated, germanium (with an appropriate impurity) seems to offer the most promise as a low-temperature thermometer, not only because it can have high sensitivity but because recent investigations show that germanium thermometers can have very good reproducibility. Friedburg [9] has made a systematic investigation of a germanium alloy containing nominally 0.001 atomic percent indium. Small homogeneous specimens with slightly different impurity concentration were obtained from different levels of a polycrystalline ingot. Those having room-temperature resistivities of about 0.08 ohm cm were found to have useful tem-

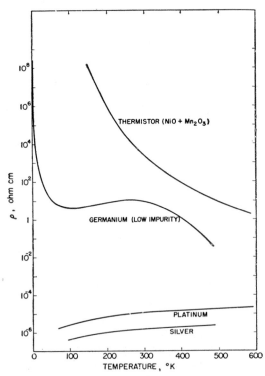

FIGURE 5.9. Comparison of temperature-resistance behavior of semiconductors and pure metals.

perature coefficients of resistance between 1.6° and 4.2°K. Thermometers were constructed of such strips (10 × 3 × 1 mm) by attaching current and potential leads with a tin-indium alloy solder. Temperatures determined with all the thermometers were found to be reproducible to 0.001 degree in the range 1.6° to 4.2°K when the thermometer was not warmed to higher temperatures between measurements. Several of the thermometers were equally reproducible after repeated cycling between liquid helium and room temperature. Kunzler, Geballe, and Hull [23] report excellent low-temperature characteristics of thermometers cut from a single crystal of arsenic-doped germanium. The thermometers were protected by mounting them in platinum capsules. They had good sensitivity between 2° and 35°K. Most important was their stability upon repeated cycling between room temperature and liquid helium temperature. The authors report that the data obtained support the tentative conclusion that the reproducibility is of the order of 10^{-4}°K at the boiling point of helium.

The principal objections to germanium semiconductors as thermometers are (1) the limited availability of suitable material and (2) the lack of a simple mathematical expression for the resistance-temperature relation. Obviously neither of these objections would be likely to withstand a concerted effort to develop germanium thermometers and determine their temperature-resistance relation.

Up to the present time carbon has been the most widely used semiconducting material for thermometry below 20°K. Giauque, Stout, and Clark [24] and Van Dijk, Keesom, and Steller [25] used stripes of carbon ink on porous paper. Fairbank and Lane [26] used commercially prepared carbon resistance strips.

Clement and Quinnel [27] measured the low-temperature characteristics of commercial carbon radio resistors and developed a very useful semi-empirical equation relating resistance and temperature. Although they made no attempt to try samples of resistors from all manufactures, they found that the 1-watt size manufactured by the Allen Bradley Company was suitable for their work. Resistors supplied by other manufacturers may be just as good or better. More measurements should be made and correlated with the methods of manufacture to determine the optimum carbon resistor for the application. Clement and Quinnel used resistors of nominal values of 10 ohms to 270 ohms. The equation fitting their data in the range 2° to 20°K is

$$\log R + K/\log R = A + B/T$$

where R is the resistance at the temperature T, and K, A, and B are experimentally determined constants. Temperatures calculated from this equation were found to be within 0.5 percent of the measured temperature between 2° and 20°K for eight different resistor samples.

Although carbon resistance thermometers are readily obtained and are quite useful for many applications, they are not as stable as the germanium just discussed. Accordingly it now appears that germanium is the favored candidate for precision resistance thermometry at very low temperatures.

5.24. Superconducting Thermometers. In some special applications it is useful to employ a superconductor in its transition range as a resistance thermometer. A typical polycrystalline superconductor has a transition curve like that shown in Figure 5.10. It is apparent that, in the very small temperature interval occupied by the transition, a superconductor is an extremely sensitive resistance thermometer. A very interesting application of this circumstance is the superconducting bolometer [28] [29] [30]. The principle of this device is illustrated in Figure 5.11.

A piece of superconducting material is mounted on a surface kept at the temperature of the midpoint of the superconducting transition. A constant direct current flows through the superconductor. Radiation passing through the window warms the superconductor. By interposing the rotating slotted wheel this radiation is interrupted at a definite frequency so the temperature of the superconductor will oscillate at the same frequency. The temperature oscillations in turn produce voltage oscillations across the superconductor and consequently energize the primary of the high-ratio transformer.

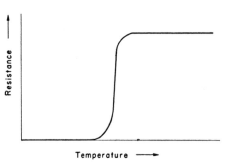

FIGURE 5.10. Resistance-temperature transition curve of a typical polycrystalline superconductor.

The secondary of this transformer feeds the input of a narrow-band-pass amplifier tuned to the proper frequency. Andrews et al. employed niobium nitride as the superconducting element because of its high transition temperature which permitted the use of liquid hydrogen as the refrigerant.

Another thermometer which utilizes the phenomenon of superconductivity is the leaded phosphor-bronze thermometer [31]. This alloy consists of a dispersion of lead or lead-bismuth alloy about 0.1 percent by weight in phosphor bronze. When this material is properly compounded and drawn into fine wire, it is found that it is quite temperature-sensitive in the region below $7.2°K$, the superconducting transition of lead. It appears that under the intense mechanical strains introduced by drawing the wire, the finely divided islands or filaments of lead, or lead-bismuth alloy, become superconducting progressively over a large temperature range. Such thermometers have been used from $1°$ to $7°K$.

5.25. Measuring Equipment for Resistance Thermometers. For accurate work either of two types of measuring equipment can be used: the Wheatstone bridge or the potentiometer and standard resistor. The bridge method

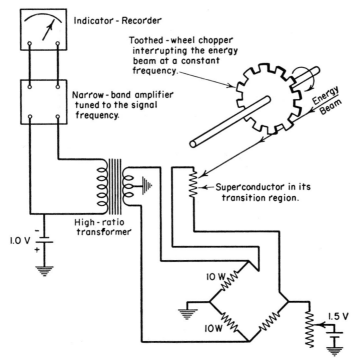

Indicator - Recorder

Toothed - wheel chopper
interrupting the energy
beam at a constant
frequency.

Narrow - band amplifier
tuned to the signal
frequency.

Energy Beam

Superconductor in its
transition region.

High - ratio
transformer

1.0 V

10 W

10 W

1.5 V

FIGURE 5.11. Superconducting bolometer.

has been developed at the National Bureau of Standards to a very high degree
of precision. The Mueller bridge will measure resistance up to 111 ohms.
It is a six-dial instrument, one division in the last dial corresponding to 0.0001
ohm. The important resistors are temperature controlled, and other elements
and compensators are provided so that an over-all accuracy of 0.0001 ohm can
be realized. Figure 5.12 is a simplified circuit diagram of a Mueller bridge
with a standard four-lead resistance thermometer. Connections to the thermometer are made through a commutator so that the thermometer can be
reversed, putting leads C and c where T and t are shown in the diagram. N
or R is the resistance shown on the bridge dials. If N is the bridge reading
with the thermometer connections in the "normal" position as shown, and R
the reading when reversed,

$$x + C = N + T$$
$$x + T = R + C$$

then
$$x = \frac{N + R}{2}$$

Thus the lead resistance is completely eliminated.

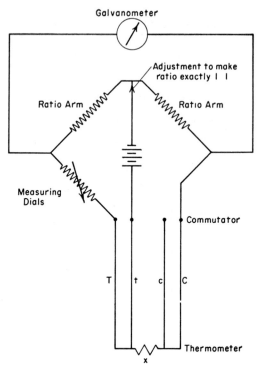

FIGURE 5.12. Diagram of a Mueller bridge with four-lead platinum resistance thermometer.

It will be noted that if lead T has the same resistance as lead C, we need make only one reading. For a great deal of work such a three-lead thermometer is quite adequate. For instance this three-lead arrangement is well suited for a resistance-operated thermostat.

It should be pointed out that the three- or four-lead thermometer demands a Wheatstone bridge with a one-to-one ratio. The multirange Wheatstone bridge cannot be used to compensate lead resistance by the method described. For high-resistance thermometers, lead resistance is sometimes small enough to ignore, so the multirange bridge is suitable. For example, resistance thermometers made of semiconductors often have high resistance, and their large changes in resistance can be followed with such a bridge. Moreover, the high dR/dT of a semiconductor does not demand as high an accuracy as that furnished by the Mueller bridge. A home-made Wheatstone bridge may be made from a one-to-one-ratio coil and a dial resistance box. Such a bridge may be quite reliable if the ratio arms, Figure 5.12, are wound with manganin wire which is a continuous piece from a single spool. If the coil mount consists of a brass tube, all the wire will all be at very nearly the same temperature and, being at a uniform temperature, the resistances of the two sections will remain equal. Such a bridge was used quite successfully for controlling the temperature of a stirred-liquid cryostat at NBS.

Figure 5.13 illustrates the potentiometer method of measuring resistances. The thermometer is connected in series with a standard resistor and a small current passed through the circuit. The resistance of the thermometer is determined by measuring in succession the potential across the terminals of the thermometer and the standard resistance. This method is very versatile, since the standard resistance can be chosen to have the same order of resistance as the thermometer. Moreover the energizing current in the potentiometer need not be set at any standard value; a value of current can be used that will utilize all the dials of the potentiometer. It is only necessary to measure successively the potentials (in dial units) across the thermometer and standard resistor in a time interval short enough to be sure that the current in neither circuit changes appreciably between readings. This method is not well adapted to themostat circuits because changes in the current in either circuit cause a change in the balance of the instrument.

VI. Magnetic Thermometry. Determining Temperatures Produced by Adiabatic Demagnetization

5.26. The very low temperatures produced by isentropic demagnetization of paramagnetic salts can be measured by utilizing properties of the salts themselves. In the first place, at moderately low temperatures, down to 1°K or a little lower, such materials closely obey the Curie relation,

$$\chi = \frac{C}{T}$$

where χ is the magnetic susceptibility, T the absolute temperature, and C the

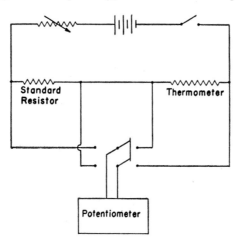

Figure 5.13. Potentiometer method of comparing resistances and thereby determining the resistance of a resistance thermometer.

Curie constant. At lower temperatures there are deviations from the Curie relation but it has become customary to go ahead and utilize the Curie formula and designate temperatures thus derived as "Curie" or "magnetic" temperatures and denote them by the symbol T^*. An apparatus designed for such measurements is shown in Figure 5.14. An alternating current in the primary coil produces alternating voltages in the secondaries. These are equal and opposite when there is no specimen present. The presence of the paramagnetic specimen inside one of the secondaries increases the mutual inductance and therefore the voltage developed by this coil. Balance is restored by adjusting the external variable mutual inductance. The mutual inductance between the primary coil and the specimen secondary is a linear function of the magnetic susceptibility of the specimen. Thus by determining the mutual inductance at a few temperatures given by the vapor pressure of helium, and plotting the values of mutual inductance against the reciprocal of temperature, lower temperatures may be measured by extrapolation. These lower temperatures are, of course, "magnetic" (T^*) temperatures since in this temperature range there are deviations from the Curie relation. A thorough discussion of modern techniques of magnetic thermometry was given by Van Dijk [7].

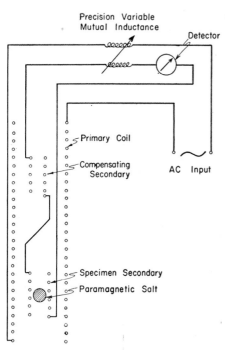

FIGURE 5.14.   Magnetic thermometer.

The conversion of these values of T^* to absolute thermodynamic temperatures T is a rather complicated experimental assignment, but is is based on a rigorous, straightforward, and relatively simple thermodynamic treatment.

Consider the processes illustrated in Figure 5.15. The paramagnetic salt is brought to a temperature T_i, known on the thermodynamic scale, for example, 1°K. First, isothermal magnetizations are performed and the amount of heat produced is measured by the evaporation of liquid helium which is in thermal contact with the salt. The entropy changes accompanying the isothermal magnetizations are then obtained simply by dividing the heat of magnetization by T_i. Thus at T_i we have an experimental relationship between the magnetic field H and the entropy of magnetization.

If next a series of isentropic demagnetizations is performed starting at T_i,

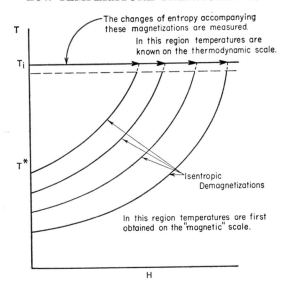

FIGURE 5.15. A method of converting "Curie" temperatures to thermodynamic temperatures.

with various values of initial magnetic field H, a different final temperature T^* will be reached in each case. Since the entropy at the start of each of these demagnetizations is known and the demagnetizations are isentropic, we now have an experimental relation between T^* and the entropy of the salt in zero magnetic field, at the very low final temperatures. From this relation we can compute values of $(\partial S/\partial T^*)_{H=0}$.

Next it is necessary to perform an ordinary calorimetric measurement in the absence of magnetic field, that is, add heat to the salt which has been cooled by adiabatic demagnetization and measure the temperature rise. This experiment yields a relation between Q, the heat added, T^*, the measured magnetic temperature, and allows us to compute $(\partial Q/\partial T^*)_{H=0}$.

From these two partial derivatives the thermodynamic temperature is obtained;

$$T = \frac{dQ}{dS} = \frac{(\partial Q/\partial T^*)_{H=0}}{(\partial S/\partial T^*)_{H=0}}$$

VII. LIQUID-IN-GLASS THERMOMETERS

5.27. There are many applications which call for the relatively simple but not necessarily inaccurate liquid-in-glass thermometer. When intended for use at low temperatures, most such thermometers are filled with organic liquids and therefore have characteristics quite different from those of mercury thermometers. A very important consideration is the drainage of the liquid. A reading taken immediately after immersion may be low by several degrees because some of the liquid clings to the walls of the capillary and drains slowly. The drainage can be speeded by first immersing only the bulb, leaving the stem warm, and then after a few minutes, completing the immersion. When the capillary is cold, drainage is slow because of the higher viscosity of the liquid.

5.28. Partial Immersion. Another important source of error is encountered when part of the thermometer stem is at a temperature different from the temperature being measured. It is always best to have all the liquid column immersed; but if this is impractical, a correction for the emergent stem should be made according to the formula

$$\text{Stem correction} = kn(T - t)$$

where k is the differential expansion coefficient, n is the number of degrees of stem emergent, T the temperature of the bath, and t the mean temperature of the emergent stem.

For toluene, a liquid often used in such thermometers, the value of k is approximately 0.001 for a centigrade thermometer. When measuring a temperature of $-50°C$ with 40 degrees of the stem at an average temperature of $-10°C$ the emergent stem correction will be

$$.001 \times 40[-50 - (-10)] = -1.6°C$$

5.29. Distillation. Since many of the organic liquids used in thermometers are quite volatile, it frequently happens that some of the liquid evaporates from the column and condenses in the expansion bulb at the top. Droplets in the capillary itself are usually evident, but it is easy to miss liquid in the expansion bulb.

5.30. Lower Temperatures. The liquid most commonly used for thermometers calibrated as low as $-200°C$ is pentane; actually the pure pentanes freeze far above this temperature, but there is a commercial crude mixture of pentanes which remains sufficiently mobile (perhaps by supercooling) to be usable to liquid-nitrogen temperature $(-196°C)$. Another liquid which has been used and appears to have some advantages is propane. Propane is less viscous than pentane, but is more volatile. In fact the vapor pressure of propane at room temperature is several atmospheres, so the thermometers are under pressure.

5.31. Liquid Metals. The disadvantages mentioned above are eliminated or greatly reduced in thermometers filled with liquid metals. The only difficulty is that liquid metals freeze at relatively high temperatures. Mercury freezes at $-40°C$. The range has been extended to about $-55°C$ by using the eutectic mixture of mercury and thallium.

5.32. Accuracy Obtainable. It is dangerous to be dogmatic about accuracy, but experience with low-temperature liquid-in-glass thermometers suggests that those filled with organic liquids can, with reasonable care, be trusted to 1° or 2°C. A good thermometer filled with a liquid metal should have less than one-tenth this error. Some very sensitive mercury-thallium thermometers have been found to be reproducible to 0.01 degree.

REFERENCES FOR CHAPTER 5

[1] H. F. Stimson, *J. Research NBS*, **42**, 209 (1949).
[2] Harold J. Hoge and Ferdinand G. Brickwedde, *J. Research NBS*, **22**, 351 (1939) RP 1188.
[3] Woolley, Brickwedde, and Scott, *J. Research NBS*, **41**, 379 (1948) RP 1932.
[4] Harold J. Hoge, *J. Research NBS*, **44**, 321 (1950).
[5] G. W. Moessen, J. G. Aston, and R. G. Ascah, *J. Chem. Phys.*, **22**, 2096 (1954).
[6] *Conférence de Physique des basses temperatures*, Paris, 2-8 September 1955.
[7] H. van Dijk and M. Durieux, in C. J. Gorter (Ed.), "Progress in Low Temperature Physics," North Holland Publishing Co., Amsterdam, Vol. 2 (1957) p. 431.
[8] H. J. Hoge in "Temperature, Its Measurement and Control in Science and Industry," Reinhold Publishing Corporation, N.Y., Vol. 1 (1941) p. 141.
[9] S. A. Friedburg in "Temperature, Its Measurement and Control in Science and Industry," Reinhold Publishing Corporation, N.Y., Vol. 2 (1956) p. 359.
[10] K. Mendelssohn, *Zt. f. Physik*, **73**, 482 (1931).
[11] R. B. Scott, *J. Research NBS*, **25**, 459 (1940) RP 1339.
[12] C. H. Meyers and M. S. Van Dusen, *B.S.J. Research*, **10**, 381 (1933) RP 538.
[13] J. R. Clement and John Gaffney. A report presented at the 1954 Cryogenic Engineering Conference, Boulder, Colorado.
[14] D. H. Weitzel and O. E. Park, *Rev. Sci. Instr.*, **27**, 57 (1956).
[15] D. H. Weitzel, W. V. Lobenstein, J. W. Draper, and O. E. Park, *J. Research NBS*, **60**, 221 (1958).
[16] W. F. Giauque, R. M. Buffington, and W. A. Schulze, *J. Amer. Chem. Soc.*, **49**, 2343 (1927).
[17] Walter P. White, *J. Amer. Chem. Soc.*, **36**, 2292 (1914) and *Rev. Sci. Instr.*, **4**, 142 (1933).
[18] G. K. White and S. B. Woods, *Rev. Sci. Instr.*, **28**, 638 (1957).
[19] J. C. Southard and F. G. Brickwedde, *J. Amer. Chem. Soc.*, **55**, 4378 (1933).
[20] C. H. Meyers, *B.S.J. Research*, **9**, 807 (1932) RP 508.
[21] Russell B. Scott and Jane W. Mellors, *J. Research NBS*, **34**, 249 (1945) RP 1640.
[22] J. A. Becker, C. B. Green, and G. L. Pearson, *Elec. Eng.*, **65**, 711 (1946).
[23] J. E. Kunzler, T. H. Geballe, and G. W. Hull, *Rev. Sci. Instr.*, **28**, 96 (1957).
[24] W. F. Giauque, J. W. Stout, and C. W. Clark, *J. Amer. Chem. Soc.*, **60**, 1053 (1938).
[25] H. van Dijk, W. H. Keesom, and J. P. Steller, *Physica*, **5**, 625 (1938).
[26] H. A. Fairbank and C. T. Lane, *Rev. Sci. Instr.*, **18**, 525 (1947).
[27] J. R. Clement and E. H. Quinnel, *Rev. Sci. Instr.*, **23**, 213 (1952).
[28] Donald H. Andrews, "Report of an international conference on fundamental particles and low temperatures held at the Cavendish laboratory Cambridge on 22-27 July 1946," Vol. 2, Low Temperatures, p. 56.
[29] Robert M. Milton, *Chem. Rev.*, **39**, 419 (1946).
[30] J. A. Hulbert and G. O. Jones, *Proc. Phys. Soc.* **B68**, (1955).
[31] W. H. Keesom, *Leiden Comm. Suppl.* **80a**; P. H. Van Laer and W. H. Keesom, *Leiden Comm.*, **252f**, *Physica*, **5**, 541 (1938).
[32] R. B. Scott, C. H. Meyers, R. D. Rands, Jr., F. G. Brickwedde, and N. Bekkedahl, *J. Research NBS*, **35**, 39 (1945).

Chapter VI

INSULATION*

6.1. Many cryogenic processes require a perfection of thermal insulation unapproached in any other field. For instance, in some experiments in which temperatures of 0.01°K were produced by adiabatic demagnetization, a 2.5-gram specimen was so well insulated from its surroundings that it received heat at a rate of only about 3.6 ergs per minute. This may be better appreciated when the energy is expressed in more easily visualized terms as follows: The specimen would produce more energy upon being dropped 1 mm than it would receive by heat transfer in an hour. Even in relatively large-scale equipment the heat flow must be kept very small to conserve precious refrigeration or to preserve liquids having small heats of vaporization. For example, there is a commercial storage vessel holding 50 liters of liquid helium with an evaporation loss of only 0.25 liter per day. Translated into terms of energy flow, this is less than 0.01 watt. Some large containers for the storage and transportation of liquid oxygen and nitrogen have evaporation losses of less than 1 percent per day. It has been mentioned earlier that in gas separation plants which deliver products in the gaseous state, practically all the refrigeration supplied for the process is lost either through imperfect heat exchange or by heat flow through the insulation. Thus an improvement in insulation pays off directly in reducing the amount of refrigeration needed, and accordingly the power required.

The choice of insulation for a particular application is usually a compromise in which such factors as economy, convenience, weight, ruggedness, volume, and other properties are considered along with the effectiveness of the insulation. Thus, although the major part of this chapter will be devoted to the principles and techniques of high quality insulation, some attention will be given to less perfect insulation methods that may be desirable for special applications. Only those methods which have been found to be useful at temperatures as low as the boiling point of liquid nitrogen (77°K) will be considered.

* Originally issued in preliminary form as *Low Temperature Insulation* by R. B. Scott, Cryogenic Engineering Laboratory, National Bureau of Standards, Boulder Laboratories, Boulder, Colo., NBS Report 5526, October 21, 1957.

I. Vacuum Insulation

6.2. James Dewar, the first to liquefy hydrogen, was also the first to use vacuum insulation. His invention, the double-walled glass vessel with a high vacuum in the space between the walls, is now a common household article in addition to being extensively used in research laboratories. The inventor is honored by the name "Dewar vessel" or sometimes simply "dewar." It is customary to call all vessels which utilize vacuum insulation to prevent heat flow into a cold space dewars. The importance of vacuum insulation is evident when it is realized that it can almost completely eliminate two of the principal modes of heat transfer, gaseous conduction and convection. When appropriate measures are taken also to minimize heat transfer by radiation and conduction by solid structural members, vacuum insulation is by far the most effective known. Two common types of vacuum insulated vessels (dewars) are illustrated in Figure 6.1. Because of its importance, a large part

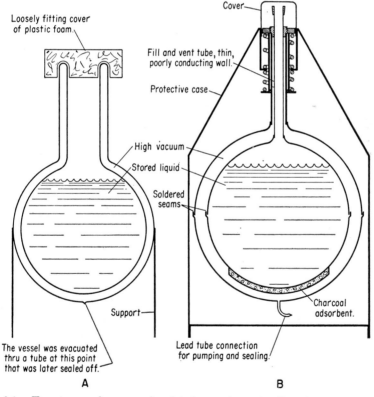

Loosely fitting cover of plastic foam.

Cover

Fill and vent tube, thin, poorly conducting wall.

Protective case

High vacuum

Stored liquid

Soldered seams

Support

The vessel was evacuated thru a tube at this point that was later sealed off.

Charcoal adsorbent.

Lead tube connection for pumping and sealing.

A B

Figure 6.1. Two types of vacuum-insulated containers for liquefied gases. Vessel A is Pyrex® glass. Surfaces of the glass facing the vacuum space are silvered to reduce heat transfer by radiation. Vessel B is metal. Spheres are copper, with surfaces facing the vacuum space cleaned to achieve the high intrinsic reflectivity of copper.

of this chapter will be devoted to a discussion of high-vacuum insulation, including material on the production and maintenance of high vacua. First let us examine the principal modes by which heat enters a vacuum-insulated low-temperature vessel and show how the heat flow can be computed.

6.3. Heat Transfer by Residual Gas. It is predicted by the kinetic theory of gases and confirmed by experiment that the thermal conductivity of a gas, in which the mean free path is small in relation to the distances between the surfaces constituting the heat source and the heat sink, is independent of the gas pressure. Thus, if one measures the rate of heat flow through air at 300°C between surfaces of slightly different temperatures with a separation of about 1 cm as the pressure is reduced from a starting pressure of 1 atmosphere, it is found that the rate is essentially unchanged until the pressure becomes quite small. However, as the pressure approaches the micron range (*ca.* 10 to 100 microns Hg), there is a marked decrease in rate of heat transfer; and at pressures below 1 micron Hg the rate is nearly proportional to the gas pressure. There is a constant small amount of heat transferred by radiation and, if this is corrected for, the transfer by the residual gas is quite precisely proportional to the pressure.

This result is also very simply explained by kinetic theory. It is a consequence of the fact that at sufficiently low pressures the molecules of a gas collide with the walls of the enclosure much more frequently than with each other; thus each molecule becomes a vehicle which travels without interruption from one boundary to that opposite and transports energy from the warm to the cold surface on each trip. It is this region of low pressure and long mean free path ("free molecule" conduction) that is of interest in vacuum insulation. It is also worth mention that under these conditions the rate of heat transfer is independent of the separation between the two surfaces; increasing the separation lengthens the time required for an individual molecule to make a trip; but if the pressure (molecular concentration) is unchanged, the total number of molecules available as heat-transfer vehicles is increased in the same proportion. If each gas molecule achieved thermal equilibrium with the wall as it collided and rebounded, the rate of heat transfer would be uniquely determined by the molecular weight, specific heat, and pressure of the residual gas. However, such thermal equilibruim is seldom if ever realized. The approach to equilibrium is a property of the wall-gas combination and has been treated quantitatively by Knudsen [1] by the concept of the accommodation coefficient α, which is defined by

$$\alpha = \frac{T_i - T_e}{T_i - T_w} \tag{6.1}$$

where T_i is the effective temperature of the incident molecules, T_e the effective temperature of the emitted (reflected) molecules, and T_w the temperature of the wall. If complete equilibrium is established between the wall temperature and that of the molecules striking it, α will be unity. If the molecules rebound from the wall without change of kinetic energy, α will be zero. In practice neither of these extremes is encountered; α is found to have values between 0 and 1, although for rough surfaces at temperatures close to the condensing temperature of the molecule the value of α approaches 1.

The residual gas in the vacuum space insulating a cryogenic vessel presents a curious situation when one considers the "temperature" of the gas. In the simple case of parallel surfaces with accommodation coefficients of unity at each wall, it is apparent that there are two distinct sets of molecules. The set leaving the warm surface has a speed distribution characteristic of the temperature of the warm surface, and each molecule has a velocity component in the direction of the cold surface. The other set of molecules has a speed distribution bestowed by the cold surface and a component of velocity towards the warm surface. Knudsen has investigated this problem and obtained a relation for the heat transfer between long coaxial cylinders as follows:

$$W = \frac{A_1}{2}\left(\frac{\alpha_1\alpha_2}{\alpha_2 + \frac{r_1}{r_2}(1 - \alpha_2)\alpha_1}\right)\frac{\gamma + 1}{\gamma - 1}\sqrt{\frac{R_M}{2\pi}}\frac{p}{\sqrt{TM}}(T_2 - T_1) \qquad (6.2)$$

where W is the rate of heat transfer, A_1 is the area of the inner cylinder, α is the accommodation coefficient, r is the radius of a cylinder, γ is the ratio of specific heats, C_p/C_v, R_M is the universal gas constant, p is the pressure, T is the absolute temperature, M is the molecular weight of the residual gas.

The subscripts 1 and 2 refer to the inner and outer cylinders respectively. The temperature T without subscript should be measured at the gage that measures the pressure p. In a system in which the mean free paths of molecules are large compared to the dimensions of the spaces, $p/\sqrt{T}$ has a constant value. This phenomenon of proportionality between p and $\sqrt{T}$ has been called thermal transpiration, thermomolecular pressure, or Knudsen effect.

This behavior can be derived quite simply from elementary kinetic theory of gases. Consider a chamber containing a gas at low density divided by an insulating partition in which there is an aperture of area A. The temperatures on the two sides of the partition are maintained at T_1 and T_2 respectively.

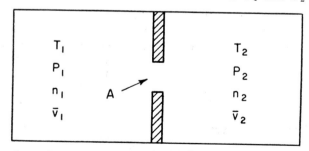

Now the number of molecules entering the aperture from the left in unit time is proportional to $n_1\bar{v}_1$, where n_1 is the number of molecules in a unit volume and $\bar{v}_1$ is their mean root square velocity. Likewise the number entering the aperture from the right in unit time is proportional to $n_2\bar{v}_2$. Moreover n and $\bar{v}$ are related to the pressure by

$$P = \tfrac{1}{3}nM\bar{v}^2$$

where M is the molecular mass. Also, $\bar{v}^2$ is proportional to the absolute temperature T. At equilibrium, of course, the rate at which molecules move through the aperture from left to right must equal the number moving through from right to left:

$$n_1\bar{v}_1 = n_2\bar{v}_2$$

Then by simple substitution it is seen that

$$P_1/P_2 = \sqrt{T_1/T_2}$$

For practical computations of heat transfer in systems other than long coaxial cylinders, it is sufficiently accurate to substitute the ratio of the areas of the inner and outer surfaces A_1/A_2 for the ratio of the radii r_1/r_2. This will allow the computation of the heat transfer between surfaces of various geometry: short cylinders, concentric spheres, etc.

Equation 6.2 is a general equation which can be used with any consistent system of units. For units commonly used in vacuum work and cryogenics it can be stated as

$$W = 2.426 \times 10^{-4}\, A_1 \frac{\alpha_1\alpha_2}{\alpha_2 + \dfrac{A_1}{A_2}(1 - \alpha_2)\alpha_1} \frac{\gamma + 1}{\gamma - 1} \frac{p}{\sqrt{MT}}(T_2 - T_1) \quad (6.3)$$

Here W is the rate of heat transfer in watts,
   A_1 and A_2 are the areas of the inner and outer walls in cm^2,
   p is the pressure in microns of mercury,
   and the temperatures T, T_1, and T_2 are in degrees Kelvin.
   The other quantities are the same as in Equation 6.2.

The following table of mean free paths may be helpful in deciding whether or not free molecule conduction exists in a given situation.

TABLE 6.1.   MEAN FREE PATHS OF SOME GASES
AT A PRESSURE OF 1 MICRON OF MERCURY

Temperature, °K	Air, cm	Hydrogen, cm	Helium, cm
4	—	—	0.11
20	—	0.30	0.67
76	0.87	1.8	3.2
300	5.1	9.5	15.

The mean free path is given by

$$L = 8.6 \times 10^3 \frac{\eta}{p}\sqrt{\frac{T}{M}} \quad (6.4)$$

Where L is the mfp in cm, η the viscosity of the gas in poises, p the pressure in microns, T the Kelvin temperature and M the molecular weight. Thus, L varies inversely with pressure and approximately as $T^{3/2}$ since η is roughly proportional to T.

The limited literature on accommodation coefficients has been summarized by Partington [2]. Except upon surfaces having had unusual preparation, the common gases have accommodation coefficients between 0.7 and 1 at or below room temperature. The light gases, hydrogen and helium, may have much lower values. Table 6.2 lists some values derived from the data of Keesom and Schmidt (1936-1937) and Knudsen (1911). The former authors suggested that α will tend towards unity as the temperature approaches the critical temperature of the gas. However, the value of the accommodation coefficient is sensitive to the condition of the surface.

TABLE 6.2. APPROXIMATE ACCOMMODATION COEFFICIENTS

T, °K	Helium	Hydrogen	Air
300	0.3	0.3	0.8-0.9
76	0.4	0.5	1
20	0.6	1.	—

Because of the great variations in accommodation coefficients, it is difficult to make accurate estimates of heat transfer by residual gas. This is usually not a serious lack, however, because as a rule the objective is to obtain a vacuum of such quality that the heat transfer by residual gas does not contribute seriously to the over-all heat transfer. It is interesting to note that in some cases residual helium in a vacuum space will transfer less heat than the same pressure of air, even though the thermal conductivity of helium is much greater than that of air. The values of accommodation coefficients given in Table 6.2 for helium and air at 300°K and 76°K will lead to this result when used in conjunction with Equation 6.3. The lower accommodation coefficient of helium more than compensates for its higher intrinsic thermal conductivity which is a consequence of its lower molecular weight.

6.4. Heat Transfer by Radiation. The rate at which a surface emits thermal radiation is given by the Stefan-Boltzmann equation,

$$W = \sigma e A T^4 \tag{6.5}$$

where e is the total emissivity at temperature T,

  A is the area,

  σ is a constant having the value 5.67×10^{-12} watt cm^{-2} (deg K)$^{-4}$

The net exchange of radiant energy between two surfaces is given by the expression

$$W = \sigma E A (T_2{}^4 - T_1{}^4) \tag{6.6}$$

where subscripts 1 and 2 refer to the cold and warm surfaces respectively.

A is an area factor. In the case of cylinders or spheres it will be taken as the area of the enclosed (inner) surface; in the case of parallel plates it is obviously the area of either surface. E is a factor involving the two emissivities. For spheres and cylinders its value depends on whether the reflections at the enclosing surface are specular (mirror-like) or diffuse (i.e., with intensity proportional to the cosine of the angle between the direction of emission and the surface). The mode of reflection at the enclosed surface is immaterial and for parallel plates the mode of reflection at both surfaces is immaterial. Table 6.3 gives values of E in terms of individual emissivities

TABLE 6.3. VALUES OF E: A_1 AND A_2 ARE THE RESPECTIVE AREAS OF THE INNER AND OUTER SURFACES

	Specular Reflection	Diffuse Reflection
Parallel Plates	$\dfrac{e_1 e_2}{e_2 + (1 - e_2)e_1}$	$\dfrac{e_1 e_2}{e_2 + (1 - e_2)e_1}$
Long Coaxial Cylinders $(L \gg r)$	$\dfrac{e_1 e_2}{e_2 + (1 - e_2)e_1}$	$\dfrac{e_1 e_2}{e_2 + \dfrac{A_1}{A_2}(1 - e_2)e_1}$
Concentric Spheres	$\dfrac{e_1 e_2}{e_2 + (1 - e_2)e_1}$	$\dfrac{e_1 e_2}{e_2 + \dfrac{A_1}{A_2}(1 - e_2)e_1}$

and geometries for gray surfaces; that is, surfaces for which the emissivity is independent of wave length. The assumption of grayness is not strictly correct but can be shown to introduce negligible error in practical situations.

The formula giving the value of E for long cylinders and concentric spheres (diffuse reflection) is a good approximation for practical vessels such as short cylinders with elliptical or flat ends, or other conservative shapes if A_1 and A_2 are taken as the total areas, facing the insulating space, of the inner and outer surfaces respectively. The mode of reflection at practical surfaces is usually not known. It is often assumed that the reflection is diffuse rather than specular, but this assumption may not be justified for the good-reflecting surfaces and long wave lengths involved in cryogenic applications. In the absence of information on this point the formulas serve only to define the limits within which E must lie. For the common case, $e_1 \cong e_2 \ll 1$, the ratio E (specular)/E(diffuse) equals $\frac{1}{2}(1 + A_1/A_2)$ and obviously ranges from $\frac{1}{2}$ to 1. In general, the heat transfer where specular reflection is involved is equal to or less than that for diffuse reflection.

Radiation transfer can be reduced by interposing thermally isolated shields parallel to the radiating surfaces. Their effect can be very concisely expressed by matrix algebra [3]. Here we will limit ourselves for simplicity to the special case of two parallel planes between which are n shields. We will further simplify by distinguishing only two kinds of emissivity, that of the two bounding surfaces, e_o, assumed to be the same, and that of the shields, e_s, assumed to be all equal to each other. Then it can be shown that the heat transfer for $n \gtreqless 1$ is

$$W = (I_2 - I_1) \frac{E_o E_s}{(n-1)E_o + 2E_s} \tag{6.7}$$

where $I = \sigma AT^4$, the black-body emission. E_o is the emissivity factor applying between either boundary and the adjacent shield. E_s is the emissivity factor applying between any two adjacent shields.

$$E_o = \frac{e_o e_s}{e_s + e_o - e_o e_s} \tag{6.8}$$

$$E_s = \frac{e_s}{2 - e_s} \tag{6.9}$$

Case A: $e_o = e_s$, and consequently

$$E_o = E_s = E$$

Here

$$W = (I_2 - I_1) \left(\frac{E}{n+1} \right)$$

This case represents the use of floating metallic radiation shields in a dewar. In an actual installation it may prove difficult to realize the reduction in heat transfer indicated by the above formula because of necessary openings, irregularities, and connecting lines that behave like areas of high emissivity.

Case B: $e_o \ll 1$, $e_s \cong 1$, i.e., bright boundaries, black shields. Here

$$W = (I_2 - I_1) \left(\frac{E_o}{(n-1)E_o + 2} \right)$$

For small values of n this becomes

$$W \cong (I_2 - I_1) \left(\frac{E_o}{2} \right)$$

But here $E_o \cong e_o$. If n were zero, we would have

$$W = (I_2 - I_1) \left(\frac{e_o}{2 - e_o} \right) \cong (I_2 - I_1) \left(\frac{e_o}{2} \right)$$

which is the same result. Hence a small number of such shields is virtually without effect. As n is made very large, the thermal resistance of the shields, though individually small, takes effect through sheer numbers and W approaches the same value as in case A. Thus the boundary emissivity is of importance only for small numbers of shields. The case of numerous black shields is simulated by opaque non-metallic powders in the vacuum space.

The net heat transfer by radiation between two surfaces depends upon two different quantities: (a) the emissivity of the warm surface and (b) the absorptivity of the cold surface for radiation having an energy–wave length distribution characteristic of the warm surface. For the sake of conciseness both of these quantities are often designated as emissivities. Figure 6.2 shows graphically the energy–wave length distribution for some representative cryogenic temperatures. Of course, the radiant energy decreases very rapidly with falling temperature, and in addition, the wave length for maximum energy becomes greater with decreasing temperature. This wave length is given by Wien's displacement formula,

$$\lambda_{max} \, T = \text{constant}$$

The constant is 2898 micron degrees K.

For completeness, it should be pointed out that the literature contains two principal classes of emissivities: (a) those measured at normal incidence and (b) those averaged over all angles between normal and grazing with the ap-

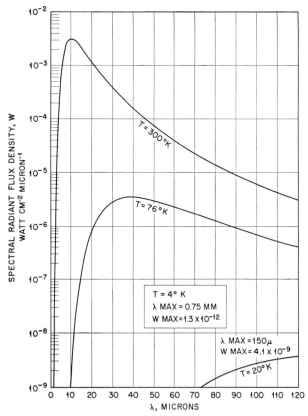

FIGURE 6.2.　Energy-wave length graph (black body radiation).

plication of a weighting factor of the cosine of the angle made with the surface. These are called "normal" emissivities and "hemispherical" emissivities, respectively. In heat transfer between extended surfaces it is the latter emissivity that is applicable. However, the difference between the two kinds can be at most 30 percent [4] and it is usually ignored in engineering calculations because of the large uncertainties that can exist due to surface contamination, the presence of piping or other complicated geometrical factors, etc. Unfortunately, the difference between normal and hemispherical emissivities is greatest for the case of greatest practical interest, namely metals for which $e \ll 1$.

A large number of low-temperature emissivities determined at the NBS Cryogenic Engineering Laboratory are included in the table of emissivities given in Chapter 10 (see p. 347).

So far we have been discussing "total" emissivities without bothering to prefix the qualifying adjective. Occasionally total emissivity data will be lacking for a substance for which "spectral" emissivities have been determined. The latter are simply emissivities determined using monochromatic radiation. Now the total emissivity is the integral over all wave lengths of the spectral emissivity weighted according to the black-body energy–wave length distribution function. For a gray body the total and spectral emissivities are equal. Fortunately, metals approximate gray bodies reasonably well at the wave lengths that are important for thermal radiators at temperatures of $300°\text{K}$ or less; that is, wave lengths of a few microns or greater. This means that spectral emissivity values in the infrared will be reasonably good approximations to the total emissivity, especially if they are available at wave lengths equal to or greater than λ_{max}. The "greater than" is specified because more energy is produced at $\lambda > \lambda_{max}$ than at $\lambda < \lambda_{max}$. It is this same fact that metals approximate gray bodies in the infrared that permits us to use the expressions "emissivity of the cold surface" and "absorptivity of the cold surface for radiation characteristic of the warm surface" as if they were interchangeable.

Examination of the available data on low temperature emissivities discloses certain generalizations:

(1) The best reflectors are also the best electrical conductors (copper, silver, gold, aluminum).

(2) The emissivity decreases with decreasing temperature.

(3) The emissivity of good reflectors is increased by surface contamination.

(4) Alloying a good-reflecting metal increases its emissivity.

(5) The emissivity is increased by treatments such as mechanical polishing which result in work-hardening of the surface layer of metal.

(6) Visual appearance (i.e., brightness) is not a reliable criterion of reflecting power at long wave lengths.

Items (2), (4), and (5) are closely related to (1) in that the electrical resistivity usually increases with temperature, impurity, and strain. The classical free-electron theory leads to an expression for reflectivity at long wave lengths in terms of resistivity. This expression is approximately correct for good conductors at room temperature and for poor conductors, such as alloys, at all temperatures; but it gives reflectivities that are much too high for good conductors at low temperatures where the electronic mean free path becomes large compared with the depth of penetration of the electromagnetic wave into the metal. This effect, the anomalous skin effect, has been successfully treated in recent years [5]. However, the strong dependence of the reflectivity on surface contamination makes this a field in which precise agreement between theory and experiment is hardly to be expected. We may note parenthetically that a superconductor does not have perfect reflectivity but rather shows little or no difference from the normal state.

As a converse of the "don'ts" implied in the above list of rules, we may state that the best reflecting surface will be a pure good-conducting metal, annealed, and cleaned in some manner which avoids strain, such as by acids and residue-free organic solvents.

Figures 6.3 and 6.4 are useful in making rapid approximate computations

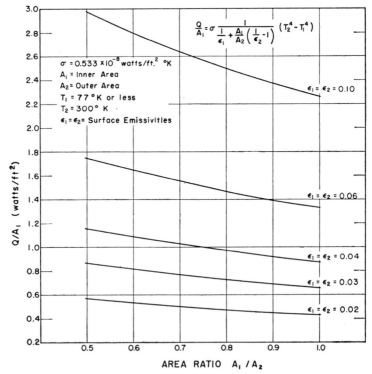

$$\frac{Q}{A_1} = \sigma \frac{1}{\frac{1}{\epsilon_1} + \frac{A_1}{A_2}\left(\frac{1}{\epsilon_2} - 1\right)} (T_2^4 - T_1^4)$$

$\sigma = 0.533 \times 10^{-8}$ watts/ft.^{2} $^\circ$K
A_1 = Inner Area
A_2 = Outer Area
T_1 = 77 $^\circ$K or less
T_2 = 300° K
$\epsilon_1 = \epsilon_2$ = Surface Emissivities

$\epsilon_1 = \epsilon_2 = 0.10$

$\epsilon_1 = \epsilon_2 = 0.06$

$\epsilon_1 = \epsilon_2 = 0.04$

$\epsilon_1 = \epsilon_2 = 0.03$

$\epsilon_1 = \epsilon_2 = 0.02$

Q/A_1 (watts/ft^2)

AREA RATIO A_1 / A_2

FIGURE 6.3. Net radiant heat transfer from a surface at 300°K to 77°K or lower.

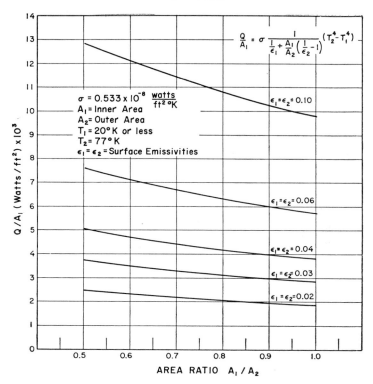

FIGURE 6.4. Net radiant heat transfer from a surface at 77°K to 20°K or lower.

of heat transfer by radiation for two situations frequently encountered by low-temperature workers. Figure 6.3 gives the net radiant-heat transfer from a surface at room temperature to one at 77°K or lower, and Figure 6.4 the net radiant heat transfer from a surface at 77°K to one at 20°K or lower.

6.5. Heat Transfer by Supports. It is a simple matter to compute the amount of heat conducted through ordinary solid supports, such as rods or cables, which may be used to bear the weight of the inner container of a dewar. The rate of heat transfer is given by

$$W = -Ak(dT/dx) \tag{6.10}$$

where A is the cross-sectional area of the support ($A = $ const.), k is the thermal conductivity and dT/dx is the temperature gradient. The negative sign merely indicates that heat flows in the direction of lower temperatures. The thermal conductivity usually varies markedly with temperature at low temperatures, so that an integration is required to obtain the heat flow. Thus

$$W = \frac{A}{L} \int_{T_1}^{T_2} k \, dT \tag{6.11}$$

where L is the length of the support with one end at the higher temperature T_2 and the other end at T_1. This expression may be evaluated by inserting an analytic function for $k = f(T)$, but as a rule there is no such simple function; $k = f(T)$ is commonly represented by a graph in which k is plotted as ordinate with T as abscissa. In this case Equation 6.11 may be evaluated by numerical integration

$$W = \frac{A}{L} \sum_{T_1}^{T_2} k_m \Delta T \qquad (6.12)$$

where k_m is the mean thermal conductivity in the temperature interval ΔT.

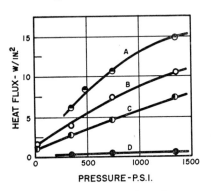

FIGURE 6.5. Heat conducted as a function of mechanical pressure by stacks of type 302 round stainless steel plates, each plate 0.0008 inch thick. (A) 148 plates; (B) 209; (C) 313; and (D) 315. Boundary temperatures for A, B, and C are 76°K and 296°K; for D, 20°K and 76°K.

By taking sufficiently small intervals of ΔT any desired accuracy can be achieved. If the thermal conductivity is a linear function of the temperature, it is correct to use an average value of k, midway between T_1 and T_2. Most convenient are thermal conductivity integrals which show directly the conduction of a unit area between any two temperatures.

When the supporting member is the tube which carries the evaporating vapor, as in the dewars shown in Figure 6.1, there is a circumstance which reduces the heat transfer to the inner container. Some of the heat which starts down the tube is intercepted by the issuing vapor and never reaches the inner container. This effect will be analyzed in the chapter on storage and transportation of liquefied gases.

There is a type of support that is of value when available space or other considerations make it difficult to use long rods or cables. This is the laminated support which consists of many layers of thin stainless steel or other poorly conducting metal. These supports, of course, are used only for compressive loads, but for such use their strength is almost the same as solid metal although the heat flow may be only a small fraction (e.g., 1 percent) of that of a similar solid support. These insulating supports owe their effectiveness to the high thermal resistance of the contact between two metal surfaces in a vacuum. Two forms have been devised; one consists of a stack of disks or washers, the other is a coiled strip like a tightly wound clock spring. It has been found that the thermal resistance of these multiple-contact supports can be increased considerably by lightly dusting the surfaces with manganese dioxide. Figure 6.5 gives data on the thermal resistance of some laminated stainless steel supports.

6.6. Analysis of Vacuum Systems. A high-vacuum system, Figure 6.6, usually consists of a mechanical pump called the fore pump which exhausts to the atmosphere and maintains an inlet pressure in the range 1 to about 100 microns of mercury, a pipe connecting this pump to the outlet of a diffusion pump capable of reducing the pressure several orders of magnitude more, and a pipe of larger diameter connecting the diffusion pump to the volume being evacuated, for example, the insulating space of a dewar vessel. Sometimes a second diffusion pump, called a booster pump, is used between the high-vacuum diffusion pump and the mechanical pump. Also it is customary to provide a cold trap to remove condensable vapors. Some judgment should be exercised in selecting pumps of the proper capacities and choosing connecting pipe and other elements of such size that their resistance to flow will not seriously limit the over-all performance.

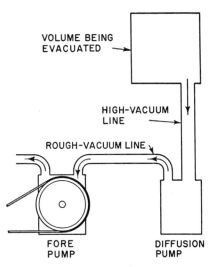

FIGURE 6.6. Schematic diagram of a simple vacuum system.

Although exact computation of the behavior of a vacuum system is neither possible nor necessary, approximate calculations can be made which are adequate for use in designing a vacuum system for a given service. The following brief discussion of vacuum-system analysis is based principally on a book by Guthrie and Wakerling [6] and an article by Norman [7] contributed to the Symposium on High Vacuum, sponsored by the National Research Corp. and the Division of Industrial and Engineering Chemistry, American Chemical Society, Cambridge, Mass., October 30-31, 1947. These references are particularly recommended as sources of easily applied practical information. For a very thorough and basic treatment of the subject, the well-known book by Dushman [10] is recommended. Current information on vacuum techniques and equipment is available from the journal *Vacuum* [8] and *Vacuum Symposium Transactions* [9].

Since the rate of flow Q of a gas through a pipe or other component which offers resistance to flow is proportional to the pressure drop $p_1 - p_2$ across the component, it is useful to employ the concept of conductance, which is simply the proportionality constant involved. Thus the conductance,

$$C = \frac{Q}{p_1 - p_2} \tag{6.13}$$

Q is the quantity of gas measured in units of pressure × volume passing across a given plane in unit time. If the temperature is constant, Q is proportional to the mass rate of flow. The conductance of a given element is a function of the dimensions of the element, of certain physical properties of the gas flowing through it, and in some cases, of the pressure of the gas. If a number of components of conductances C_1, C_2, C_3, etc., are connected in series, the net conductance C will be given by

$$\frac{1}{C} = \frac{1}{C_1} + \frac{1}{C_2} + \frac{1}{C_3} + \cdots \tag{6.14}$$

Also, if these individual conductances are connected in parallel the resultant conductance is

$$C = C_1 + C_2 + C_3 + \cdots \tag{6.15}$$

Another concept needed for analysis of vacuum systems is the speed of a vacuum pump. For the purposes of this discussion the speed of a vacuum pump is defined as the volume rate of flow of gas into the pump at the existing inlet pressure. If a pump of speed S is connected by a pipe of conductance C to a chamber being evacuated, the effective pumping speed of the system, S', will be given by

$$\frac{1}{S'} = \frac{1}{S} + \frac{1}{C} \tag{6.16}$$

Thus it is seen that the pumping speed can be seriously reduced if connecting elements have inadequate conductance.

Conductance of High-Vacuum Lines. In the high-vacuum region of a system the pressure is usually so low that the mean free paths of the molecules are considerably greater than the lateral dimensions of the channels, and hence the molecules collide much more often with the walls than they do with each other. Under these conditions the mode of gas flow is called free molecular flow. For practical purposes it may be assumed that this type of flow exists if

$$pD < 15$$

where p is the average gas pressure in microns of mercury, and D is the lateral dimension of the gas passage in centimeters. A simple working formula for the conductance of a long circular pipe carrying a gas in the region of free molecular flow is

$$C = 12.1 \left(\frac{28.7}{M} \cdot \frac{T}{293} \right)^{1/2} D^3 / L \tag{6.17}$$

where C is the conductance in liters per second* and D and L are the diameter and length of the pipe in centimeters. The factor $\left(\dfrac{28.7}{M} \cdot \dfrac{T}{293} \right)^{1/2}$, where M is the molecular weight and T the Kelvin temperature, permits the use of the

---

* This unit does not clearly express the nature of the conductance C. It would be more complete to say that C is expressed in micron-liters per second for a Δp of 1 micron.

formula with gases other than air and at temperatures other than room temperature. For air at 20°C this factor is unity. This formula neglects the end correction. It is applicable when L is very much greater than D. The end correction can be included by considering the problem of the conductance of an aperture. The conductance of an aperture is

$$C_A = 11.6 \left(\frac{28.7}{M} \cdot \frac{T}{293}\right)^{1/2} A \qquad (6.18)$$

where A is the area of the aperture in square centimeters. If the aperture is circular, this becomes

$$C_A = 9.1 \left(\frac{28.7}{M} \cdot \frac{T}{293}\right)^{1/2} D^2 \qquad (6.19)$$

where D is the diameter of the aperture in centimeters. This equation is valid when the dimensions of the vessel being evacuated are large compared with the diameter of the aperture through which the gas is leaving. Since in actual vacuum systems it is important to keep lines short, the normal design is something like that shown in Figure 6.6. The connection between the principal volume and the diffusion pump may be considered to be an aperture in series with a connecting pipe of the same diameter. The net conductance may be conveniently represented by

$$C = \left(\frac{28.7}{M} \cdot \frac{T}{293}\right)^{1/2} f D^2 \qquad (6.20)$$

where f is a dimensionless factor which depends upon the ratio of the length to the diameter of the connecting tube. Values of f are given in Figure 6.7. For $L/D = 0$, Equation 6.20 gives the conductance of an aperture and for $L \gg D$ it reduces to the formula for a long pipe. For L/D greater than 20, Equation 6.17 can be used. The error from end effect will be less than 10 percent.

ILLUSTRATION: Suppose that a diffusion pump with a speed of 100 liters per second is to be used to evacuate hydrogen from a large volume at $-200°C$, and design considerations require a connecting line 100 cm long. If a reduction of pumping speed of only 25 percent is permitted, what must be the diameter of the connecting pipe? From Equation 6.16

$$\frac{1}{S'} = \frac{1}{100} + \frac{1}{C}$$

and $S' = 75$ liters per second.

Therefore C must be at least 300 liters per second. Then Equation 6.20 becomes

$$300 = \sqrt{\frac{28.7}{2} \cdot \frac{73}{293}} f D^2$$

$$f D^2 = 159$$

And, from Figure 6.7, D is found to be 11.5 cm.

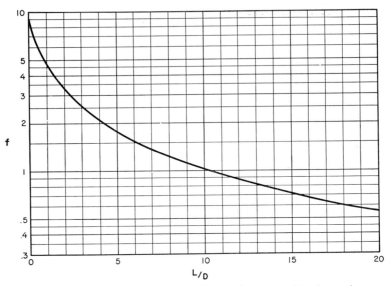

FIGURE 6.7. Values of factor f in equation for conductance of a short pipe,

$$C = \left(\frac{28.7}{M} \cdot \frac{T}{293} \right)^{\frac{1}{2}} fD^2.$$

L and D are length and diameter of pipe (in cm), C is net conductance in liters per second and T is Kelvin temperature.

Practical vacuum systems usually have one or more bends in the connecting lines and may contain baffles, cold traps, and valves. It is common practice to consider that a right-angle bend in a pipe is equivalent to increasing the length by one or two diameters. Some well-designed valves are essentially right-angle bends, offering no greater resistance to flow. Baffles and cold traps present such wide variations in shapes and dimensions that computation of conductance is very difficult. The safe procedure is to try to design such elements so that their passages and apertures are considerably larger than those of the rest of the system.

Conductance of Rough-Vacuum Lines. The mode of gas flow in the fore-vacuum region of a vacuum system may range from viscous flow, where the mean free paths of the molecules are short compared with the dimensions of the channel, to free molecular flow considered above. The flow may be considered viscous or streamline if the pressure is below atmospheric and

$$pD > 500$$

where p is in microns of mercury and D in cm. It is seen that there is a wide transition region

$$15 < pD < 500$$

where the flow is mixed, having some attributes of viscous flow and some of free molecular flow. It happens that for small vacuum systems using oil diffusion pumps requiring a backing pressure of less than 100 microns and fore-vacuum lines of a few centimeters diameter, the mode of gas flow is frequently in the transition region. From Poiseuille's law of viscous flow, the conductance of a long cylindrical tube is

$$C = \frac{\pi}{128\eta} \frac{D^4}{L} p \tag{6.21}$$

in cgs units, where C is in cm^3 per second, η is the viscosity in poises, and p is the pressure in dynes per cm^2. In the units previously used

$$C = 3.3 \times 10^{-5} \frac{D^4 p}{\eta L} \tag{6.22}$$

where C is in liters per second and p in microns. It will be noted that here the conductance is proportional to the pressure of the gas; so one must know the pressure in order to apply the formula. The conductance for mixed flow, where

$$15 < pD < 500,$$

is approximately

$$C = 3.3 \times 10^{-5} \frac{D^4 p}{\eta L} + \frac{10D^3}{L} \tag{6.23}$$

End corrections for the viscous and mixed flow are difficult to compute. Some experiments indicate that for pressures below 200 microns the end correction may be made by assuming an increase in length of about one diameter.

ILLUSTRATION: What is the conductance of a pipe 2.5 cm I.D., 200 cm long, for air at 20°C and at a mean pressure of 25 microns? From Equation 6.23

$$C = 3.3 \times 10^{-5} \times \frac{2.5^4 \times 25}{1.78 \times 10^{-4} \times 200} + \frac{10 \times 2.5^3}{200}$$

$$= .905 + .78 = 1.68 \text{ liters per second}$$

6.7. **Outgassing.** When a vacuum enclosure is pumped, the surfaces gradually release sizable quantities of gas, and accordingly the attainment of a good vacuum is greatly retarded. Some of the gas being liberated is bound to the surfaces by physical adsorption, some is dissolved in the solid, and some exists in chemical combination—for example, in oxide on the surfaces. The most effective means of removing these gases, and thus speeding up the evacuation process, is by heating during evacuation. When this is not feasible, heating the components in a vacuum oven just prior to assembly may accomplish nearly the same result. Heating in a hydrogen atmosphere will remove surface oxides, adsorbed air, and water vapor, but it is believed that for components to be used for a cryogenic insulating vacuum, heating in vacuum is greatly preferable because this will also remove some of the dissolved hydrogen. Residual hydrogen in an insulating vacuum is particularly objectionable because of its high thermal conductivity and its resistance to condensation on cold surfaces. In some metals large quantities of hydrogen trapped in pores during the smelting process may slowly diffuse to the surface and spoil the vacuum. Diffusion is more rapid in steel than in copper or aluminum.

It is advisable to avoid, as far as possible, organic materials in a vacuum system. These as a rule contain appreciable quantities of air in solution and also may contain entrapped or dissolved solvent or plasticizer. Particularly bad are rubber and phenolic plastics. Teflon®, Kel-F ®, polyethylene, polystyrene, and epoxy resins are much better.

It is very important that the interior of a vacuum system be scrupulously clean. A film of oil on the pipes or soldering flux at the joints may make it almost impossible to achieve a satisfactory vacuum. In cleaning a vacuum system it is good practice to use hot water to dissolve the water soluble dirt and after drying, follow this with an organic solvent. If the principal contaminant is not water-soluble, the order of washing should be reversed. Of course, the presence of soluble plastics may proscribe the use of organic solvents. In this case a detergent in hot water may be satisfactory.

Because of the difficulty of outgassing metals, many large vacuum-insulated metal containers are continuously pumped with a diffusion pump and fore pump permanently attached. Smaller metal vacuum vessels are usually provided with adsorbents which take up the residual gas when cold.

Diffusion of Gases Through Metals. Measurements made at high temperatures indicate that the rate of diffusion of a gas through a metal can be expressed by a relation of the form

$$q = \frac{k_0}{d} \sqrt{P}\, e^{-(b_0/T)} \tag{6.24}$$

where q is the diffusion rate, k_0 and b_0 constants characteristic of the gas-metal system, d the thickness of the metal, P the gas pressure, and T the Kelvin temperature. Dushman [10] has reduced this equation to the form

$$\log Q = C - B/T \tag{6.25}$$

for constant gas pressure and thickness of metal. He summarized the results of various observers in a table which listed values of C and B as well as temperatures at which specified diffusion rates would be expected.

In Figure 6.8, representative entries from Dushman's table are presented in the form of graphs and extended to temperatures likely to be encountered in the normal use of evacuated equipment. It is recognized that this extensive extrapolation is subject to question, and values thus obtained should be regarded accordingly. However, even if diffusion data were completely reliable, the gas emitted from the vacuum side of an enclosure could not be predicted with much confidence because much of the gas would exist in the

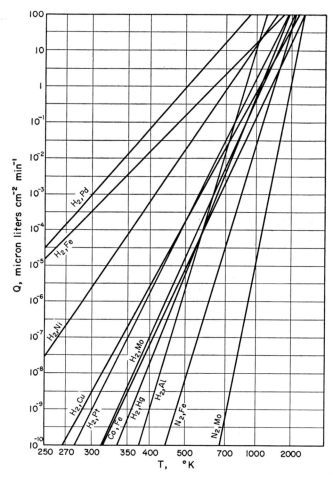

FIGURE 6.8. Diffusion of gases through metals. Graphs of log $Q = C - B/T$, where Q is the rate of diffusion in micron liters per minute per cm² through a thickness of 1 mm when the gas pressure is 1 atmosphere on one side and zero on the other. Values of C and B are from Dushman, "Scientific Foundations of Vacuum Technique," p. 611. Diffusion for different pressures and through different thicknesses may be obtained by assuming that the rate of diffusion is proportional to $p^{\frac{1}{2}}$ and inversely proportional to the thickness.

interior of the metal and the concentration would depend upon previous treatment.

6.8. Getters. A "getter" is a substance which takes up gas at very low pressures and so is used to improve or maintain a vacuum in a closed system. The processes responsible for the action of various getters include physical adsorption of the gas upon an extended surface adsorbent, chemical combination with suitable active materials, and the solution of gases in certain metals.

Chemical Getters. The term "getter" originated with substances of this type used to maintain vacuum in electronic tubes. The one having the most general utility is barium, but other alkali and alkaline earth metals have been used. All common gases except the rare gases can be removed by a suitable selection of metals. In order to be effective at ambient temperatures, such substances must be finely dispersed so as to present a large surface area. This is usually done by subliming the substance onto the walls of the vacuum space.

The only thermodynamic requirement for successful use of the chemical getter is that the pressure to be achieved cannot be less than the dissociation pressure of the compound formed by the metal and the gas. Of course, it is also required that the reaction take place with reasonable speed. Protective surface films may create difficulties in this respect.

Solution Getters. These consist of certain transition metals of which titanium, zirconium, and thorium are the most widely used. These take common gases such as N_2, O_2, H_2 into solid solution either as dissociated atoms or possibly by dissolving compounds formed by the gas and the metal. Stoichiometric proportions are not maintained over all.

Where a diatomic gas is taken into the lattice as dissociated atoms (as occurs with hydrogen), the solubility at low pressures varies with $\sqrt{P}$. Unfortunately, many of the available solubility data are at atmospheric pressure. The simple $\sqrt{P}$ law may not extend this far, and extrapolation of such data to the region of high vacuum is attended by very large uncertainties.

The more active of these metals may absorb very large volumes of gas. The system palladium-hydrogen is one of the most striking of these, especially at ordinary temperatures. Systems of this class show thermochemical and electrical properties that indicate them to be more properly considered as a special class of alloys than as ordinary solutions.

Gas-metal systems of this type show decreasing gas solubility with increasing temperature. On the other hand, *rate* of solution increases with increasing temperature. The optimum operating temperature is determined by balancing these factors. For oxygen and nitrogen this temperature may be about 1000°C, while for hydrogen it is usually considered to be about 400°C. However, a recent paper by Stout and Gibbons [11] reports that bulk titanium will rapidly take up hydrogen at room temperature provided the surface is kept free from oxide. Getters of this type can be regenerated by flashing at a very high temperature in vacuum. They do not take up the rare gases. There is a commercial high speed pump [12] which obtains most of its action from gettering by continuously sublimed titanium. Finely divided metals of this class are active at room temperature.

Adsorbents. Adsorbents such as activated coconut charcoal have long been used to maintain good insulating vacua in vessels used to store cryogenic liquids. This is a particularly apt utilization because the effectiveness of an adsorbent is greatly enhanced by lowering the temperature, and in this case the low temperature is furnished by the liquid being stored. Figure 6.1B (p. 143) is a cross section of a typical commercial vessel used for storing and transporting liquid oxygen and liquid nitrogen. The adsorbent is activated charcoal contained so as to be very nearly at the temperature of the liquid being stored. Although the vacuum between the walls of such a vessel may not be particularly good when it is empty (warm), as soon as the cryogenic liquid is introduced the adsorbent will take up gas and greatly improve the insulating vacuum.

When an adsorbent is thus used to improve a high vacuum it must take up gas at a very low pressure. Figure 6.9 is a plot of the temperature-pressure data obtained by several different observers who measured the adsorption of nitrogen and hydrogen by carbon. Quantitative comparison of the data of different observers is not readily made because of the wide variations in

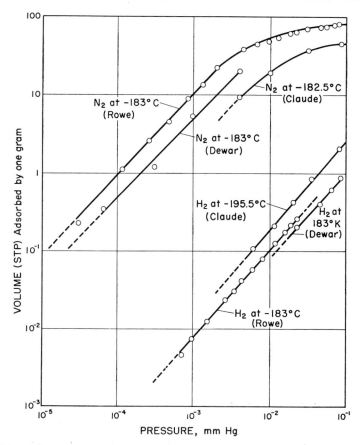

FIGURE 6.9. Adsorption of nitrogen and hydrogen by activated charcoal at low temperatures and pressures [14], [15], [16].

the adsorptive capacity of the carbon used. However, the figure does show a striking similarity between the trends of the various curves at very low pressures. The data of the early experimenters Claude 'and Rowe indicate that the amount adsorbed is very nearly proportional to the pressure (a slope of unity on this log-log graph). However, the very recent measurements of Lopez-Gonzalez, Carpenter and Dietz [13] show a much weaker pressure dependence for nitrogen at somewhat higher pressures. These recent data can be represented by a relation proposed by Freundlich [17]:

$$\log v = k + (\log p) / n \tag{6.26}$$

where v is the volume (STP) of gas adsorbed by a unit mass of adsorbent, k and n are experimental constants, and p is the equilibrium pressure of the gas in contact with the adsorbent. Thus a plot of log v versus log p should yield a straight line, but not necessarily one of unit slope ($n = 1$). However, Hill [18] has shown from a statistical mechanics treatment that all adsorption isotherms should approach the Henry's law relation, $v \propto p$, at very low pressures. Thus all adsorption isotherms would be expected to bend downwards and attain a slope of unity if extended to sufficiently low pressures. The data on hydrogen indicate that Henry's law is obeyed approximately for adsorption upon charcoal at pressures of 0.1 mm Hg and lower for a temperature of 77°K.

Estimates of Amount of Adsorbent Required. From the available data it may be possible for the designer of vacuum-insulated equipment to make an order-of-magnitude estimate of the amount of charcoal needed to adsorb a given quantity of hydrogen or nitrogen and achieve an acceptable residual pressure. However, this is only half the problem. The other half, how much gas will need to be adsorbed, is even more uncertain. It is known that metals contain objectionable quantities of gases, but the rates at which the gases will be released into the vacuum space at ordinary temperatures cannot be predicted. Because of this lack of sufficient quantitative information about adsorption, solution, diffusion, and the effects of outgassing treatments, an account of some over-all results regarding the use of adsorbents in practical equipment may be of value.

A typical commercial container for liquid oxygen or nitrogen has an insulating vacuum of about 7000 cm³ with a total boundary surface of approximately 15,000 cm². It has been found that an adsorber consisting of 1000 grams of activated charcoal in contact with the cold surface will maintain a good insulating vacuum for as long as five years.

It is very probable that hydrogen is the residual gas most responsible for heat conduction in an insulating vacuum. All the other gases with the exceptions of helium and neon are much more strongly adsorbed at liquid oxygen, nitrogen, or hydrogen temperatures and helium and neon are not likely to be present in appreciable amounts in a space from which the atmospheric air has been removed by pumping. Moreover, adsorbed, dissolved, or entrapped hydrogen is found in nearly all metals and may be gradually released into the insulating vacuum.

R. B. Jacobs [19] made some experiments on the adsorption and condensation of air by charcoal at liquid-hydrogen temperature. It was found that 527 grams of charcoal would serve in lieu of a pump to produce an insulating vacuum in a liquid-hydrogen transfer line. The pressure before cooling was 1 atmosphere and after liquid hydrogen was introduced the pressure fell to 9×10^{-6} mm Hg in five hours. The volume of the insulating space was 3680 cm^3. Of course most of the pressure reduction resulted from the ordinary condensation of nitrogen, oxygen and argon on the liquid-hydrogen-cooled surface. However, if there had been no adsorber present the final pressure of the helium, hydrogen, and neon constituents of atmospheric air would have been 0.064 mm Hg.

The cryogenic engineer needs more data on the adsorption of nitrogen, oxygen, carbon monoxide, argon, and hydrogen, since these are the gases most likely to give trouble in an insulating vacuum. In particular it would be very valuable to have data on the adsorption of hydrogen by charcoal, silica gel, and other materials at 20.4°K, the normal boiling point of hydrogen. Hydrogen is the only gas likely to be found in a vacuum insulating space bounded by a wall at liquid-hydrogen temperature. It may be of interest here to report that a commercial liquid-nitrogen-shielded dewar designed for the storage of liquid hydrogen and liquid helium was found to have considerably less heat leak when it contained liquid helium than when it contained liquid hydrogen. This is attributed to the superior cleanup of residual hydrogen from the insulating vacuum when a surface is cooled to the temperature of liquid helium.

In addition to further data on adsorption of gases, quantitative values are needed of desorption from metals commonly used, and the effects of various treatments of the metals.

It should be pointed out that adsorption measurements at very low pressures are not easy. In the first place, the measurement of very low pressure is an exacting task. Then it has been shown that the attainment of equilibrium is a slow process. Lopez-Gonzalez [13] et al., found that about 8 hours were required to attain equilibrium on a bone char for nitrogen at 90°K and an equilibrium pressure of 0.4 micron Hg. Dushman [10, p. 494] indicates that equilibrium for hydrogen may take ten times as long as for oxygen (and by inference for nitrogen). Finally, measurements at very low pressures may be ruined by desorption or adsorption of gas from the walls of the apparatus, or cleanup by an ionization gage. Thus it appears that the experimenter would be well advised to use rather large quantities of adsorbent and a vacuum gage that will not itself remove or add appreciable amounts of gas.

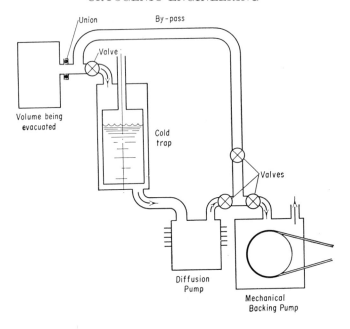

FIGURE 6.10. High-vacuum pumping system designed for general use in a low-temperature laboratory.

6.9. Vacuum Equipment. Figure 6.10 is a flow diagram and photograph of a complete small high-vacuum pumping system which was designed for general laboratory use in the NBS Cryogenic Engineering Laboratory. It is used principally to evacuate systems and components which are being checked for leaks and to evacuate and outgas equipment prior to seal-off. This system includes a bypass connection with appropriate valves which permit the isolation of the diffusion pump when it becomes necessary to let air into the rest of the system to repair a leak or to connect the pumping system to another object being tested. Serious damage (oxidation) may result if air at atmospheric pressure is allowed to come into contact with the hot oil in the pump. The valves and bypass connection make it unnecessary to wait for the diffusion pump to cool. The general characteristics of the principal elements of a high-vacuum system may be treated by considering one by one the components shown in Figure 6.10.

Mechanical Pumps. Most of the mechanical pumps now used to produce the intial low pressure needed to back up high-vacuum diffusion pumps are of the rotary volumetric-displacement type. They are available in a wide range of capacities and in several makes which differ principally in the detailed means by which a large volume of low-pressure gas is compressed to atmospheric with each revolution of the pump. Figure 6.11 illustrates the principle of one such pump.

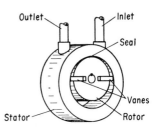

FIGURE 6.11. Mechanical pump having vanes in the rotor.

The inner cylinder rotates with the upper side almost in contact with the inside of a larger cylinder. The gas which enters the space between the two cylinders is compressed to a very small volume and discharged through a check valve which prevents the return of air into the discharge side of the pump. Small clearance is maintained between the ends of the cam and moving cylinder and the end plates of the stationary hollow cylinder. A complete gas seal is maintained by providing a copious bathing of oil over all the moving parts. In fact a little oil is discharged with the air at each revolution, and an oil-air separation tank is provided from which oil continuously returns to the moving parts of the pump. Figure 6.12 illustrates a two-stage pump using a somewhat different device to accomplish a similar function. Here a sliding vane in the stationary part separates the intake and exhaust portions of the displacement volume.

It is seen that in each pump the gas being pumped is admitted into a large volume and then this volume is isolated from the intake and the gas compressed into a very small volume and discharged. Obviously each of these styles of pumps can be compounded of two or more stages so that the first stage discharges into the intake of the second, thereby attaining a lower ultimate pressure. Other factors influencing the ultimate vacuum are (1) vapor pressure of the oil, (2) solubility in the oil of the gas being pumped, (3) completeness of the discharge of gas at each revolution, and (4) absence of leaks, either external or bypassing the oil seals.

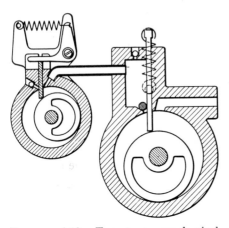

FIGURE   6.12.   Two-stage   mechanical pump.

The most common cause of poor performance of a mechanical pump is contamination of the oil with a volatile substance, usually water. A moderate water contamination can be removed by pumping air for several hours. The flow or air entering the pump should be kept at a rate below that which causes frothing of the oil. Water contamination can be avoided by bleeding a little air into the pump intake while the wet system is being pumped. By this means the partial pressure of the water is kept below its condensation pressure. Some modern pumps have this feature incorporated into the design. Of course the quickest way to remove an oil contaminant is to drain the oil and replace it. The oils recommended by the pump manufacturers are, as a rule, specially refined and have very low vapor pressures. If the ultimate in performance is not required, a good grade of motor oil of viscosity SAE 20 (without additives) may be very satisfactory. In fact, such an oil used in a pump serving a clean system will improve with use as the more volatile constituents are discharged with the gas being pumped.

Most pumps have check valves which prevent the flow of oil into the vacuum system when the pump is stopped. However, these sometimes leak, so it is always safest to close the valve between the mechanical pump and the rest of the system and have a valve to let air into the mechanical pump when it is stopped. A precaution that should be observed with large pumps having oil separation reservoirs is to turn them over by hand before turning on the motor so that any excess oil in the working volume of the pump is gently discharged into the reservoir. Failure to do this may cause damage when the rapidly turning rotor encounters an appreciable volume of the almost incompressible oil.

Contaminants more harmful than volatile impurities are corrosive gases and liquids and abrasive solids. If reasonable care and cleanliness are observed when constructing cryogenic equipment, it is unlikely that corrosive substances will be a problem. However, abrasive solids may be encountered. In an ordinary system there may be scale, metal droplets from welds, filings, drill chips, etc. The best procedure is to thoroughly clean each subassembly and make the final connections by a method that leaves no residue. If this cannot be done, a trap or filter should be used to protect the mechanical pump. Care should be taken to avoid excessive pressure-drop in these protective devices. When a mechanical pump is used to evacuate powder insulation, an adequate filter should be provided because the insulating powders are light and prone to be carried along with the air as they are evacuated. Moreover, many of the good powder insulations are of basically hard material (e.g., silica) and are very abrasive to metals.

The speed of a given mechanical pump depends upon the pressure of the gas being handled. A typical behavior is illustrated in Figure 6.13. At

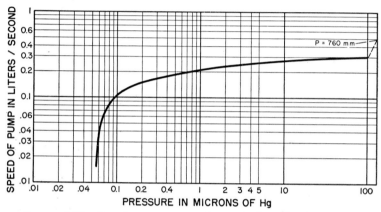

FIGURE 6.13. Speed vs. pressure of a typical mechanical pump.

high pressures the speed approaches the volumetric displacement rate. At lower pressures the speed diminishes greatly, reaching the value zero at the minimum pressure attainable by the pump. In choosing a mechanical pump for a particular system, the speed should be chosen so that the backing pressure for the diffusion pump will be comfortably lower than the permitted maximum after making due allowance for pressure drop in the connecting lines and valves. Mechanical pumps are available having volumetric displacement rates ranging from a few liters up to 20,000 liters per minute.

Diffusion Pumps. Figure 6.14 illustrates the action of a diffusion pump. A liquid of low vapor pressure is boiled; the vapor is ejected at a high velocity in a downward direction through the jet and is condensed on the cold wall of the pump. Molecules of the gas being pumped enter the vapor stream and are given a downward velocity component by collisions with the vapor molecules. The gas molecules are then removed through the discharge line by means of a backing pump such as the mechanical pumps just discussed.

Pumps of this type operate only at quite low pressures. The backing pressure usually required is 25 to 300 μ Hg. The ultimate vacuum attainable depends somewhat upon the vapor pressure of the pump liquid at the temperature of the condensing surfaces. However, by providing a cold trap between

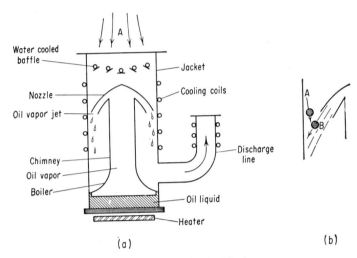

FIGURE 6.14.   Schematic of diffusion pump.

the diffusion pump and the region being evacuated, pressures far below the vapor pressure of the pump liquid may be achieved. For a good insulating vacuum the required pressure may be from 10^{-5} to 10^{-7} mm Hg.

The first liquid used for diffusion pumps was mercury, but today most commercial pumps use an oil of low vapor pressure. Silicone oils have excellent characteristics, notably, high chemical stability and resistance to oxidation. The NBS Cryogenic Engineering Laboratory uses silicone oils in most of the diffusion pumps. Oil diffusion pumps of a great range of capacities and characteristics are available as stock items from several commercial suppliers, and it is usually a simple matter for the engineer to choose a pump capable of maintaining a required insulating vacuum by studying the pump characteristics listed by the manufacturer. Diffusion pumps often have two or more stages and in some oil pumps the liquid return flow is arranged so that the more volatile constituents of the oil are not allowed to enter the high-vacuum jet. This is the "fractionating" oil pump illustrated in Figure 6.15.

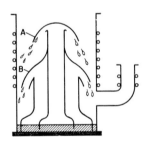

FIGURE 6.15. Fractionating oil diffusion pump. The high-vacuum nozzle, A, is fed with oil vapor from which the more volatile components have been distilled into the first stage, B.

Ideally a diffusion pump should remove gas molecules as fast as they diffuse into the jet area. This would be equivalent to replacing the jet with a perfect vacuum. Thus the speed of such an ideal pump would be given by the conductance of an aperture, Equation 6.18,

$$S = C_A = 11.6 \left(\frac{28.7}{M} \cdot \frac{T}{293} \right)^{1/2} A \qquad (6.27)$$

where A is the area of the pump jet in cm², and S is the pump speed in liters per second.   The ratio of the actual rate of gas removed to this ideal is known as the "Ho coefficient."   For the best pumps the Ho coefficient has a value approaching 0.4 when pumping air.

Equation 6.27 indicates that the pumping speed will be greater for gases of low molecular weight and less for heavy gases.   This is sometimes observed in actual pumps, but in some cases the reverse is true.   The performance of a pump handling light gases is usually improved by increasing the heater power and maintaining lower-than-normal backing pressure.

The performance of a diffusion pump depends upon the heat input, so that in some installations it is desirable to vary the heat input to obtain the optimum performance for the specific application.   Figure 6.16 shows in a qualitative way the effects of varying the heat input.   Figure 6.17 shows how the

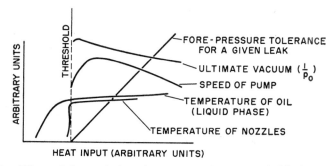

FIGURE 6.16.   Effect of change in heat input on performance of diffusion pump.   From Guthrie and Wakerling [6].

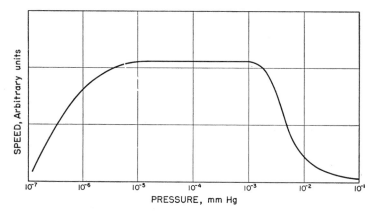

FIGURE 6.17.   Representative plot of speed versus pressure for a three-stage oil diffusion pump.   Some pumps do not have such a wide range in which the pumping speed is constant, but nearly all diffusion pumps have a broad maximum.   Intake pressure is not critical.

speed of a diffusion pump varies with the pressure of air being pumped. Commercial oil diffusion pumps are available in sizes from 5 liters per second with a pumping connection about 1 inch in diameter, to 15,000 liters per second with a 32-inch connection. Also special booster pumps are available which will discharge against a backing pressure of 1 to 3 mm Hg. Such a pump is sometimes used between the regular diffusion pump and the mechanical pump, thus greatly reducing the size of the mechanical pump needed.

Since the molecules of oil vapor issuing from the jets of a diffusion pump have a random thermal motion superimposed upon the bulk motion, a small fraction will migrate back toward the volume being evacuated. Such backstreaming of oil from the diffusion pump into the high-vacuum region is particularly objectionable in some cryogenic applications. Since the region being evacuated has at least one cold wall, oil vapor escaping from the pump is likely to condense on such a surface and spoil its reflectivity. Accordingly when a diffusion pump is close-coupled to the insulating vacuum (which is good practice for optimum pumping speed), a cold trap or baffle should be provided to intercept migrating oil vapor.

Cold Traps. The cold trap shown in Figure 6.11 is essentially a dewar flask with its insulating vacuum constituting a part of the high-vacuum connecting line between the diffusion pump and the region being evacuated. Its function is to capture any readily condensable vapors. Thus it adds greatly to the over-all pumping speed by removing condensable vapors such as water, and at the same time keeps pump-oil vapor out of the volume being evacuated. Since the cold trap is situated in the high-vacuum region of the system, it will intercept nearly all the condensable molecules if the cold surface is so disposed that it blocks any straight line path between the inlet and outlet of the trap. Therefore, the gas passages, and accordingly the conductance of the trap, can be made large. It is often advantageous to isolate the trap so that it may be warmed and the condensed vapors removed while a good vacuum is still maintained in the rest of the system. Some cold traps can be readily disassembled and cleaned. This is most easily accomplished by providing flanges and an O-ring seal as shown in Figure 6.18.

Since vacuum-insulated cryogenic equipment will in use have extensive cold surfaces, one may quite logically question the usefulness of an auxiliary cold trap. Actually the trap is very worthwhile in this application. The best technique for achieving a good vacuum is first to pump while the system is warm; if feasible, the surfaces should be heated to drive off absorbed gases and vapors. During this process the cold trap helps the pumping operation by condensing the vapors. (It is profitable to isolate the cold trap occasionally, warm it, and remove the condensed materials by pumping with the fore pump.) After this phase is completed and the cold regions of the cryogenic apparatus are cooled, the cold trap prevents pump-oil vapor from backstreaming and spoiling the reflectivity of the cold surfaces.

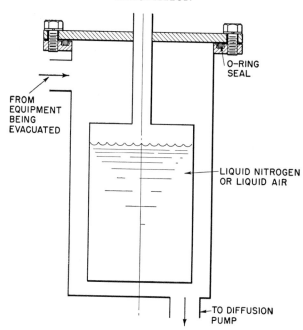

FROM
EQUIPMENT
BEING
EVACUATED

O-RING
SEAL

LIQUID NITROGEN
OR LIQUID AIR

TO DIFFUSION
PUMP

FIGURE 6.18. Demountable cold trap.

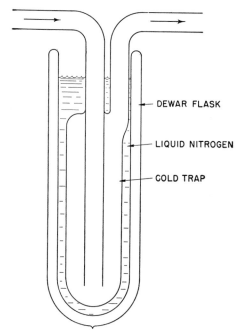

DEWAR FLASK

LIQUID NITROGEN

COLD TRAP

FIGURE 6.19. Cold trap of type extensively used with glass vacuum systems.

The type of coldtrap shown in Figure 6.18 should have the attributes of a dewar flask, a good insulating vacuum and highly reflecting walls and a neck of low thermal conductivity. If the application is such that the vacuum will be poor for extended periods, the cold trap shown in Figure 6.19 may be preferable.

When a system being evacuated with a mechanical pump alone emits a large amount of water—for example, an adsorbent being reactivated—it is often advisable to provide a cold trap to prevent the entry of water into the mechanical pump. This may be done with the dry-ice trap shown in Figure 6.20. This trap can be easily disassembled to remove the frost which collects

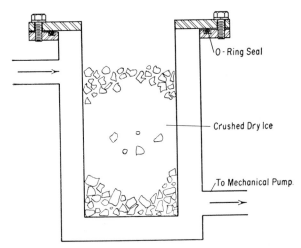

O - Ring Seal

Crushed Dry Ice

To Mechanical Pump.

FIGURE 6.20.   Dry-ice trap to protect a mechanical pump from water vapor.

on the cold surface. The principal difference between this trap and those shown in Figures 6.10 and 6.18 is the large opening for filling. This results in greater heat leak but is necessary when using dry ice as the refrigerant.

Vacuum Gages. Since vacuum gages must measure pressures many orders of magnitude smaller than atmospheric, the familiar simple liquid manometer is of little value in this service. Therefore, most vacuum gages are secondary gages; that is, they do not respond directly to pressure but are sensitive to another pressure-dependent property of a rarefied gas. At least four different physical principles have been utilized for secondary gages and a multitude of different designs have been evolved. However, because the manometer is an absolute pressure gage, several methods of increasing its sensitivity have been devised. The most valuable of these is the classical McLeod gage. It is still widely used as the sole pressure-measuring device in some vacuum systems, but its most important current application is for the calibration of secondary gages.

Because of the great variety of vacuum gages that have been devised, there will be no attempt here to describe them all. This discussion will be limited to brief descriptions of some types of vacuum gages that have been found to be the most suitable for cryogenic work.

The McLeod gage is illustrated in Figure 6.21. When the mercury is allowed to rise, it traps the gas in the volume V and compresses it to V′, V″, V‴, thereby increasing the pressure by the corresponding volume ratio according to Boyle's law. The commonly used volumetric ratios are 10^2, 10^3, 10^4, and 10^5. The pressure is indicated by the difference in level of the mercury in the central capillary and in the side tubes. In order to compensate for capillary depression of the mercury, identical capillaries are used for the corresponding parts of the central and side tubes. The principle advantage of the McLeod gage is that for noncondensable gases it is an absolute instrument. Its principle disadvantages are that it is not continuous reading and that it does not indicate condensable vapors.

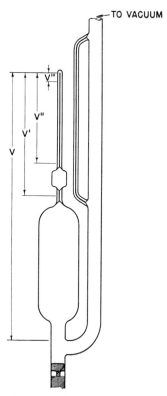

FIGURE 6.21. McLeod gage.

There are two types of gages that depend on the fact that the thermal conductivity of a low-pressure gas depends upon the pressure. One of these is the Pirani gage shown in Figure 6.22. The electric current through the platinum filaments is sufficient to raise their temperatures to about 125°C. With a high vacuum in both bulbs, R_3 is adjusted until the bridge is balanced; there is no current through the meter. Now any gas in bulb I will conduct heat away from the filament, cooling it and causing a change in resistance which is shown by the current through the meter. Since at low pressure the thermal conductivity of a gas is pressure-dependent, the indication of the meter will be a measure of the pressure. Figure 6.23 shows the response of a typical Pirani gage. Of course the calibration depends upon the thermal conductivity of the gas being measured.

Another vacuum gage that responds to changes in thermal conductivity is the thermocouple gage. In this gage the junction of a thermocouple is in thermal contact with a small resistance heater (Figure 6.24) and the assembly mounted in a tube which communicates with the vacuum being measured. Since the junction of the thermocouple is cooled by thermal conduction of the gas, the current indicated by the microammeter will be a measure of the

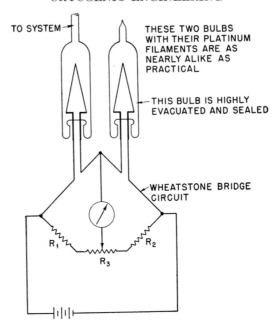

FIGURE 6.22. Pirani vacuum gage.

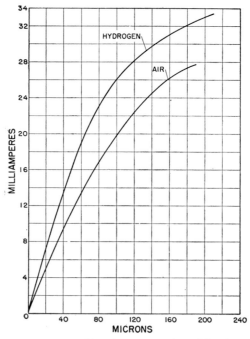

FIGURE 6.23. Calibration curves for a Pirani gage.

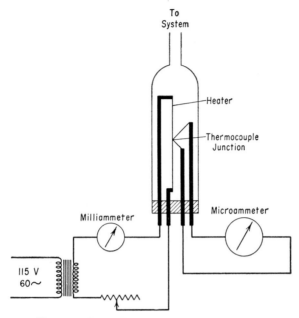

FIGURE 6.24. Thermocouple vacuum gage.

pressure. Figure 6.25 shows the calibration curves of a thermocouple gage for dry air. The thermocouple gage is used extensively to measure the pressure produced by the mechanical pump of a vacuum system. It is simple, easy to use, its pressure range is about right for this application and its accuracy is adequate.

There is a class of vacuum gages that makes use of the change of viscosity

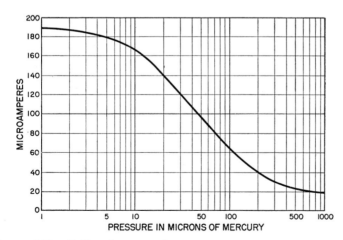

FIGURE 6.25. Calibration curve for a commercial thermocouple gage.

with pressure at low pressures. One such gage that has been found quite convenient is an adaptation of the Langmuir [20] molecular gage. As manufactured by the General Electric Co., this gage consists of two coaxial vaned cylinders, one rotating at 3600 rpm and the other restrained by a spring. The radial distance between the two cylinders is about ⅛ inch. Molecules are set in motion by the rotating cylinder and transfer their momentum to the spring-restrained cylinder, displacing it from its rest position. The angle of displacement is indicated by a pointer. The indication depends upon the pressure and molecular weight of the gas. Calibration curves for some different gases are shown in Figure 6.26.

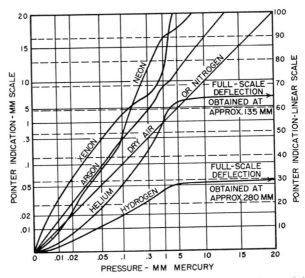

FIGURE 6.26. Typical calibration curves showing scale distribution and full scale values for typical gases for the General Electric molecular vacuum gage.

The Knudsen gage is shown in principle in Figure 6.27. The suspended element AA is given a torque because of the bombardment of high-speed molecules coming from the heated strips BB. Of course AA receives a torque of the opposite sign from molecules striking the other sides, but this latter torque is weaker because the average velocity of these impinging molecules is less than that of those which were heated by BB. When the mean free path of the molecules is greater than the distance between A and B, the pressure is given [10] by

$$P = \frac{4\pi^2 I\theta}{rA\tau^2} \cdot \frac{T}{T_1 - T} \tag{6.28}$$

where I is the moment of inertia of the suspended system and τ is its period of vibration, r is the mean radius of the moving vane and A its area, T_1 is the absolute temperature of the heated surface, T is the ambient temperature, P is the pressure, and θ is the angular deflection of the moving system. Any consistent set of units may be used. For example, if cgs units are used and θ is measured in radians, P will be in dynes cm^{-2} or microbars. Very important features of this gage are that (1) it is an absolute gage, (2) its indications are independent of the molecular weight of the gas being measured, and (3) it will measure the pressures of condensable vapors. Several different designs of Knudsen gages have been devised and sensitivities as high as 10^{-8} mm Hg have been reported.

The ionization gage, Figure 6.28, is probably the most widely used high-vacuum gage. The principle of operation of the thermionic ionization gage is as follows: The filament temperature is adjusted so that a constant electron current flows to the anode. These electrons ionize gas molecules with

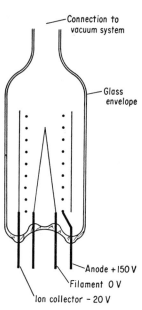

Connection to vacuum system

Glass envelope

Anode + 150 V
Filament 0 V
Ion collector – 20 V

FIGURE 6.28. Representation of an ionization gage. Potentials indicated are those used for a specific commercial gage. Other gages use potentials as low as +10 volts for the anode and −280 volts for the ion collector.

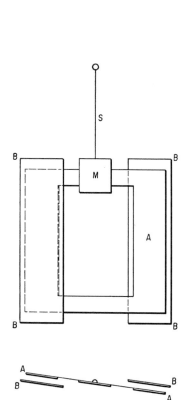

FIGURE 6.27. Diagrammatic sketch of Knudsen type of gage.

which they collide, and the resultant positive ions are attracted to the negatively charged ion collection electrode, producing a current which is usually measured with a microammeter. Since the supply of electrons is fixed and they are accelerated by a fixed potential difference, the rate of ion formation, and accordingly the ion current, is proportional to the molecular concentration. The proportionality constant, of course, depends upon the construction of the gage tube and upon the nature of the gas. A typical commercial gage has a constant of 100 microamperes per micron.

To avoid errors caused by the release of adsorbed gas as an ionization gage warms up, a means is usually provided for preheating and degassing the gage prior to use. In the gage shown in Figure 6.28 this is done by providing another connection to the helical anode and using it as a heater. At very low pressures leakage currents can cause appreciable error, particularly after long operation has produced leakage paths by evaporation of the filament and transfer of tungsten to the glass walls. At pressures adequate for vacuum insulation, of the order of 10^{-6} mm Hg, errors from leakage are not likely to be serious.

The Philips gage, Figure 6.29, is another type of ionization gage. It is

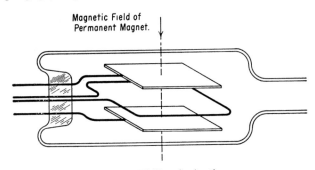

Magnetic Field of
Permanent Magnet.

FIGURE 6.29. Philips ionization gage.

designed so that the small number of electrons emanating from cold electrodes will cause measurable ionization in a rarefied gas. An electron that happens to be near the upper plate is accelerated downward by the positively charged ring. The magnetic field causes it to move in a tight helical path. It passes through the ring and continues on toward the lower cathode until its direction is reversed because of the reversal of the direction of the electrical field. These repeated oscillations so greatly extend the path that a relatively few electrons can create a sizable ionization current. The principal advantage of the Philips gage is its ruggedness; a loss of vacuum does not destroy a filament. Its range extends to higher pressures than those reached by the thermionic ionization gage. Electrical leakage is more serious because higher voltages are used.

Figure 6.30 shows the useful ranges of the vacuum gages discussed.

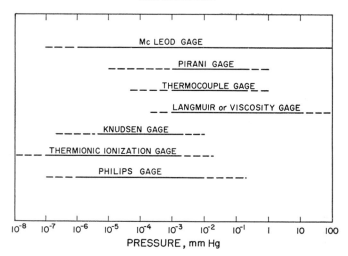

FIGURE 6.30. Useful ranges of vacuum gages. Solid parts of lines indicate normal range; dashed parts indicate ranges extended by taking special pains. These ranges are based upon performance of gages that are commercially available.

High-Vacuum Valves. Of the many valves designed for high-vacuum use, the most reliable are those which do not depend on packing to separate the vacuum region from the atmosphere. Figure 6.31 is an example of a valve which avoids packing by making use of a metal bellows.

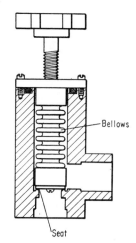

Some valves have an elastic diaphragm of synthetic rubber which is pressed onto a seat by a metal member which is on the atmospheric side of the diaphragm. These are not very suitable for high-vacuum work because air will diffuse slowly through the diaphragm. Of course, some diffusion can occur through the organic washer used in the valve of Figure 6.31, but the available area is so small that the diffusion is seldom of any consequence.

There is a valve developed at the NBS Cryogenic Engineering Laboratory [21] that has proved to be very useful for temporary or permanent sealing of evacuated vessels. It is shown in cross section in Figure 6.32. After pumping is completed the valve is closed and then the valve handle and bonnet can be removed, leaving only the closed valve seat on the evacuated apparatus.

FIGURE 6.31. High-vacuum valve.

Most of the manufacturers of high-vacuum equipment now supply valves, so it is unnecessary for the user to concern himself with the details of valve design. In choosing a valve, one should make sure that it does not seriously restrict the flow and that its seals are positive. In an emergency an ordinary brass globe valve can be used for a time by replacing the fiber sealing washer with neoprene or teflon and using vacuum grease liberally on the packing. Some of the high-vacuum valves now on the market utilize a standard globe-valve body with the bonnet replaced by one which is modified to accommodate a metal bellows and valve-actuating mechanism similar to that shown in Figure 6.31.

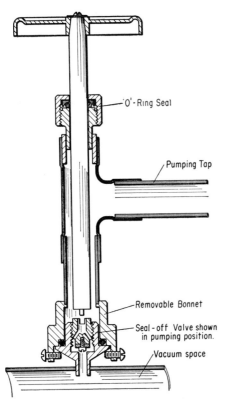

FIGURE 6.32. Richards seal-off valve.

6.10. Techniques of Construction of Vacuum-Insulated Cryogenic Equipment: *Materials.* Glass was the first material to be used for a vacuum-insulated vessel—the original dewar flask. Glass has many advantages: (1) it is a poor conductor of heat, (2) it is readily fabricated into intricate shapes, (3) it is relatively easy to produce leak-free glass vessels, and if leaks exist, they are easily discovered and repaired, (4) the internal surfaces of a glass vessel (those facing the insulating vacuum) can be rendered highly reflecting by silvering, and (5) glass can be heated to a relatively high temperature during evacuation so that adsorbed and dissolved gases can be effectively removed. For these reasons glass is admirably suited for small experimental apparatus where ruggedness is not a requirement. There are a few special considerations that should be taken into account when fabricating glass apparatus for use at low temperatures. The vessel may be subjected to local cooling by the introduction of a cryogenic fluid and this can set up mechanical strains which will crack the glass. This difficulty can be reduced by using thin glass, avoiding abrupt changes in thickness and using glass which has a low coefficient of expansion—for example, a glass containing a high percentage of silica. Unfortunately helium will diffuse through high-silica glass such as Pyrex®, so some workers prefer other glasses for use with helium. However, the diffusion of helium is quite slow at low temperatures; so if the helium is not permitted to remain in contact with the Pyrex® vessel when it is warm, the vacuum may be maintained for long periods.

Nearly all of the common structural metals may be used for vacuum-insulated equipment. Ordinary carbon steel is not often used for those parts which become cold, because of the low-temperature embrittlement; but it is often used for the outer, room-temperature enclosure of an insulating vacuum in large equipment. It has a relatively high emissivity, so some means such as electroplating or lining with highly reflecting foil is usually employed to reduce thermal radiation. Steels are more permeable to gases than are most other metals.

Copper has long been used as the principal material for the construction of laboratory containers for liquid oxygen and nitrogen. Such containers range in capacity from 5 to 1000 liters. Copper is readily shaped by spinning or drawing and can be soldered very easily. It has high reflectivity for thermal radiation, so it is particularly suitable for the boundaries of an insulating vacuum. Its softness and rather low mechanical strength are disadvantages, but its malleability at low temperature makes it a relatively safe material; it will stretch and deform with little danger of complete failure. The high thermal conductivity of copper is a useful property for many applications, but makes it unsuitable to use for filling or discharge lines which communicate between cold and warm regions. It should be pointed out that there are many different commercial coppers and their low-temperature thermal conductivities are widely different, depending upon the kind and quantity of impurity. The designer should consult the data on thermal conductivity given in Chapter 10 (pp. 343-346). Seamless copper tubing and sheet is remarkably free of imperfections, pinholes, and porous regions.

Brass is frequently used for vacuum equipment. Free-cutting brass is useful for special fittings, flanges, etc., because it is easily machined and is readily soldered to most other ordinary metals. It is somewhat stronger and harder than copper, but in the annealed condition it is still rather soft and has a low yield strength. It has the relatively high emissivity and low thermal conductivity characteristic of an alloy, but it is not outstanding in the latter respect—there are many other alloys with smaller thermal conductivities. Rolled or drawn brass is usually relatively free of imperfections that may show up as vacuum leaks. However, one exception should be noted—rolled bar stock of many metals, including brass, may have imperfections in the shape of tiny elongated voids parallel to and near the axis. These result from the stretching of a small bubble during the rolling process. There have been some reports also of porosity in cast brass fittings.

Stainless steels of types 304 or 347 are extensively used in cryogenic apparatus where good tensile properties and impact resistance are needed. Also these steels have low thermal conductivities, so they are very good for use as insulating supports and for entry and exit lines communicating between cold and warm regions. Type 347 is preferred because of its stability—areas adjacent to welds are less apt to be damaged by overheating. The emissivity of stainless steel is rather high, 5 to 8 percent compared with about 2 percent for aluminum and 1.5 to 2.0 percent for copper. These are emissivities for room temperature radiation and were obtained with commercial materials having surface treatments realizable in actual construction of cryogenic equipment. Stainless steels are more difficult to soft-solder than copper and copper alloys. A rather corrosive flux is required to remove the refractory oxide. Such a flux must be used carefully and be completely removed after the joint is finished, because residual flux may corrode through thin stainless steel. Even droplets of flux spattered at a distance of several inches from the actual joint have caused leaks. Type 303 stainless steel is particularly obstinate in its aversion to soft solder. It is also rather difficult to silver solder.

The copper-nickel alloys, ranging from 80 Cu–20 Ni to 30 Cu–70 Ni and including Monel®, K-Monel® and S-Monel®, which have small additions of other elements, all have good mechanical properties at low temperatures, have low thermal conductivities, and are readily soldered. Their emissivities are rather high.

Inconel®, an alloy of nickel, chromium, manganese, and iron, has low temperature properties somewhat similar to those of Monel®.

Everdur® (96.1% Cu, 2.75 Si, 1% Mn, and 0.15 Fe) has good low-temperature mechanical properties and a thermal conductivity about twice that of stainless steel. It was selected for a specific low-temperature application in which materials which became appreciably magnetic at low temperatures could not be used because of the presence of intense magnetic fields.

In recent years there has been an increase in the use of aluminum and aluminum alloys for low-temperature vacuum-insulated apparatus. Aluminum has good low-temperature mechanical properties and in addition has a rather low emissivity, so it is suitable for the boundaries of an insulating vacuum space. Also, aluminum is very resistant to diffusion of gases. The disadvantage of aluminum is that it is difficult to solder; however, it can be welded by the electric arc shielded with rare gas. Aluminum of high purity is a very good conductor of heat at low temperatures.

Joints and Seams. The development of shielded-arc welding has made it possible to weld almost all metals, and it appears that if the welder is sufficiently skilled he can consistently produce vacuum-tight welds. Such skill is particularly valuable in fabricating cryogenic equipment of aluminum and stainless steel. Even copper can be successfully welded if the plate is not too thin. Welded vacuum-insulated equipment of carbon steel, stainless steel, and aluminum is widely used. With proper techniques the mechanical strength of a weld is not much less than that of the parent material. Since shielded-arc welding is a highly specialized skill developed by practice plus expert instruction, there will be no attempt here to describe procedures. It should be remarked, however, that it is quite possible that a flaw which would have negligible effect on the mechanical strength of a weld could constitute a serious vacuum leak. Some fabricators make a practice of covering welded seams of thin stainless steel with soft solder, even before checking for leaks.

The most versatile means of making vacuum-tight joints in metals is by soldering. Many dissimilar metals can be joined with solder, and in many cases soldering is preferable to welding in joining similar metals. Mebs and Roeser [22] have compiled a survey article describing soldering procedures and the various types of solders and fluxes that are commonly used. Most of this information is applicable to the construction of vacuum-insulated cryogenic equipment, and will not be repeated here. However, there are some procedures that should be emphasized because of their importance in vacuum work, and some special techniques that have important applications in cryogenic equipment. Of primary importance is the requirement for cleanliness. The parts to be soldered should be thoroughly degreased and oxide films removed throughout, not only to facilitate the soldering operation itself but also to avoid insoluble deposits (oxide or carbon) which will spoil the reflectivity of surfaces and slow down evacuation. Likewise, fluxes should be completely removed after soldering to avoid corrosion, to improve the reflectivities, and to avoid sources of volatile contaminants or dissolved gases. Care should be exercised to avoid carbon deposits on interior surfaces caused by a smoky flame from the soldering torch. In cryogenic equipment using organic materials as insulating supports, care should be taken not to overheat and decompose the supports during the soldering operation.

Although aluminum has excellent low-temperature mechanical properties, its high thermal conductivity makes it undesirable to use for filling lines which constitute thermal paths between low-temperature and high-temperature regions. For this reason considerable attention has been given to the construction of transition joints between aluminum and a poorly conducting metal such as stainless steel. This permits the exploitation of the advantages of aluminum for the isothermal surface (e.g., the inner shell of a vacuum-insulated storage vessel) and at the same time allows one to use the insulating property of a stainless steel or Monel tube to connect to the warm exterior.

Several different types of transition joints have been tried in the NBS Cryogenic Engineering Laboratory. The method preferred at this time is the relatively simple joint made by friction-tinning the interior of the end of an aluminum tube with tin-lead solder and then completing the joint by standard soft-soldering techniques to stainless steel or other readily soldered alloy. There is some advantage in joining the stainless steel to a brass or copper sleeve with silver solder and then connecting this sleeve to the aluminum with tin-lead solder. The aluminum is "tinned" with tin-lead solder by abrading the surface with a steel scraper while molten solder covers it. It should be pointed out such a soft-soldered joint should not be required to support much mechanical stress in shear or tension. Soft solder should be considered the sealing material and mechanical stress should be supported by other means. It is important that the aluminum tube be the outer or female member of the joint. This insures that a compressive stress will result when the joint is cooled, because of the greater thermal expansivity of the aluminum. When aluminum is used as the inner member, the resultant tensile stress in the solder may cause failure.

As a rule, soldered joints or seams are considered to be permanent connections. However, since soft solder melts at a relatively low temperature, such joints are sometimes used as regular access areas in experimental apparatus. A particularly convenient and successful soldered joint for this purpose is shown in Figure 6.33. Here the solder usually employed for low-

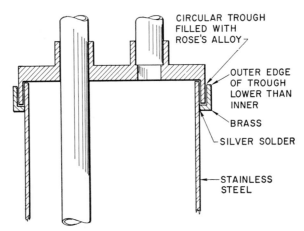

FIGURE 6.33. Soldered joint designed for easy separation and reassembly. Sometimes this type of joint is provided with an electric heater wound upon the outside of the trough making assembly and disassembly more convenient.

temperature work is Rose's alloy, which melts at 100°C. Before applying the Rose's metal the surfaces are tinned with tin-lead solder by the usual methods. The Rose's metal will alloy readily with surfaces so prepared.

The low-temperature worker is often warned against "tin pest," the transition at moderately low temperatures of ordinary white tin to the gray allotropic form in a soldered joint and the resultant failure of the joint. These warnings are usually based on hearsay evidence because very few experimenters have actually encountered the phenomenon. The reason for this seems to be the fact that a rather small amount of alloying impurity inhibits the transition. It is reported that 0.5 percent antimony, 0.1 percent bismuth, or 5 percent of lead is sufficient to prevent the transition to gray tin. Even when pure tin is used on brass or copper, there is usually enough copper dissolved into the tin during the soldering operation to inhibit the transition to gray tin.

Gasketed Seals. A gasketed seal is a closure effected by mechanical pressure on a deformable material. Most seals employ relatively soft gaskets between hard compression flanges. One of the most widely used vacuum seals is the O-ring seal shown in Figure 6.34. Here a rubber ring of toroidal shape fits into a groove and is deformed sufficiently to make a leak-free seal when the cover is bolted on. O-rings of standard sizes are commercially available, and the manufacturers have established recommended dimensions for the groove. As a rule the O-ring is covered with a film of vacuum grease when it is installed. Care should be taken that the variety of rubber used is not attacked by the grease. Since gases will dissolve in rubber and are

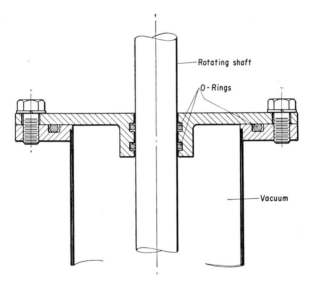

Rotating shaft

O - Rings

Vacuum

FIGURE 6.34. O-rings used as a vacuum seal for a sliding or rotating shaft transmitting motion into a vacuum enclosure.

slowly evolved, there should be a minimum area of the gasket exposed to the vacuum. Some of the synthetic rubbers such as neoprene and butyl rubber are less permeable to gases than is natural rubber. Plastic materials other than rubber are sometimes used for gaskets. One such material which is desirable because it gives off very little gas is polytetrafluoroethylene, or Teflon®. It is somewhat elastic but not rubber-like; moreover, it tends to flow somewhat under continuous loading. Therefore a closure using such a gasket should be designed to maintain pressure; for example, by using spring washers under the bolt heads. If a groove is used for Teflon® it should not be so deep that the metal flanges touch when the bolts are tightened. Although Teflon® has been used successfully at low temperatures, special precautions must be taken to compensate for the large thermal contraction. Rubber becomes very hard and brittle at low temperature in addition to having an undesirable contraction.

Soft metals (lead, copper, aluminum, and others) have been successfully used as gasket materials. These can be vacuum-tight over a wide range of temperatures, from far above room temperature down to the temperature of liquid helium. A type of metal-gasketed seal is shown in Figure 6.35. As the seal is tightened, raised V-rings on the steel flanges penetrate deeply into the gasket causing drastic permanent deformation. This illustrates the basic principle of such seals; deformation sufficient to close any tiny irregularities that might constitute leaks. Elastic deformation of the bolts and flanges is sufficient to maintain pressure on the gasket when dimensions change upon heating or cooling. Seals of this type have been used at temperatures

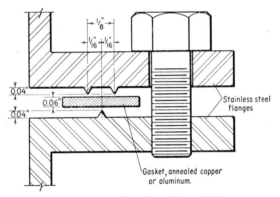

FIGURE 6.35. Method of using a metal gasket for a high-vacuum seal. Illustration shows a cross section through one edge of a pair of circular flanges.

from 600°C to −196°C. Some were repeatedly cycled between room temperature and −196°C and remained leak-free.

The details of seals using soft metal gaskets are not critical. Another successful type consists of a round wire ring compressed into V-grooves in both flanges. Sometimes the gasket is simply a wire ring compressed between flat plates. The critical features are the requirement for sufficient pressure on the gasket to produce substantial flow, or permanent deformation of the metal, and surfaces finished so as to avoid radial marks or scratches which cross the seal. The plastic deformation may not close such a scratch. It has been found beneficial to use a film of vacuum grease on gaskets to be used at low temperatures.

One of the most difficult problems in low-temperature vacuum sealing was encountered by research workers at the University of California Radiation Laboratory in connection with the design of liquid hydrogen bubble chambers. It was necessary to seal a massive glass window to a metal tank so that the assembly would remain vacuum-tight when cooled to the temperature of

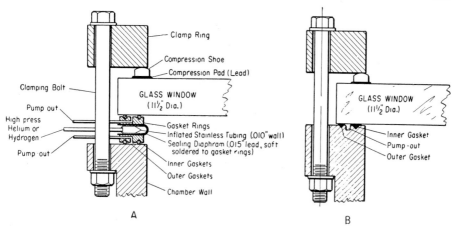

FIGURE 6.36. Gasketed seals with bubble chamber windows used at the University of California Radiation Laboratory.

liquid hydrogen and subjected to pressures which pulsated between 6 and 2 atmospheres. Their solutions are shown in Figure 6.36A and 6.36B. Lead gaskets were used. It was found necessary to insure that the lead-wire gaskets were clean and free of surface carbonate by drawing the wire through a die shortly before assembling the seal.

Glass-to-Metal Seals. One of the first glass-to-metal seals was developed by Housekeeper. In its common form, Figure 6.37, it consists of a metal tube, usually copper, with the end, which connects to the glass, thinned so that differential expansion will cause the copper to yield rather than separate from or break the glass. The glass (usually Pyrex®) is rather thick, to provide the required mechanical strength. A successful technique in making such seals is to torch the copper (at red heat) until a thin layer of black oxide, CuO, covers the surface to be sealed. Then the Pyrex® tube is slipped on and heated until it shrinks down into intimate contact with the copper. The cupric oxide is reduced to the red cuprous oxide when contact with the glass excludes the atmosphere. The red oxide of copper is readily wetted by the glass and forms a leak-free seal. A good seal of this type shows a clear, smooth red color without bubbles or areas of unoxidized copper under the glass.

A type of Housekeeper seal more often used today, and now commercially available, is made with alloys having coefficients of expansion very closely matching that of the glass. Usually a glass of intermediate expansivity is used to connect the sealing glass to Pyrex®

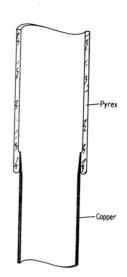

FIGURE 6.37. Housekeeper seal.

(Figure 6.38). Two alloys which have been used for these seals are Kovar®, developed by the Westinghouse Electric and Manufacturing Company; and Fernico®, developed by the General Electric Company.

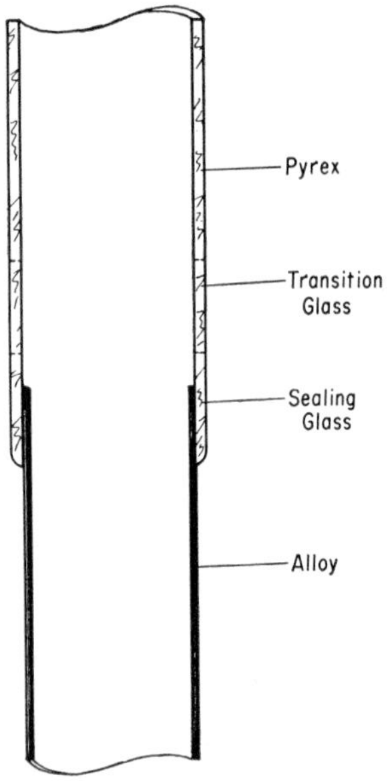

Some soft glasses seal readily to platinum; thus platinum-glass seals are much used for laboratory apparatus.

Organic waxes and cements of various types are often used in the laboratory to join metal to glass. Many kinds of fusible waxes of low vapor pressure are available at scientific supply houses and are quite suitable for making removable connections between glass and metal tubing. It is good practice always to have the glass tube inside the metal tube so that as the joint cools, the greater contraction of the metal squeezes down upon the cement. A very reliable waxed seal is shown in Figure 6.39. Epoxy resin cements have been recommended for joining metal to glass. Such a joint is, of course, not readily disassembled because these cements harden by polymerization and cannot subsequently be melted.

A quite useful glass-to-metal seal is shown in Figure 6.40. This is often used to connect glass ionization gages to metal vacuum systems.

Of all these seals the only ones that have been demonstrated conclusively to be reliable when cooled to very low temperatures are of the House-

FIGURE 6.38. Glass-to-metal seal using an alloy having the same expansivity as the sealing glass.

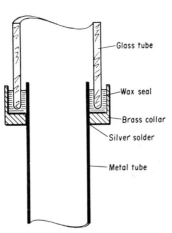

FIGURE 6.39. Waxed seal joining glass and metal tubing.

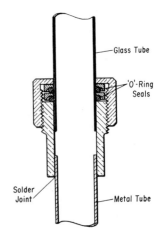

FIGURE 6.40. Glass to metal O-ring seal.

keeper type, wherein there is direct adhesion between the metal (or its surface oxide) and the glass, and the soft metal gasket with elastic compression bolts or washers. The tenacity of the epoxy resin cements suggests that it may be possible to utilize them in seals that will withstand cooling. The ordinary fusible waxes are of little value in this application.

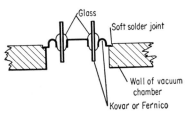

FIGURE 6.41. Commercial seal for introducing electrical connections into a highly evacuated enclosure.

Seals for Electrical Leads. Many of the sealing methods just described can be used to bring electrical leads through the wall of a high-vacuum enclosure. One of the most widely used is the commercial seal illustrated in Figure 6.41. Bare wires can be threaded through the small tubes and soldered into place. This is quite satisfactory for most work and, if necessary, the seal can be operated at very low temperatures. However, for electrical measurements dealing with very small DC potentials, for example when measuring small temperature differences with thermocouples, the dissimilar metals at the seal can introduce errors because of their thermoelectric effect. For such a service the seal shown in Figure 6.42 is greatly preferred. Here an all-copper circuit can be maintained and errors arising from thermal emf's at metal junctions are avoided. This is obviously just another application of the seal shown in Figure 6.39. It has been found that wires insulated with enamel and silk can be used if the wax is kept fluid until it penetrates the silk insulation. Leaks can be repaired by painting the external junctures of the wires and wax with shellac while the system is at reduced pressure.

Rubber gaskets can be used to bring electrical leads into a vacuum system as shown in Figure 6.43. The wires are spaced so that they emerge between the flange bolts. By using vacuum grease on the rubber gaskets this assembly can be made vacuum tight. Without the grease, tiny channels are left along the sides of the wires.

A discarded metal radio tube is a very convenient device for bringing electrical leads into a metal vacuum enclosure. By sawing off the upper end of the tube, connections can be soldered to the internal ends of the leads and then the tube is soldered to

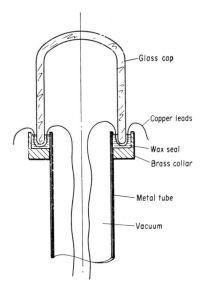

FIGURE 6.42. Method of bringing copper leads out of a high-vacuum enclosure without introducing junctions between dissimilar metals.

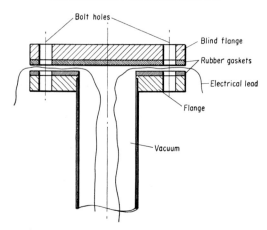

FIGURE 6.43. Gasketed seal carrying electrical leads.

the vacuum system with the base exposed, providing a male plug which constitutes a terminal for a standard receptacle.

Seals for Moving Parts. Perhaps the most useful device for transmitting motion through the wall of a vacuum enclosure is the metal bellows. One application is the valve illustrated in Figure 6.31. While the bellows is particularly suited to linear motion of small amplitude, it can be used to transmit rotary motion. Figure 6.44 illustrates the "wobble stick" method of achieving rotary motion through a bellows.

O-rings can be used as seals on smooth-sliding or rotating shafts. A somewhat better seal, although not as perfect as the metal bellows, is the Wilson seal shown in Figure 6.45.

6.11. Leak Hunting and Repairing. Most of the early techniques of vacuum leak finding make use of the equipment normally associated with a vacuum system—gages, pumps, valves, etc. In the hands of a skilled and experienced experimenter these methods are successful. However, finding very small leaks by such means often is time-consuming and tedious to the point of frustration. Fortunately, in recent years specialized leak-detection devices have been developed which, because of their high sensitivity and rapid response, have greatly reduced the labor of leak finding. The new equipment and techniques will, of course, be described, but the older methods will not be ignored because they still are often useful even when a modern leak detector is also available. This discussion will attempt to emphasize those considerations which apply to insulating vacua for cryogenic equipment. However, most of the material has general applicability to all vacuum systems. It is recommended that the reader also consult more extensive treatises—for example, Guthrie and Wakerling [6] and Dushman [10].

Determining That a Leak Exists. When it is found that a reasonable amount of pumping will not produce an adequate vacuum in a system, the

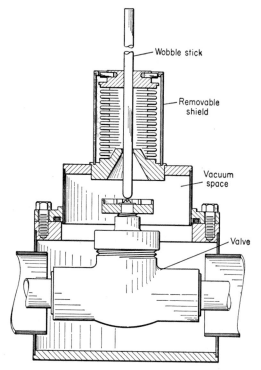

FIGURE 6.44.   Wobble-stick valve.

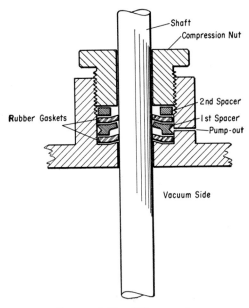

FIGURE 6.45.   Wilson seal.

novice may assume that there are leaks. However, there are many circumstances other than leaks that will prevent the attainment of a good vacuum. For example, a little water left in the system will continue to evaporate and spoil the vacuum. Often upon lowering the pressure, the water will freeze and evaporate quite slowly because of the poor thermal contact between the ice and the wall of the vacuum system. Other volatile materials will behave similarly. Porous materials, many organic plastics, greases, and oils can slowly release large quantities of gas. Also ordinary outgassing, even from clean walls of the vacuum system, may prevent the attainment of the required low pressure. Finally the pumping system may not be functioning properly, perhaps because of a volatile contaminant, such as water, in the pump oil. In short the experimenter should always bear in mind that failure to attain a good vacuum is evidence only, not necessarily proof, of a leak. Countless hours have been wasted hunting for non-existent leaks. In fact sources of gas such as those mentioned above are sometimes called "virtual" leaks. Most of the methods to be described can be used to differentiate between virtual leaks and real leaks.

Bubble Tests. An excellent way to locate large leaks is to pressurize the interior of the system or component with air or other gas and immerse the apparatus in water. Gas bubbles issuing from the leak show its precise location. Sometimes rather small leaks are located this way by close observation. It is necessary to make sure that the surface being tested is free of trapped bubbles, or bubbles that arise from air coming out of solution with the water. When the system cannot be immersed in water, leaks can be located by painting the suspected area with a soap solution. This is not quite as reliable as the immersion test because some areas can be skipped accidentally. It is necessary that the surfaces be clean before the soap-solution test, because oil films or small amounts of soldering flux will destroy the bubble-producing quality of the soap solution. Bubble tests can be used to locate leaks as small as 0.1 micron liter per second. Very large leaks are sometimes missed by the soap-solution test because a bubble will not form across a high-velocity gas jet. Such leaks are really not a serious problem because they can be located by holding a flame close by and observing the wavering when a leak is approached.

Locating Leaks by Isolation. In a vacuum system consisting of different regions which can be valved off one by one from the pumping system, the region responsible for the principal source of trouble can be located by observing the decrease in pressure attained by the pump when the appropriate valve is closed. This of course only narrows the search; it does not even distinguish between a real and a virtual leak.

Spark Coil Method. When the pressure in a vacuum system is between 50 microns Hg and 1 cm Hg, the gas will support a glow discharge from a high-potential electrical source. If the system consists wholly or partly of glass, the discharge can be produced by passing the ungrounded electrode of a small Tesla coil over the outside of the glass. When the electrode approaches a hole in the glass the spark will be seen entering the hole, concentrating the discharge at that point.

The spark coil can also be used to maintain a continuous discharge in a glass part of the system leading to the pump and the leak found by painting suspected areas with an organic liquid such as alcohol. The color of the discharge will change markedly when alcohol enters the system. This permits the location of leaks in metal parts of the system.

Evacuation of the Pressure Side. A leak in the inner wall of a dewar vessel is readily indicated by reducing the pressure inside the vessel with a mechanical pump. If there is a leak, the vacuum in the insulating space will improve. This principle may be extended to outer walls of evacuated enclosures by devising hoods which can be fitted over suspected areas and evacuated. A rather widely used adaptation of this technique is the "pump-out" on gasketed seals. The scheme is to use two gaskets separated by a space which communicates with a pumping tap, Figure 6.46. An improvement in the main vacuum, when the pressure between the gaskets is reduced, is proof of a leak in the inner gasket.

Change in Indication of Vacuum Gage When Probe Gas or Liquid Is Applied at Leak. This method requires that the system be equipped with a continuously indicating vacuum gage such as an ionization gage, Knudsen gage, or Pirani gage. When a probe material is applied at the leak the indication of the gage will change, either because the material entering the leak causes a change in composition of the gas inside the system or because the leak is temporarily sealed. The system is continuously pumped. Helium sprayed on a leak will decrease the reading of an ionization gage, but it will increase the reading of a Pirani gage. Hydrogen or oxygen will decrease the electron emission of an ionization-gage filament.

A more sensitive method is to paint the suspected areas with a volatile liquid

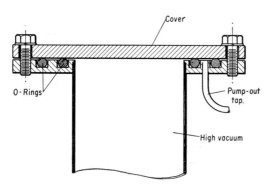

FIGURE 6.46. Pump-out method of locating leaking gaskets.

that will prevent the entry of air through the leak. In this case it is good practice to protect the vacuum gage with a cold trap cooled with liquid nitrogen or liquid air, so that vapor from the probe liquid will be condensed. When the leak is sealed, the gage indication falls rapidly. Water is often used as the sealing liquid, but it has the disadvantage of a rather low vapor pressure so that it may keep the leak closed for several hours and thus greatly postpone a confirmation of the location of the leak. It is always good practice to repeat the test when a leak is found, because the lowering of pressure could have been a coincidence resulting, for example, from improved pump performance caused by an increase in line voltage. Alcohol, benzene, ether, and acetone have been used as sealing liquids. It may be of interest to point out that any leak which has a measurable effect on the vacuum attainable in a continuously pumped system can be detected by this method. Total immersion of the suspected area in the sealing fluid is the most certain means of determining the existence of a leak. After the presence of the leak is known, its exact location can be found by painting small areas with the sealing liquid.

Leak Detectors. Several instruments have been developed for the specific purpose of finding leaks in high-vacuum enclosures. The most sensitive, reliable, convenient (and most expensive) of these devices is the helium mass-spectrometer leak detector. This consists of a small mass spectrometer adjusted to detect only ions of mass 4. Thus there will be a response when helium, sprayed on a leak, enters a vacuum system which communicates with the leak detector. Since the normal concentration of helium in the atmosphere is only 4 parts per million and other molecules or atoms of mass 4 are practically non-existent in the atmosphere, the background response of the instrument is very low; hence it can be made extremely sensitive.

Figure 6.47 illustrates the principle of the helium mass-spectrometer leak detector. Electrons are emitted from the filament and are accelerated through the ionization chamber. The positive ions produced by the collision of electrons with gas molecules in the ionization chamber are accelerated in a direction perpendicular to the permanent magnetic field by the negative potential between plates S_1 and S_2. The magnetic field causes these charged particles to move in curved paths and the collimating slits allow only those of mass 4 to strike the helium target. The ion current from the helium target is amplified and sent to a meter which shows the intensity of the beam of helium ions. This signal also is rendered audible by means of a circuit with a loudspeaker arranged so that the frequency of the note emitted by the loudspeaker increases with the intensity of the ion beam. This enables the operator to give his full attention to probing for leaks; he does not have to watch a meter. By causing an alternating voltage on the electron accelerator, the ion beam is made intermittent so that AC amplifying equipment can be used. The leak detector has its own high-vacuum pumping system so that helium

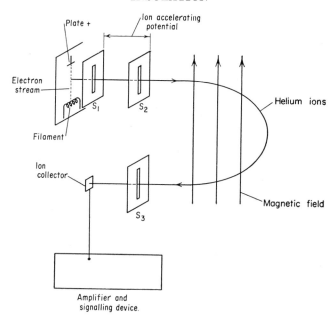

FIGURE 6.47. Helium mass spectrograph. Helium ions are formed in the electron stream, are accelerated by the potential difference between S_1 and S_2, and follow a circular path because of the magnetic field. The proper combination of accelerating voltage and magnetic field causes the ions of mass 4 to enter the slit S_3 and strike the ion collector. The ion current is amplified and actuates the signaling device.

entering the equipment under test will be drawn through the ionization chamber. Also a cold trap is provided to protect the mass spectrograph from volatile substances which may be evolved by the test object. The optimum operating pressure for such a leak detector is about 0.1 micron Hg. It has been reported that this type of leak detector will indicate a leak which admits only 5×10^{-3} micron liters per hour.

Figure 6.48 illustrates a typical setup for leak finding with the helium mass-spectrometer leak detector. It will be noted that extra protection is provided by additional cold traps. The valves and disconnects allow the operator to admit air to the test object and repair a leak without letting air into the leak detector. This saves time when the object is retested after repairs. There are two techniques utilizing this setup. The most common procedure is to provide a fine jet of helium by means of a nozzle connected to a helium supply with a rubber tube. This jet is sprayed systematically over all the joints and seams of the test object. It is important that one start at the top in this probing because helium, being light, will rise, so that the operator may think that he has discovered a leak at a certain point when actually the helium is entering a hole above the area being tested. The other method

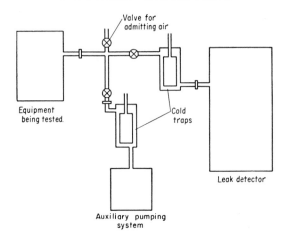

FIGURE 6.48.   Typical setup for leak hunting.

of leak finding is more positive and more sensitive.   It consists in providing a hood or enclosure which will completely envelop the object or area being tested so that it can be subjected to an atmosphere of almost pure helium. This is the most sensitive application of the leak detector.   Obviously it will not show the specific location of a leak, but it will indicate the presence of a leak so that the operator will know if further search is needed.   There is one warning that should be given; if the helium-filled hood encloses a temporary connection made of rubber tubing, diffusion through the wall of the rubber tube may appear to be a leak.

Another way of operating the helium leak detector is to fill the vessel being tested with helium at a pressure greater than atmospheric and use a "sniffer" probe which connects with the leak detector.   The sniffer is a fine valve at the extreme end of a probing tube which admits gas very slowly so that the pressure in the leak detector can be kept in the operating range (*ca.* 0.1 μ Hg). The sniffer probe is attached to the leak detector with a length of rubber vacuum tubing.   This method is not as sensitive as the first method described, because a large amount of air is always taken into the probe along with the small amount of helium escaping from the leak.   It is imperative that the valve be as close as possible to the end of the probe, so that helium from the leak can enter without displacing a large amount of air.

There are several mass-spectrometer leak detectors on the market today, and although their cost is substantial, the money is well spent wherever considerable time is devoted to leak hunting.   It has been estimated that the normal use of a helium leak detector will save enough manpower to pay for the instrument during the first year of its use.   Guthrie and Wakerling [6] give detailed descriptions of a helium leak detector developed at the University of California Radiation Laboratory which can be constructed by a competent experimenter.

Another type of leak detector commercially available that has had some popularity is the halogen leak detector. It is less expensive and less sensitive than the helium leak detector. Figure 6.49 illustrates the principle of this device. Its action depends upon the fact that the positive-ion emission of a hot platinum surface in air is markedly enhanced by the presence of the vapor of a halogen compound. Positive ions produced by the hot platinum cylinder P are collected by C and produce a current in the microammeter. The sensitivity can be increased by amplifying the positive-ion current. White and Hickey [23] state that the sensitivity of the detector under these conditions is of the same order of magnitude as that obtained with the helium mass specrometer. The halogen compound commonly used with this leak detector is one of the Freons®, halogen-substituted methanes and ethanes. The techniques of hunting leaks with this detector are the same as those used with the helium leak detector. It may be noted, however, that the halogen leak detector is sensitive to tobacco smoke and that some halogen vapors may be present accidentally in the laboratory; so its response is not as specific as that of the helium leak detector. Also, since the test gas is heavier than air, probing should start at the bottom of the evacuated test object.

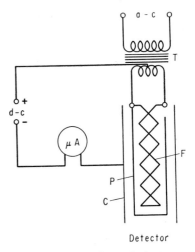

FIGURE 6.49. Halogen leak detector.

Repairing Leaks. Leaks are usually found in seams, joints, and seals, and the preferred repair is to redo the connection. In the case of welded or hard-soldered joints and seams it is sometimes more convenient to seal a leak by covering it with tin-lead solder. However this should not be done if there is a probability that additional welding or silver soldering is to be done in the vicinity, because when tin-lead solder is heated to the temperatures required for hard-soldering or welding it will oxidize and vaporize, spoiling the seal and making additional repair very difficult. Leaks in joints that are kept at room temperature are sometimes sealed by painting with a varnish such as Glyptal ®. However if such a patch is cooled to the temperature of liquid air, it usually fails. Leaks in gasketed seals usually require renewing or regreasing the gasket. Where soft metal gaskets are used, a leak can sometimes be cured by annealing the gasket and replacing it. Leaks in aluminum welds can be repaired by additional welding or by soldering. As was pointed out in the section on techniques of construction, soldering aluminum requires special techniques because of the refractory nature of the surface oxide film. One method that has been successful is to scrape or abrade the surface while it is covered with molten solder.

Cold Leaks. One of the most exasperating situations that afflicts the cryogenist is the leak that shows up only when the equipment is cold. In some instances the leak really exists at ordinary temperatures but it is too small to detect. Upon cooling, differential contraction, higher gas density and lower viscosity may cooperate to increase the leak rate. In other cases a substance such as grease or soldering flux may completely seal the pore when the material is liquid or plastic, but the hardening and contraction accompanying the cooling causes a leak to open up. The latter difficulty can usually be avoided by thorough cleaning—long immersion in boiling water and soaking in organic solvent. A possible procedure for finding the former type of leak is meticulous attention to leak detection so as to squeeze the greatest possible sensitivity from the instrument being used. In some cases it may be possible to evacuate the offending component, cool it with liquid nitrogen, and locate the leak with a helium leak detector before the condensation of moisture from the atmosphere seals the leak. Sometimes cold leaks can be found by bubbling helium through the liquid nitrogen in which the object is immersed. Sometimes time is saved by simply admitting defeat in locating the leak, resoldering all the joints and covering welded seams with a layer of soft solder.

Occasionally the investigator using helium below its lambda point is plagued with even worse troubles—"superleaks." Since helium II, the liquid modification that exists below $2.19°K$, can traverse submicroscopic pores at rates that are orders of magnitude greater than the rate of flow of helium above $2.19°K$, leaks that are far below the limit of detection at ordinary temperatures become ruinous below $2.19°K$. Here there is no hope of accurately locating the leak, so the only remedy is blind resoldering. Pellam [24] once cured such a difficulty by immersing the entire low-temperature enclosure in a molten bath of Rose's alloy.

Leaks into an Enclosure Containing an Adsorbent. Since an adsorbent gives off gas and constitutes a virtual leak, it makes the detection of real leaks in the enclosure more difficult. For this reason it is best to do all the leak hunting possible before the adsorbent is introduced. It is usually practical to provide a filler opening with a gasketed seal so that there is small chance of producing a leak when the adsorbent is put in and the enclosure resealed. Of course the final seal must be tested after the adsorbent is in place. The helium leak detector can best be used in its most sensitive way (vacuum inside, helium jet or hood outside). The clean-up time after helium has entered a leak will be increased by the adsorbent. However if leak hunting is done by the method in which the vacuum space is pressurized with helium and the sniffer probe is used outside, the adsorbent will take up so much helium that days of pumping may be required to reduce the helium concentration to a level that will permit the first type of test to be used.

6.12. General Remarks on Vacuum Construction and Leak Testing. It seems that respect for the skill required to produce leak-free vacuum equipment and an appreciation of the perfection demanded of the fabricator are usually acquired only by experience. There is a tendency to assume that the techniques used to produce such items as tanks for compressed air or gasoline can be applied with equal success to the manufacture of high-vacuum equipment. It is not realized that seams that are perfect by ordinary standards may contain leaks that will ruin vacuum insulation. The professional welder is sometimes amazed to discover that his work will not stand the test of the helium leak detector. However, modern shielded-arc welding is a highly developed process and there are many experts who can consistently produce vacuum-tight seams, either by hand or by the use of automatic welding machines. It is a rather curious fact that equal skill in soldering is relatively scarce. Perhaps the explanation is that soldering is considered to be rather easy. Therefore little or no specialized training is given. It is good practice to have the mechanic who makes the soldered and welded seams observe and participate in the leak hunting so that he will better appreciate the need for perfect work. Some of the more common faults are (1) a poor bond between the solder and the metal surfaces caused by dirty surfaces, inadequate flux, or insufficient heating, (2) overheating which may cause porous welds or soldered joints, (3) a hole temporarily closed with flux, and (4) allowing a corrosive flux to remain on thin surfaces until it penetrates and causes holes. Thin stainless-steel sheet or tubing and metal bellows made of brass, bronze, or stainless steel are particularly subject to leaks caused by corrosion.

Sometimes a piece of equipment is completely assembled before leak testing only to find that it must be disassembled before a leak can be repaired. Such troubles can usually be avoided by proper coordination of assembly and leak hunting. For example, the inner part of a vacuum-insulated vessel should be checked for leaks before it is enclosed. If the inner wall of the vessel will not withstand the crushing effect of the atmosphere upon evacuation, it may be tested in an auxiliary vacuum chamber or by making a temporary assembly using waxed or gasketed seals on the outer vacuum enclosure.

To conclude this discussion on the construction of vacuum-insulated equipment on an encouraging note, it may be remarked that leak-free radio tubes are being manufactured by the hundreds of millions. This is abundant proof that proper techniques will consistently produce even the perfection demanded of high-vacuum equipment.

6.13. Evacuated Porous Insulation. When an insulating space is filled with a powder having a low gross density (a large ratio of volume of gas-filled voids to that of the solid material) it is found that the apparent thermal conductivity is approximately that of the gas. It appears that the amount of heat transferred by solid conduction through the powder is relatively small. Also the presence of the powder inhibits, to some extent, heat transfer by convection and radiation. Now if the gas pressure in the interstices is reduced by pumping the enclosure, the rate of heat transfer is little affected at first because the thermal conductivity of the gas is almost independent of pressure in this higher-pressure region. However, when the gas pressure approaches the value at which the mean free paths of the molecules are comparable with interstitial distances, there is a marked reduction in the apparent thermal conductivity. This is illustrated in Figure 6.50. For most powders used with

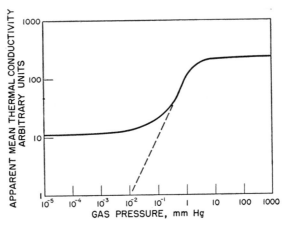

FIGURE 6.50. Variation of the apparent thermal conductivity of an insulating powder as the pressure of the interstitial gas is changed.

nitrogen as the interstitial gas it appears that the condition of free molecule conduction sets in at pressures of the order 1.0 to 0.1 mm Hg. If the only mechanism for heat transfer were that of gaseous conduction, the rate of heat transfer at all lower pressures would be proportional to the pressure of the gas. However this is found not to be the case; at quite low pressures the rate of heat transfer becomes almost independent of pressure, showing that heat is being transmitted by other means. This residual heat transfer can be by solid conduction through the powder or by radiation or by both. Figure 6.50 is somewhat idealized to represent the behavior of a powder with voids of uniform size and therefore having a rather sharp transition into the range of free molecule conduction. For most actual powders this transition is more diffuse.

Measuring Heat Transfer Through Powders. Heat transfer through powders has been studied at the National Bureau of Standards [25] with the calorimeter illustrated in Figure 6.51. This calorimeter determines the rate of heat transfer from the warmer outer surface to the colder inner surface by measuring the rate at which a cryogenic liquid (nitrogen, hydrogen, or helium) evaporates. Heat conducted or radiated from above to the measur-

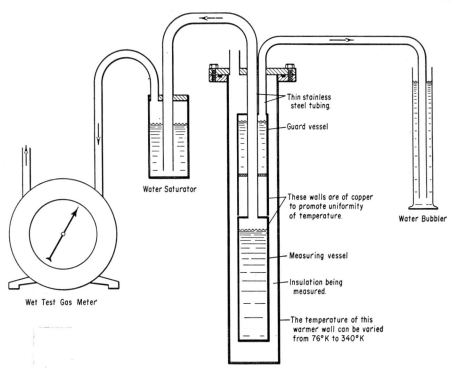

FIGURE 6.51.   Calorimeter for studying insulation at low temperatures.

ing vessel is intercepted by the guard vessel.   In order to prevent condensation of vapor from the measuring vessel on the wall of the tube which is in contact with the liquid in the guard vessel, the guard vessel is maintained at a temperature just slightly above that of the measuring vessel by bubbling the vapor evaporated from the guard vessel through a few inches of water and thus maintaining its equilibrium pressure a little above that in the measuring vessel.   Insulations of thickness 0.5 inch, 1 inch, and 1.8 inches can be measured by using outer vessels of various diameters.

The rate of heat transfer to the measuring vessel is computed by the relation

$$W = L_v(dM/dt) \cdot \rho_{\text{liq}}/(\rho_{\text{liq}} - \rho_{\text{vap}}) \tag{6.29}$$

where W is the rate of heat transfer in watts, L_v is the heat of vaporization in Joules per gram, dM/dt is the rate at which vapor leaves the calorimeter and ρ_{liq} and ρ_{vap} are the densities of the saturated liquid and vapor respectively at the temperature existing in the measuring vessel.   The factor $\rho_{\text{liq}}/(\rho_{\text{liq}} - \rho_{\text{vap}})$ corrects for the vapor that is formed but does not leave the calorimeter; merely occupying the space vacated by the evaporated liquid. For nitrogen at its normal boiling point this factor is 1.006, for hydrogen 1.019.

Figure 6.52 shows some of the NBS data [25] obtained for several powders. It is seen that when the cold surface is at 76°K the apparent thermal conductivity is reduced only slightly by lowering the pressure below 10 microns Hg. The mechanism responsible for the residual heat transfer has been investigated by varying the temperature of the outer, warm surface of the calorimeter. Since heat transferred by radiation is proportional to the differences of the fourth powers of the temperatures of the two surfaces, while that transferred by solid conduction is approximately proportional to the difference of the first powers of the temperatures, a moderate variation of the temperature of the warm surface will distinguish between the two modes. With silica aerogel as the insulating medium the temperature of the outer surface was varied from 273° to 329°K while the inner surface was kept at 76°K, and it was found that the residual heat transfer was nearly proportional to the difference of the fourth powers of the temperatures. From this, it was concluded that solid conduction is unimportant for this temperature span. However for heat transfer from a surface at 76°K to one at 20°K there is evidence

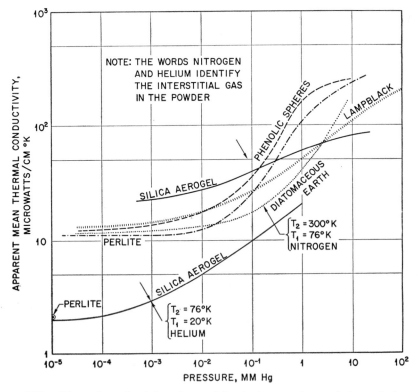

FIGURE 6.52.   Thermal conductivity of several insulating powders and the variation with interstitial gas pressure.

that solid conduction through the powder is a major factor. Since the energy radiated from a surface at 76°K is only about 0.004 of that radiated at room temperature, it is not surprising that the relative importance of the two modes of heat transfer can be reversed by such a temperature change.

The radiant-heat transmission through a partially transparent powder is not simple. Some of the heat is radiated directly from the warm to the cold surface, some is absorbed by the powder and re-radiated, and some is reflected by the powder. For the layers of silica aerogel (less than 1 inch) the apparent thermal conductivity depends upon the thickness and upon the emissivities of the boundaries. Thus the concept of thermal conductivity cannot be properly applied to thin layers. However for layers 1 inch or more in thickness the apparent thermal conductivities given in Figure 6.52 may be employed in the conventional way with errors not exceeding 10 percent.

Convenient Formula for Porous Insulation. A good approximation for the heat transfer through a porous insulation of constant thickness in a vessel of conservative shape is given by

$$W = \frac{\bar{k}(T_2 - T_1)}{t} \times \sqrt{A_1 A_2} \tag{6.30}$$

where $\bar{k}$ is the mean effective thermal conductivity between the temperature T_2 and T_1, T_2 is the temperature of the outer surface, T_1 is the temperature of the inner surface, A_1 and A_2 are the areas of the inner and outer surfaces respectively, and t is the thickness of the insulation. This formula is exact for concentric spheres. For cylinders with spherical, dished, or elliptical heads it has been estimated that it will give results within 5 percent if the thickness of the insulating space is not more than 50 percent of the radius of the inner cylinder. It is correspondingly reliable for other shapes in which the thickness of the insulation is a small fraction of the minor perimeter of the vessel. In reporting values of the thermal properties of insulators the mean effective thermal conductivity is often given between commonly encountered temperatures. If the available data are presented in the more general form of instantaneous conductivities as a function of temperature the mean effective thermal conductivity can be obtained from the relation.

$$\bar{k} = \left[\int_{T_1}^{T_2} k\,dT \right] / (T_2 - T_1) \tag{6.31}$$

where k is the thermal conductivity at the temperature T. If k is a linear function of T, $\bar{k}$ is the arithmetic mean conductivity between T_1 and T_2.

Other Relevant Properties of Insulating Powders. There are some properties of insulating powders other than thermal conductivity that should be taken into consideration when designing equipment which makes use of this kind of insulation. First is the difficulty of evacuation. The gas being removed usually has to filter through the powder for rather long distances, and the resistance to flow is serious. Evacuation time can be reduced by providing a number of pumping taps, or better still, a number of pumping channels with many openings distributed so that the paths of the gas through the powder are short. Since the powders are light and fine, they tend to be carried along with the gas; so the openings must be protected by filters. Some of the powders, notably silica aerogel, adsorb large amounts of water from a humid atmosphere. It saves pumping time to dry them by heating before they are introduced. Also evacuation time can be reduced by heating to drive off adsorbed gases while the vessel is being pumped.

The cost of the powder is important when it is used to insulate a large vessel. For transportable equipment the density may be of some concern. Table 6.4 lists properties of several insulating powders tested at the National

TABLE 6.4. COMPARISON OF RELEVANT PROPERTIES OF SOME EVACUATED
INSULATING POWDERS TESTED AT THE NATIONAL BUREAU
OF STANDARDS CRYOGENIC ENGINEERING LABORATORY

Material	Mean Apparent Thermal Conductivity (300° to 76°K), milliwatts/cm deg K	Density, lbs/ft³	Approximate Cost, $/ft³
Silica aerogel	0.022	5.0	5.00
Perlite 30-mesh	0.017	6.6	.40
Perlite 30- to 80-mesh	0.012	8.4	.40
Perlite 80-mesh	0.010	8.7	.50
Lampblack	0.011	12	1.20
Diatomaceous earth	0.011	20	1.00

Bureau of Standards. M. M. Fulk [26] has prepared a review article on evacuated powder insulation.

II. GAS-FILLED POWDERS AND FIBROUS MATERIALS

6.14. Permeable materials of low density, such as powders and fibers with gas at atmospheric pressure in the interstices, have been used to insulate air liquefiers, gas separation columns, tanks for liquid oxygen and nitrogen, and other equipment in which the temperature does not fall below the boiling point of nitrogen. In this type of insulating material, the volume of the gas in the voids may be 10 to 100 times the volume of the solid material. Figure 6.53 shows the thermal conductivities of some of the more common permeable insulations. It is seen that the best of these approach the conductivity of air, indicating that the air which occupies the voids is the agent responsible for most of the heat conduction. This suggests the principle of gas-filled insula-

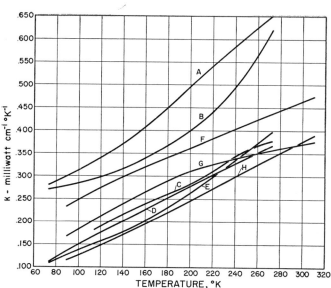

FIGURE 6.53. Thermal conductivities of several permeable materials at low temperatures. Curves A to E are from the data of Chow [26]; Curves F, G, and H are from the data of Wilkes [27]. A, vermiculite 10-14-mesh; B, sawdust; C, granulated cork, 50 percent 10-20-mesh, 50 percent less than 20-mesh; D, seaweed product (powder); E, crude cotton wadding; F, vegetable fiber board; G, cork board; H, glass fiber board.

tion. The solid portion stops radiation and gas convection. In the ideal case the conduction through the solid would be negligible and the gas in the voids would be responsible for the heat flow. In actual insulations the solid particles of powder or the fibers short-circuit the heat flow through the gas to some extent and the resultant thermal conductivity is usually somewhat greater than that of the gas alone. There is one exception; very fine powders sometimes have such small distances between the solid particles that the mean free path of the gas is greater than the interstitial distance; hence its thermal conductivity is reduced as it would be by decreasing the pressure. Thus it is possible for a powder insulation to have a thermal conductivity less than that of the gas which fills the voids even when the gas is at atmospheric pressure.

Needless to say permeable insulations must be kept dry. If the warm surface of an insulation of this type is exposed to the atmosphere, water vapor will diffuse through and deposit as ice in the inner cold layers of the insulation, greatly increasing the thermal conductivity. Sometimes the warm surface can be sealed completely by providing an outer metal jacket as is done for vacuum insulation. However, it is not usually convenient to make the outer surface completely leakproof. A good way to keep moisture out of the insulation is to provide a few small vents in the outer boundary and allow a small amount of dry gas to flow outward through the insulation and escape through the vents. This effectively prevents the diffusion of moist air into the cold insulation.

Since the gas in the insulation is at atmospheric pressure, the temperature of the cold surface must not go below the condensing point of the gas, about 81.5°K for air, 77°K for nitrogen. If the gas in the insulation condenses, it will constitute a bad heat leak due to reflux—condensation on the cold surface, the liquid dripping off into the warmer insulation and being evaporated. Also if the insulation is combustible, the condensation of air constitutes a real hazard. The condensate can be almost 50 percent oxygen, and combustible materials soaked in such a mixture are explosive. The most practical gas to use in gas-permeated insulation below 77°K is helium. However, the high thermal conductivity of helium (7.5 times that of nitrogen at 100°K) is a serious disadvantage. If helium were substituted for air in the voids of the materials listed in Figure 6.53 one would expect that the resultant thermal conductivities would be larger by an amount approximately equal to the difference between the thermal conductivity of helium and that of air. This would mean that the conductivities of the better insulations would be raised by a factor of 5 or more. However, for a very fine powder such as silica aerogel or some grades of perlite, the ordinary thermal conductivity of helium may not apply. Since helium has a mean free path about three times that of air, its thermal conductivity would be reduced more by the small interstitial distances. Thus if it is necessary to use a permeable insulation at atmospheric pressure and at temperatures lower than 77°K, the best practical choice appears to be a very fine powder with helium as the interstitial gas. Of course neon would be better than helium, but its cost would probably be prohibitive. Also neon could not be used below its boiling point (27°K) and so would not be applicable for insulating a liquid-hydrogen vessel.

III. Solid Foams

6.15. There is a class of insulating materials which have a cellular structure caused by the evolution of a large volume of gas during manufacture. When the cells in such a material are small and do not communicate with each other, the material has some properties that make it a useful insulator for certain low-temperature applications. Foams of this type have been made of polystyrene, polyurethanes (isocyanates), rubber, silicones and other materials. Probably all organic plastics can be produced as foams if proper techniques are used. At present polystyrene foam is the most widely used.

Since gas can penetrate such a foam only by diffusion through the cell walls, the material behaves as though it were completely impermeable when the exposure to a foreign gas lasts only a short time. Also if the temperature of the cold side of the foam is so low that the gas in the nearby cells is condensed and has negligible vapor pressure, the thermal conductivity is greatly reduced by eliminating gaseous conduction in these regions. However it should be remarked that the insulating value of such foams seldom approaches that of ordinary permeable materials such as powder because the solid conducting paths in the foam are continuous even though they may be tortuous. The foaming gas used in the manufacture of many of these foams is carbon dioxide, which has a small vapor pressure at the temperature of liquid nitrogen. Thus when the foam is fresh, its thermal conductivity is reduced considerably by contact with liquid nitrogen. However, after the foam has been stored for several months, the foaming gas is largely replaced by air owing to slow diffusion, and the reduction of thermal conductivity by the condensation of the gas is of little consequence if the lowest temperature is that of liquid nitrogen. If the cold side is at the temperature of liquid hydrogen, the conductivity will be greatly lowered even if the cells of the foam contain air. However, if such a foam is left in an atmosphere of hydrogen or helium for a week or more, there will be another partial substitution by these gases and the thermal conductivity of the foam will be seriously increased. This has been demonstrated experimentally. Because the diffusion of gases through solids is greatly reduced by lowering the temperature, it is probable that little harm will ensue from contact of the insulation with hydrogen or helium while the temperature is below that of liquid nitrogen.

Since these solid-foam insulations are almost impermeable to gases, they may be used to insulate regions below the condensing temperature of air or nitrogen. One of the applications is simply to hollow out a block or cylinder of foam and use it as an insulating vessel as shown in Figure 6.54. Small vessels of this type have been quite useful. However, the logical extension of this idea—using a solid foam to insulate a large vessel made of metal—is attended with considerable difficulty. The principal cause of the trouble is the relatively high expansivity of the plastic foams. In general the expansivi-

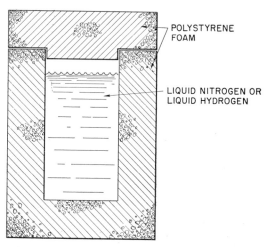

POLYSTYRENE FOAM

LIQUID NITROGEN OR LIQUID HYDROGEN

FIGURE 6.54.   Vessel for cryogenic liquids made from plastic foam.

ties of plastics are from two to ten times as large as those of ordinary structural metals. Measurements made at the Cryogenic Engineering Laboratory show that plastic foams have an expansivity greater than that of the same polymer without voids. These measurements were made with an ambient pressure of about 1 atmosphere, and it is thought that the observed enhancement of thermal expansion is probably caused by the change in pressure of the gas in the cells.

In any event the great difference between the expansivities of plastic foams and ordinary structural metals constitutes a serious problem. For example, if one were to insert a close-fitting rigid metal liner inside the vessel illustrated in Figure 6.54, the polystyrene foam would probably crack when liquid nitrogen is introduced, because the outer foamed-plastic vessel would tend to an inside diameter smaller than that of the metal liner. This is also confirmed by experiments.

At this point it may be well to digress somewhat and remark that some of the solid foams may be foamed in place by mixing the appropriate monomer, foaming agent, and catalyst and pouring this mixture into the space which is to be filled with foam. Moreover it is quite feasible to have this foamed-in-place insulation bonded to a surface of the metal enclosure.

The National Bureau of Standards has tested several of these bonded, foamed-in-place insulations, with mostly disappointing results. Upon cooling the inner surface with liquid nitrogen, the contraction sets up thermal stresses which cause cracks to appear in the insulation and spoil its imperviousness to gas and liquid. However, one of the foams tested had a rubbery consistency and withstood the cooling without cracking. Although this foam was not a particularly good insulator, its mechanical behavior points the way toward the development of satisfactory materials for this service.

Because of the large difference in the thermal expansions of metals and plastic foams, a great deal of thought has been given to schemes for utilizing plastic foams that are not bonded to the metal and have expansion joints to absorb changes in dimensions. If unprotected, the joints would, of course, constitute channels which would admit atmospheric air or cryogenic liquid and defeat the function of the insulation. However it is possible to seal such openings by using plastic films. One way to employ such a film is illustrated in Figure 6.55. Here a metal vessel is insulated with segments of solid foam, and the entire interior of the insulation is covered with a plastic bag.

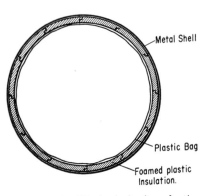

Metal Shell

Plastic Bag

Foamed plastic Insulation.

FIGURE 6.55. Method of using plastic-foam insulation to insulate a metal tank for use with cryogenic liquids.

One plastic film that has been found to be usable at very low temperatures is Mylar®. Plastic films have not been widely explored for this function; there may be many other varieties that are suitable. The requirements are that the film remain pliable and strong at the low temperatures. It appears that only rather thin films will be sufficiently pliable. Mylar® one-thousandth of an inch thick will withstand repeated severe flexure at liquid-hydrogen temperature.

IV. COMPARISON OF INSULATIONS

6.16. The boundary temperatures most frequently encountered in cryogenic design are room temperature, about 300°K; the oxygen boiling point, 90°K; the nitrogen boiling point, 77°K; the hydrogen boiling point, 20°K; and the helium boiling point 4.2°K. Of course a combination of any two of these may constitute the boundary temperatures of a specific insulation application. However, three combinations most frequently encountered require somewhat different treatments in the selection of appropriate insulating procedures. These combinations are (a) warm surface at 300°K, cold surface at 77°K (or 90°K); (b) warm surface at 300°K, cold surface at 20°K; (c) warm surface at 77°K, cold surface at 20°K (or 4°K). Combination (a) is the condition existing in ordinary containers for liquid oxygen or nitrogen, combination (b) could refer to a container for liquid hydrogen which does not have a liquid-nitrogen-cooled shield, and combination (c) is encountered in vessels for liquid hydrogen or liquid helium which have a protective shield cooled with liquid nitrogen.

When high-vacuum insulation is used, heat is transferred from a surface at 300°K to one at 90°K or lower almost entirely by radiation. The radiant heat transfer is practically unaffected by reducing the temperature of the cold surface below 90°K, since 300^4 is so much greater than 90^4. However, with boundaries at 77°K and 20° or 4°K, even a small amount of residual gas (hydrogen or helium) will account for a large part of the total heat flow. If the separation between the walls which are at 300° and 90° or less is a few inches, the substitution of evacuated powder for high vacuum alone will usually improve the insulation by reducing the radiant heat transfer. Of course this applies to surfaces having emissivities that are practically realizable, of the order of 1 or 2 percent. If the emissivities could be made low enough, the powder would not help. For the 77° and 20°K boundary condition the radiant heat transfer is so low that powder will increase the heat transfer because of its thermal conduction, unless the separation between the surfaces is quite large.

An adequate thickness of evacuated powder will have less heat leak than that through high-vacuum insulation between room temperature and the hydrogen boiling point. However, in some cases—for example, liquid transfer lines that are used only for short periods of time—the additional heat capacity of the powder may consume more liquid than the additional heat leak when using high vacuum alone.

Permeable insulations, such as gas-filled powders, are at least an order of magnitude poorer than vacuum for the 300°-77°K boundaries and are still worse for the 77°-20°K conditions because the gases available for filling the voids have high thermal conductivities. The principal virtue of this type of

TABLE 6.5.   HEAT TRANSFER BETWEEN PARALLEL SURFACES
THROUGH VARIOUS TYPES OF INSULATION[a]

	Heat Transfer Through Insulation Having the Indicated Boundary Temperatures, milliwatts cm^{-2}		
Temperature of warm surface → Temperature of cold surface → Kind of insulation	300°K 77°K	300°K 20°K	77°K 20°K
High vacuum, $p = 10^{-6}$ mm Hg (H_2 residual). Emissivity 0.02 at each surface	0.45	0.46	0.002
Gases at atmospheric pressure (no convection). 15 cm between the warm and cold surfaces H_2	19.3 ($k = 1.30$)	19.6 ($k = 1.05$)	0.8 ($k = 0.22$)
He	17.1 ($k = 1.15$)	17.7 ($k = 0.95$)	1.7 ($k = 0.45$)
Air or N_2	2.68 ($k = 0.18$)	—	—
Evacuated powder (expanded perlite with density of 5-6 lb ft^{-3}), 15-cm layer	0.16 ($\bar{k} = 0.011$)	0.13[b] ($\bar{k} = 0.007$)	0.007 ($\bar{k} = 0.002$)
Gas filled powder (expanded perlite 5-6 lb ft^{-3}) 15-cm layer He	18.7 ($\bar{k} = 1.26$)	18.7 ($\bar{k} = 1.0$ est.)	2.2 ($\bar{k} = 0.5$)
N_2	4.8 ($\bar{k} = 0.32$)	—	—
Polystyrene foam (2 lb ft^{-3}) 15-cm layer	4.9 ($\bar{k} = 0.33$)	5.1 ($\bar{k} = 0.27$)	0.57 ($\bar{k} = 0.15$)

$\bar{k}$ is the apparent effective mean thermal conductivity for the temperature interval.
k is the actual mean thermal conductivity.
The units for k and $\bar{k}$ are milliwatts cm^{-1} °K^{-1}.

[a] These computations were made by M. M. Fulk, National Bureau of Standards.
[b] This value is not consistent with that given for the boundary temperatures 300° and 77°K because it shows a smaller total heat transfer for a larger temperature difference. The cause of this discrepancy has not yet been identified.

insulation is that it does not require vacuum-tight boundaries and therefore can be lighter and less expensive than most evacuated insulations.

Solid foams are inferior to good gas-filled permeable insulation in the upper temperature region but they usually improve greatly as the temperature is lowered to 20°K because the gas in the cells is condensed and the thermal conductivity of the solid constituting the cell walls is greatly reduced. One notable exception is a glass foam which contains hydrogen gas in the cells. Solid foams also can be used without vacuum-tight boundaries.

Table 6.5 summarizes representative behavior of the various kinds of insulation for the three sets of boundary temperatures most frequently encountered. The values of heat transfer listed are for parallel surfaces; in an actual case the appropriate area factor discussed earlier must be applied.

REFERENCES FOR CHAPTER 6

[1] M. Knudsen, *Ann. d. Physik,* **31,** 205 (1910); **32,** 809 (1910); **33,** 1435 (1910); **34,** 593 (1911); and **6,** 149 (1930).
[2] J. R. Partington, "Advanced Treatise on Physical Chemistry," Longmans, Green & Co., Inc., N.Y., 1952, Vol. I, pp. 930-932.
[3] A. W. Lawson and Robert Fano, *Rev. Sci. Instr.,* **18,** 727 (1947); J. B. Garrison and A. W. Lawson, *ibid.,* **19,** 574 (1948).
[4] M. Jakob, "Heat Transfer," John Wiley & Sons, Inc., N.Y., 1949, Vol. I, pp. 43, 51-52, 124, 128.
[5] Reuter and Sondheimer, *Proc. Roy. Soc.,* **A195,** 33 (1948); Ramanathan, *Proc. Phy. Soc.,* **A65,** 532 (1952); Dingle, *Physica,* **19,** 311, 348 (1953).
[6] A. Guthrie and R. K. Wakerling, "Vacuum Equipment and Techniques," 1st ed., McGraw-Hill Book Co., Inc., N.Y., 1949.
[7] C. E. Norman, *Industrial and Eng. Chem.,* **40,** 783 (1948).
[8] "Vacuum," Edwards and Company Ltd., London.
[9] "Vacuum Symposium Transactions," sponsored by the Committee on Vacuum Techniques, Inc., Box 1282, Boston 9, Mass.
[10] Saul Dushman, "Scientific Foundation of Vacuum Techniques," John Wiley & Sons, Inc., N.Y., 1949.
[11] Vergil L. Stout and Martin D. Gibbons, *J. Appl. Phys.,* **26,** 1488 (December 1955).
[12] Robert H. Davis and Ajay S. Divatia, *Rev. Sci. Instr.,* **25,** 1193 (1954).
[13] Juan de Dios Lopez-Gonzales, Frank G. Carpenter, and Victor J. Dietz, *J. Research NBS,* **55,** 11 (1955).
[14] J. Dewar, *Proc. Roy. Dist. Gt. Brit.,* **18,** 751 (1907).
[15] G. Claude, *Compt. rend.,* **158,** 861 (1914).
[16] H. Rowe, *Phil. Mag.,* **1,** 109, 1042 (1926).
[17] H. Freundlich, "Kapillarchemie," Leipzig, 1930, Vol. I, pp. 153-172.
[18] T. L. Hill, *J. Chem. Phys.,* **18,** 246 (1950).
[19] R. B. Jacobs, NBS. Unpublished measurements (1956).
[20] I. Langmuir, *Phys. Rev.,* **1,** 337 (1913).
[21] R. J. Richards, *Rev. Sci. Instr.,* **25,** 520 (1954).
[22] R. W. Mebs and W. F. Roeser, *NBS Circ.* 492 (April 28, 1950).
[23] W. C. White and J. S. Hickey, *Electronics,* **21,** 100 (1948).
[24] J. R. Pellam. Private communication.

[25] R. J. Corruccini, J. E. Schrodt, and M. M. Fulk, NBS. Unpublished measurements (1957).

[26] M. M. Fulk, Evacuated Powder Insulation. Submitted for publication in K. Mendelssohn (Ed.), "Progress in Cryogenics," Heywood & Co., Ltd., London.

[27] C. S. Chow, Proc. Phys. Soc., 61, 206 (London 1948).

[28] J. Wilkes, Ref. Eng., 52, 37 (1946).

Chapter VII

STORING AND TRANSPORTING LIQUEFIED GASES

7.1. Methods of insulation and formulae for computing heat leak through various types of insulation for different geometrical configurations have been given in the preceding chapter. This chapter will deal with the applications of these methods and formulae to the insulation of containers for liquefied gases. Some additional material having a general applicability to the insulation and the expected performance of such containers will be given, but a large part of the discussion will consist of descriptions of actual containers. Accessories such as liquid level devices will be described. Some special techniques dealing with precooling containers and utilizing the refrigerative value of the escaping cold vapor will also be discussed.

The invention of the vacuum-insulated vessel for liquefied gases by James Dewar in 1892 was a break-through in the field of thermal insulation that has not yet been matched by further developments. All of the advances since Dewar's time have been improvements on Dewar's original concept, usually means of reducing radiant heat transfer by attaining surfaces of higher reflectivity or by interposing shields which reflect or intercept the radiant energy.

At its best the vacuum is so good that heat transfer by residual gas is almost negligible. Accordingly, the designer is mainly concerned with reducing the heat transferred by mechanical supports and that which is conveyed across the insulating vacuum by radiation. The heat transferred by the supports is a problem involving the mechanical strength required for a specific application and has no general solution. If there is no restriction on the dimensions of the vessel, the heat conducted through the supports can usually be made quite small simply by using supports of low thermal conductivity and making their lengths great enough. Even in restricted space the clever designer can usually find a way to provide a long thermal path through the solid supports. On the other hand the heat transferred by radiation is little affected by the thickness of the insulating space. In fact the insulation is somewhat better for a thin vacuum space which approaches the ideal configuration of parallel surfaces. However heat transfer by radiation can be reduced by interposing thermal shields between the warm and cold surfaces of the vessel.

One of the most effective shields for vessels containing liquid hydrogen or helium is a surface cooled with liquid nitrogen. By interposing in the insulating vacuum of a helium or hydrogen container a surface cooled to 77°K, the radiant heat transfer is reduced by a factor of about 250 under that emanating from a surface at 300°K (room temperature). Nearly all the heat radiated from the room temperature surface is intercepted and causes the evaporation of relatively inexpensive liquid nitrogen. Small vessels utilizing liquid-nitrogen-cooled shields have been described by several workers [1-6].

Although the refrigerated shield is very effective, a simple non-refrigerated "floating" shield will cause a substantial reduction in energy transfer by radiation. The floating shield is an opaque, highly reflecting surface, geometrically similar to the surface of the liquid container and suspended with the minimum of thermal contact approximately midway between the inner and outer walls of the vacuum space. If the shield has the same reflectivity as that of the boundary walls and contains no openings or irregularities, the radiant heat transfer to the liquid being stored will be reduced by about one-half. Additional shields will further reduce the heat transferred by radiation. However, the design of mechanical supports which will hold the shields in place without providing objectionable heat leaks becomes a formidable task as the number of shields is increased. Also, openings and irregularities which are needed to accommodate the piping and supports for the inner container greatly reduce the effectiveness of this type of multiple shielding.

Fortunately a method has been discovered which does not complicate the mechanical design and yet provides a barrier to thermal radiation comparable with multiple shields. This method consists of filling the insulating vacuum space with a fine light powder such as perlite, silica aerogel, carbon black, or diatomaceous earth. If the thickness of the insulating space is sufficient, filling with powder will greatly reduce the radiant heat transfer. Moreover when powder is used, the vacuum requirement is quite modest; the minimum heat transfer is very closely approached when the interstitial gas pressure is reduced to 10 microns of mercury in an insulating powder (e.g., perlite or silica aerogel) with one boundary at room temperature, 300°K, and the other at the temperature of liquid nitrogen, 77°K. A layer of evacuated powder several centimeters thick will effectively stop radiation and yet not provide an objectionable amount of thermal conduction through the touching particles of powder. When the space between the walls must be small, of the order of 1 centimeter or less, the thermal conduction through the powder is objectionable. In this case the most effective insulation is a high vacuum bounded by highly reflecting walls.

Since the principal function of the powder is to stop radiation, it is useful only when radiation constitutes an important heat leak. If an insulating vacuum is bounded by highly reflecting surfaces such as clean annealed copper, silver, or aluminum, and the surfaces are at 77° and 20°K respectively, adding powder may actually increase the heat transfer by providing paths of solid conduction. The radiant heat transfer between the surfaces of these temperatures is so small that its elimination by adding powder is of little consequence. Radiation from a surface at 77°K is only about 0.004 of that from an identical surface at 300°K, since it is proportional to the fourth power of the absolute temperature. Of course the thickness of the insulating space must be considered in such a comparison. It is probably more correct to say that for boundaries at 77° and 20°K a rather large thickness of powder would be required to compete with high-vacuum insulation.

It appears then that evacuated powder insulation is very desirable if the warm boundary is at ordinary room temperature and the insulating space is thick enough (10 cm or more) that solid conduction through the powder is not serious.

Of course, evacuated powder insulation is not new. It has been used for many years in large industrial containers for liquid oxygen and liquid nitrogen. It is particularly suitable for large containers. Now that liquid hydrogen is being stored and transported in large quantities, evacuated powder appears attractive as the insulation to use in large liquid-hydrogen vessels. Evacuated powder has been used in conjunction with a liquid-nitrogen-cooled shield for some vessels holding 750 liters of liquid hydrogen, and some liquid-hydrogen vessels of 6000 liters capacity have recently been constructed which utilize only powder insulation (no refrigerated shield).

I. Dependence of Rate of Evaporation upon Size and Shape of Vessel

7.2. It is quite easy to formulate for liquefied gas containers some general relationships between the size and shape of the vessel and the rate of evaporation of the liquid it contains. First, since the heat leak into the container increases as the surface area increases, the most favorable shape is the sphere (the greatest ratio of volume to surface). The sphere also has some advantages of mechanical strength, but in large sizes it may be expensive to fabricate. The next most favorable common shape is the square cylinder in which the length equals the diameter. The practical approach to this shape is the cylinder with standard commercial dished or elliptical heads. This design has good mechanical strength and is readily fabricated. It is stronger and has a somewhat larger ratio of volume to surface than the cylinder with the flat ends. Also the ratio of surface to volume of the cylinder with dished ends is only about 10 percent greater than that of the sphere. However in many cases, particularly vessels which are to be transported by rail or highway, the maximum diameter is fixed.

Thus most of the designs for large insulated tanks for storing and transporting liquefied gases can be assigned to two categories: (1) fixed shape and (2) fixed diameter. It is of interest to see how the performance of such containers varies with the size of the vessel. The effectiveness of a container for liquefied gas is commonly given as the fraction (or percent) of the total contents which evaporates in one day.

7.3. Vacuum-Insulated Vessels. For vacuum-insulated containers of fixed shape—that is, containers of geometric similarity but of different sizes—the heat leak by radiation and residual-gas conduction is proportional to the surface area of the inner container—that is, proportional to L^2, where L is a linear dimension of the container. The heat leak through the supports may also be considered proportional to L^2, since they will probably have a length nearly proportional to the linear dimension and a total cross-sectional area proportional to the volume (and weight) of the inner container. Then the total rate of heat leak is

$$W = CL^2 = C_1 V^{2/3}$$

where C_1 is a constant and V is the volume of the inner container. The fractional rate of evaporation is

$$\frac{W}{L_v \rho V} = \frac{C_1 V^{2/3}}{L_v \rho V} = \frac{C_1}{L_v \rho V^{1/3}}$$

where L_v is the heat of vaporization of the liquid and ρ its density.

7.4. Vessels with Porous Insulation. For containers insulated with porous materials, e.g., evacuated powders, the situation is somewhat different because for similar geometry the thickness, and therefore the effectiveness of the insulation, is proportional to the linear dimension of the container. The relation between the size and the performance of such vessels is not simple unless the heat conducted by the supports can be neglected. In this case the total heat leak is proportional to the linear dimension; so the fractional evaporation is proportional to $1/V^{2/3}$. Thus it is seen that for vessels utilizing this type of insulation, large size is even more advantageous than it is for high-vacuum-insulated vessels.

7.5. Vessels of Fixed Diameter and Different Lengths. The container for rail or road transportation, in which the maximum diameter cannot exceed a certain value but the length may be varied, can be conveniently analyzed on the assumption that the ends are spherical; so its shortest length and minimum volume are those of a sphere having the permitted diameter. In this case, since the thickness of the insulation is greatly restricted, it will be assumed that the thickness is constant. This means that the heat leak through the insulation will be proportional to the surface area both for high-vacuum insulation and for porous insulation. It should be emphasized that this does not imply that the effectiveness of the various insulations is the same. It only means that in this circumstance the heat leak for unit area is constant for a given type of insulation and is not a function of the total area. Then if we again ignore the heat leak through the supports

$$W = C[4\pi r^2 + 2\pi r(L - 2r)]$$

where C is a constant, r is the maximum permissible radius, and L the length of the container.

The fractional evaporation is

$$\frac{W}{L_v\rho V} = \frac{2CL}{L_v\rho r(L - \frac{2}{3}r)}$$

As one would expect, the fractional evaporation changes very little with length, decreasing by only one-third when the length of the container is changed from $2r$ to infinity.

7.6. Comparison of Evaporation Rate Versus Size for Different Vessels. Figure 7.1 shows graphically how the fractional rate of evaporation depends upon the volume of the container for the three conditions just discussed. The three curves should be compared with each other in regard to trend, not in regard to magnitude. The actual rates of evaporation can be determined only by computing the heat leaks for the particular insulation being used.

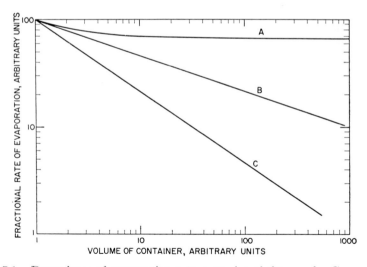

FIGURE 7.1. Dependence of evaporation rate upon size of the vessel. Curve A represents vessels of fixed diameter and various lengths; B, high-vacuum-insulated containers or containers having constant insulating thickness and similar geometry; and C, powder-insulated vessels of similar geometry throughout, including the feature that the insulation thickness bears a constant ratio to the other linear dimensions of the vessel.

II. Portable Commercial Containers for Liquid Oxygen and Nitrogen

7.7. Most low-temperature research laboratories use silvered-glass dewar flasks for small quantities of cryogenic liquids. These are available in a wide variety of shapes and sizes. Two of the commonly used types are shown in Figure 7.2. The cylindrical shape is often used as a part of an experimental assembly; sometimes parts are left unsilvered, providing transparent windows or slits for visual observation of the interior. Since glass can be heated to a high temperature while being evacuated, adsorbed and dissolved gases can be thoroughly removed. Accordingly, a sealed glass dewar will maintain a good vacuum for many years. Cylindrical metal laboratory dewars also are available commercially with inside diameters ranging from 3 or 4 inches to 17 inches and lengths up to several feet. In large diameters the manufacturer is usually willing to make the length to the customer's specifications.

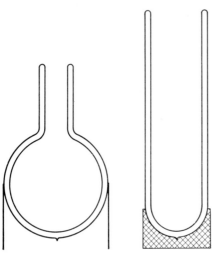

FIGURE 7.2. Two types of glass dewars. For best insulation the surfaces facing the vacuum space are silvered. For some experiments the vessel is left unsilvered, or a strip or window is left unsilvered for visual observation.

For the storage and transportation of somewhat larger quantities of liquid, 15 liters or more, the vessel commonly used is the metal dewar flask illustrated in Figure 6.1, Chapter 6 (p. 143). Vessels of this type are rather rugged, but should not be subjected to severe shocks. With proper handling they will maintain a good insulating vacuum for several years. In time, however, the gas given up by the metal accumulates in the vacuum space to a degree that the charcoal adsorbent cannot maintain a sufficiently good vacuum, and it is necessary to recondition the container by heating and pumping. Containers of this type are manufactured in sizes up to 1000 liters capacity. The larger containers are usually of the form of vertical cylinders with spherical ends, so that the diameter does not become excessive.

Another type of commercial container frequently used for the storage of moderate quantities of liquid oxygen and nitrogen is the horizontal cylindrical vessel mounted on a cart with pneumatic tires as shown in Figure 7.3. The insulation for these vessels may be either high vacuum or evacuated powder. In sizes up to 500 liters these "buggies" can be conveniently moved from place to place in the laboratory.

Larger containers of this general shape are manufactured in the form of

FIGURE 7.3. A 50-gallon commercial portable container for liquid oxygen or nitrogen. (Courtesy of Ronan and Kunzl, Inc.)

integrated tank-trailers for highway transportation and still larger vacuum-powder-insulated tanks are mounted on railroad cars.

III. A LARGE STATIONARY CONTAINER FOR LIQUID OXYGEN

7.8. Figure 7.4 is a longitudinal cross section of a cylindrical storage container for liquid oxygen having a capacity of 26,000 gallons. Although this vessel was designed for stationary storage, the maximum diameter was fixed by the requirement that it be delivered to the site by railroad. The inner vessel and piping are made of type 304 stainless steel. The outer shell is carbon steel. The insulation consists of −80-mesh perlite, evacuated. The designation −80-mesh signifies that the material passes an 80-mesh screen. The thickness of the insulation in the cylindrical part is 8.5 inches; at one end the thickness is 5.8 inches and at the other end almost 3 feet. The inner vessel is supported at the reinforcing rings by means of four stainless steel

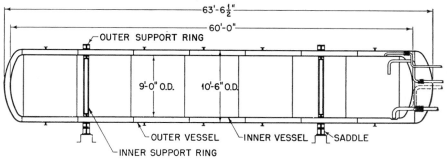

FIGURE 7.4. Large stationary container for liquid oxygen. (Courtesy, Stearns-Roger Manufacturing Company)

rods each $2\frac{3}{4}$ inches in diameter and having a free length of about 50 inches between the points of thermal contact with the inner and outer walls. The piping consists of a 6-inch discharge pipe, a 4-inch fill pipe and a 3-inch vent pipe, all "schedule 40" type 304 stainless steel, arranged approximately as shown. Stainless metal bellows sections in each pipe provide for dimensional changes accompanying cooling.

The heat leak through the perlite insulation was computed by means of Equation 6.30, p. 205, assuming that the insulation is everywhere 8.5 inches thick. The resultant value is believed to be slightly high because extra insulation thickness at the right end of the tank more than compensates for the thinner insulation at the left end; also the area factor $\sqrt{A_1 A_2}$ is slightly high because of the extra length of the outer shell. Three different values of mean effective thermal conductivity of -80-mesh perlite for the temperature interval $300°$ to $90°\mathrm{K}$ were used: 11 microwatts per cm degree for a good vacuum (less than 10 microns Hg), 19 microwatts per cm degree for a pressure of 25 microns Hg, and 26 microwatts per cm degree for a pressure of 50 microns Hg. The heat conducted through the supports and piping was computed using a mean thermal conductivity of 0.10 watt per cm degree for stainless steel between $90°$ and $300°\mathrm{K}$. The additional thermal resistance afforded by the bellows was neglected; the computations were made as though there were no bellows inserts.

Table 7.1 gives the results of the heat-leak computations.

TABLE 7.1. THERMAL CHARACTERISTICS OF A LARGE LIQUID OXYGEN CONTAINER. (THE TEMPERATURE OF THE OUTER WALL IS TAKEN AS $300°\mathrm{K}$.)

Characteristic	Good Vacuum, $<10\mu$ Hg	Pressure, 25μ Hg	Pressure, 50μ Hg
Heat leak through the powder insulation, watts	195	337	461
Heat leak through the piping, watts	13	13	13
Heat leak through supports, watts	27	27	27
Total computed heat leak, watts	235	377	498
Computed evaporation rate = percent per day	0.085	0.14	0.18

This is a very well designed vessel and its loss rate is rather low. However, there exist opportunities for improvement. For example, the discharge line constitutes an unnecessary heat leak. It is quite likely that during static storage a small amount of liquid oxygen flows continuously along the bottom side of the discharge pipe, evaporates when it reaches warmer regions and the resultant vapor is recondensed in that part of the discharge line which is surrounded by the liquid in the tank. This loss is difficult to evaluate because it involves heat transfer from an undetermined area of wetted surface to the liquid which evaporates in the tube, and heat transfer from the condensing vapor to the cold parts of the tube. The maximum temperature difference available for condensation is obviously that corresponding to the difference in vapor pressure accruing from the hydrostatic head of liquid afforded by the diameter of the discharge pipe, because if the gas pressure in the pipe is greater than that of the liquid at the level of the bottom of the pipe, liquid will be prevented from flowing towards warmer regions and this source of heat leak will cease to exist.

The remedy for this is to design the discharge line so that it emerges from the outer shell at a higher point. This will have the added advantage of decreasing heat leak by increasing the length of the heat path between the warm part of the line and the part at the temperature of liquid oxygen. A practical recommendation is shown by the dotted lines in the diagram.

Another improvement could be realized by arranging the fill and discharge tubes so that the cold gas being vented will intercept some of the heat entering through these avenues of solid thermal conduction. Of course the vent pipe must communicate with the topmost part of the tank and the discharge line with the lowest part. However there is no apparent advantage in having separate fill and discharge lines. Thermal communication between the cold escaping gas and solid members which are conducting heat into the vessel is often very advantageous; sometimes nearly all the heat which enters is absorbed by the vent gas and never reaches the liquid container.

IV. Liquid-Nitrogen-Shielded Dewars

7.9. References [1] to [6] describe liquid-nitrogen-protected vessels designed in several research laboratories. Figure 7.5 illustrates a very successful commercial container for liquid helium or hydrogen. Vessels of this type are manufactured in sizes ranging from 15 to 100 liters. The rate of evaporation of the stored liquid is very small; in the larger sizes the helium loss is less than 1 percent of the capacity per day. Many laboratories take advantage of this high-quality storage and maintain a continuous supply of liquid helium and liquid hydrogen for their research projects. By careful handling such vessels can be shipped. Regular shipments of liquid helium in 50-liter containers are being made by air between Boulder, Colo., and Washington, D.C.

Figure 7.6 is a cross section of a dewar designed at the NBS Cryogenic Engineering Laboratory [7]. This vessel, intended for liquid hydrogen storage and transportation, has a capacity of 500 liters and a loss rate of 0.26

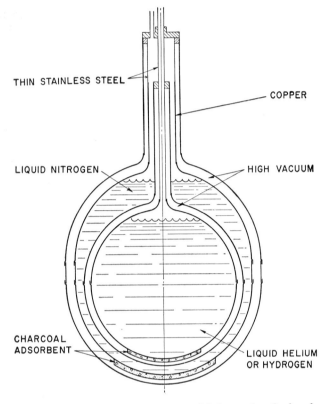

THIN STAINLESS STEEL

COPPER

LIQUID NITROGEN

HIGH VACUUM

CHARCOAL
ADSORBENT

LIQUID HELIUM
OR HYDROGEN

FIGURE 7.5. Simplified cross section of a commercial dewar for the low-loss storage and transportation of liquid hydrogen and helium.

percent or 1.3 liters of liquid hydrogen per day. It was designed for the ruggedness required for transportation by truck.

A brief description may make the illustration more easily understood: The liquid hydrogen compartment is suspended by the long stainless steel tube which makes thermal contact with the cold vessel at its bottom end. Three stainless steel cables $3/32$ inch in diameter at the top and bottom keep the hydrogen compartment centered with respect to the liquid-nitrogen-cooled shield. The liquid-nitrogen shield is in turn supported at the top by rigid members and at the bottom by another spider of $\frac{1}{8}$-inch cables. Since the shield is made of high-conductivity aluminum, liquid nitrogen in the upper reservoir is sufficient to maintain the entire shield at a temperature within a few degrees of that of boiling nitrogen. The fill and discharge lines are made of thin-wall stainless steel and their length is sufficient that heat conduction through them can be disregarded. In order to reduce the consumption of liquid nitrogen a floating shield was mounted as shown (the shell nearest

PART NO	DESCRIPTION
1	LIQUID H₂ VALVE
2	H₂ RELIEF VALVE
3	N₂ RELIEF VALVE
4	LIQUID H₂ FILL & EMPTY
5	H₂ VENT LINE
6	LIQUID N₂ FILL & EMPTY

7	N₂ VENT LINE
8	MULTIPLE —CONTACT INSULATING SUPPORTS
9	RADIATION SHIELD
10	TEFLON BUMPER
X	ALUMINUM TO STAINLESS SOLDERED CONNECTIONS

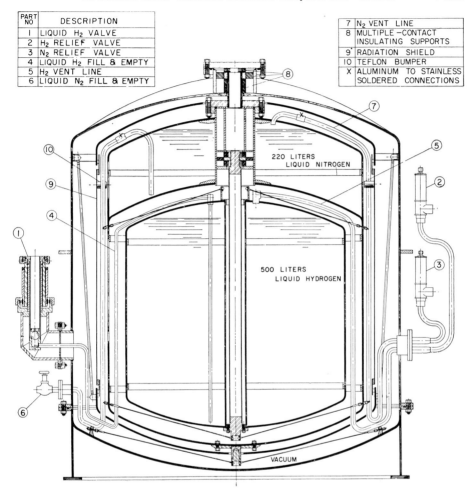

FIGURE 7.6. A 500-liter experimental dewar for liquid hydrogen. (Cryogenic Engineering Laboratory, National Bureau of Standards)

the outer wall). The use of powder insulation in the outer space was rejected because this would require a leak-tight liquid-nitrogen-cooled shield in order to maintain a high vacuum for the inner insulating space. The rate of evaporation of liquid nitrogen from this container is 15.8 liters per day.

V. A HELIUM-REFRIGERATED TRANSPORT DEWAR

7.10. A dewar designed for transporting and storing liquid hydrogen uses a helium refrigerator as well as a liquid-nitrogen-cooled shield to preserve the contents. Figure 7.7 shows a cross section of the vessel and Figure 7.8 a flow diagram of the refrigeration circuit. This vessel also is of rugged design

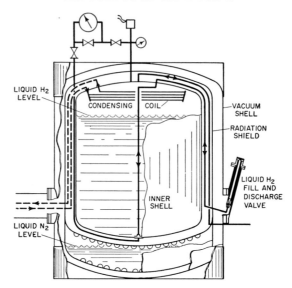

FIGURE 7.7.   Schematic section of the helium-refrigerated transport dewar.   (Courtesy, The Cambridge Corporation)

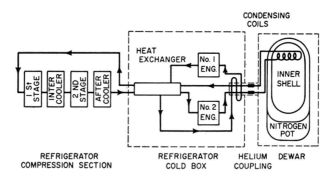

The broken lines indicate the three vacuum insulating shells.

FIGURE 7.8.   Flow diagram of the helium refrigerator associated with the transport dewar depicted in Figure 7.7.   (Courtesy, The Cambridge Corporation)

intended for highway transportation.   The suspension system consists of numerous stainless steel cables arranged to withstand severe shock loads in any direction.   The capacity is 2000 liters of liquid hydrogen and the heat leak to the liquid hydrogen is of the order of 4 to 5 watts.   When the refrigerator is not operated, the rate of evaporation of liquid parahydrogen is well under 1 percent per day.

At its inception this equipment was intended to store liquid normal hydrogen without loss; so the refrigerator was sized to absorb the heat produced by the spontaneous exothermic conversion of normal hydrogen (75 percent orthohydrogen) to the low-temperature equilibrium concentration (99.8 percent parahydrogen at 20.4°K), in addition to removing the heat which flows in from the exterior. For this reason the refrigerator has a capacity of 150 to 200 watts, considerably greater than that needed to store liquid parahydrogen without loss. This excess refrigerative capacity is convenient, however, because in storing liquid parahydrogen the refrigerator can be operated for a short time every several days and in between times the dewar is valved off and the heat influx causes a slow rise in temperature and pressure of the liquid hydrogen.

It appears now that for storing liquid parahydrogen the most economical practice is to use a good unrefrigerated container and accept the evaporation loss caused by heat leak. For a more valuable cargo such as liquid deuterium it is probable that the over-all economy would be best served by using a refrigerated container which would avoid any loss of the contents.

VI. A HYDROGEN-REFRIGERATED DEWAR

7.11. Figure 7.9 is a vessel described by Birmingham [8] which uses a hydrogen refrigerator to prevent loss. In this design all the cold parts of the refrigerator are housed inside the insulating vacuum of the dewar itself. Thus since there are no cold external connections, these can all be standard couplings. A single gas compression system can be conveniently used to refrigerate several dewars. The capacity of the refrigerator is such that a few hours' operation will remove all the heat which enters a dewar in a day. Disconnecting the compression system from one container and connecting it to the next is easily done with the couplings or valves operating at ambient temperature.

Figure 7.10 is a flow diagram of the refrigerator. The operation is as follows: after the liquid hydrogen compartment has been filled and valved off, the heat leak to it will cause a slow rise of temperature (and pressure). When this pressure reaches about 2 atmospheres (absolute) the refrigerator is started. Cold hydrogen vapor flows through the low-pressure channels of the heat exchangers, cools incoming high-pressure hydrogen, is compressed to 100 atmospheres or more, and is returned through the high-pressure channels of the exchangers. It is seen that the action is identical with that of the Joule-Thomson hydrogen liquefier described in Chapter 2 (pp. 41-42). The principal difference lies in the fact that the mass rates of flow in the high-pressure and low-pressure channels are essentially the same; consequently a larger fraction of the gas which expands through the J-T valve is liquefied. This is a consequence of the relatively greater flow of low-pressure cold gas up through the final heat exchanger, which results in a lower temperature of the high-pressure stream entering the J-T valve.

Another way of looking at this is to compare the refrigeration load imposed upon this refrigerator with that imposed upon a regular liquefier having the

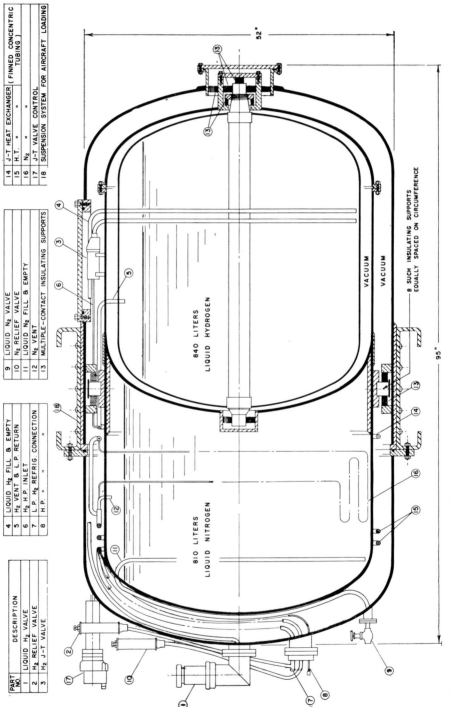

PART NO.	DESCRIPTION
1	LIQUID H₂ VALVE
2	H₂ RELIEF VALVE
3	H₂ J-T VALVE

4	LIQUID H₂ FILL & EMPTY
5	H₂ VENT & L.P. RETURN
6	H₂ H.P. INLET
7	L.P. H₂ REFRIG. CONNECTION
8	H.P. " "

9	LIQUID N₂ VALVE
10	N₂ RELIEF VALVE
11	LIQUID N₂ FILL & EMPTY
12	N₂ VENT
13	MULTIPLE-CONTACT INSULATING SUPPORTS

14	J-T HEAT EXCHANGER (FINNED CONCENTRIC TUBING)
15	H.T. " "
16	N₂ " "
17	J-T VALVE CONTROL
18	SUSPENSION SYSTEM FOR AIRCRAFT LOADING

FIGURE 7.9. Hydrogen-refrigerated transport dewar.

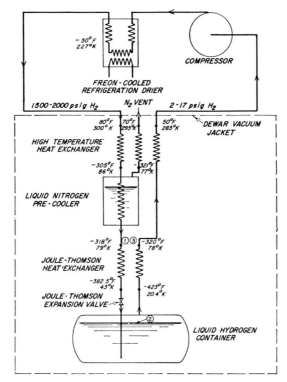

FIGURE 7.10. Flow diagram of the hydrogen-refrigerated transport dewar.

same compressor capacity.   The liquefier is required to cool the gas it liquefies and then condense it, while this refrigerator is required only to condense
saturated vapor.   Thus, since in the latter case all the refrigerative effect
can be devoted to condensing cold vapor, a larger fraction of the total flow
will be condensed.

VII. A LARGE POWDER-INSULATED TRANSPORT DEWAR FOR LIQUID HYDROGEN

7.12. A recent development in the design of transport dewars for liquid
hydrogen dispenses with refrigerated shields and achieves an acceptable evaporation rate with evacuated powder insulation alone.   This is made possible
because of the large volume of the container and the room to accommodate
a substantial thickness of powder insulation.   The advantage of large size
in a powder-insulated dewar was discussed at the beginning of this chapter
(see Figure 7.1).   Figure 7.11 is an axial cross-sectional diagram of the vessel
as designed by the Beech Aircraft Corporation in consultation with the Los
Alamos Scientific Laboratory and the National Bureau of Standards.   The
evacuated perlite insulation is approximately 12 inches thick.   A feature that

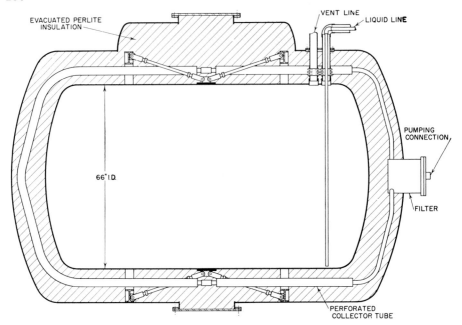

FIGURE 7.11. Transport vessel for liquid hydrogen with evacuated powder insulation. (Courtesy, Beech Aircraft Corporation).

should be mentioned is the collection pipe, which shortens the time required for evacuation by decreasing the distance that the gas must travel through the powder. The powder offers such a great resistance to the flow of low pressure gas that it usually takes several days to obtain a satisfactory vacuum in a large powder-insulated vessel. The filter keeps powder out of the vacuum pump.

The internal volume of this container is 6000 liters. In normal use it carries 5400 liters of liquid, leaving a vapor space of 600 liters. The loss rate is approximately 1.5 percent of the rated capacity in 24 hours. It is mounted on a trailer for highway transportation.

VIII. SHIPPING HELIUM AS LIQUID RATHER THAN HIGH-PRESSURE GAS

7.13. The National Bureau of Standards Cryogenic Engineering Laboratory with the support of the Department of the Navy, Bureau of Aeronautics, has studied the feasibility of large-scale shipment of helium as a liquid rather than as a high-pressure gas [9]. At first it appeared that the evaporation losses during long-distance shipment by railroad or highway might be too costly. However, further study showed that if the vessel were capable of withstanding a moderate pressure, e.g., 150 pounds per square inch, it could be closed and the shipment made without loss even for transit times of several days. In such a case it is not strictly correct to call the contents of the vessel "liquid" helium, because the temperature and pressure will rise above the critical values (5.2°K and 2.26 atm.) as the heat influx is absorbed. Since the objective is to transport *helium*, there is no particular advantage in having it reach its destination in the liquid state.

Figure 7.12 shows the pressure rise to be expected in a vessel initially filled to 90 percent of capacity with liquid helium at its normal boiling point. Since this is a constant-volume process the computations were made by equating the change in internal energy to the heat added. The thermodynamic properties used were taken from the temperature entropy chart for helium, Chapter 9 (pp. 310-313). The heat capacity of the container is negligible at these temperatures. The slope of the curve of Figure 7.12 is proportional to the ratio of heat leak to volume of vessel. Figure 7.12 is representative of what may be achieved in a well-designed transportable container having a capacity of several thousand liters.

There is a special consideration in handling liquid helium that the designer should always keep in mind. Most cryogenic liquids have a substantial heat of vaporization; therefore a vessel for liquid oxygen, nitrogen, or even hydrogen may be cooled by the evaporation of the first liquid to strike it, and the consumption of liquid in cooling the container is not excessive. With liquid helium the situation is quite different. The heat of vaporization of liquid helium is only 20.5 joules per gram. On a volumetric basis, liquid helium has less than $\frac{1}{12}$ the heat of vaporization of hydrogen.

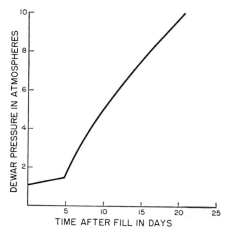

FIGURE 7.12. Increase of pressure in a large liquid-nitrogen-shielded helium container filled initially to 90 percent of capacity with liquid helium at 1 atmosphere.

A more instructive viewpoint is to compare the heat of vaporization and the specific heat of the vapor. The refrigeration furnished by the evaporation of a given mass of liquid helium is approximately equal to that supplied by warming the same quantity of gaseous helium by 4°K. Thus in cooling a vessel from 80°K (precooled with liquid nitrogen) to 4°K, the refrigerative value of the helium vapor is much greater than the latent heat of vaporization of the liquid helium. Low-temperature researchers have been quite properly aware of this, and, as a rule, they have utilized the refrigerative effect of the vapor issuing from liquid helium to furnish the major portion of the refrigeration required to cool apparatus to 4°K. The over-all effectiveness of vessels for the storage and transportation of liquid helium can be substantially improved if a means of utilizing the refrigerative effect of the helium vapor is incorporated. In a design that has been suggested the vapor formed during cool-down passes through narrow channels next to the inner wall of the vessel. Because the specific heats of metals increase rapidly with temperature, the refrigerative effect of the helium vapor can be very fully utilized. For example in cooling a copper container from 80° to 4°K, about 90 percent of the heat is removed at temperatures above 40°K.

IX. Using Refrigerative Value of Escaping Vapor to Reduce Storage Loss

7.14. It has been noted that losses of liquid while filling a helium dewar can be substantially reduced by causing the vapor to furnish the major part of the refrigeration needed to cool the container. After the vessel has been filled, the vapor resulting from normal evaporation can be used to absorb some of the heat leaking into the vessel. In most vessels part of this refrigeration is utilized more or less accidentally in absorbing some of the heat which flows by solid conduction down the vent pipe. An analysis of this process will be given later.

7.15. Vapor-Refrigerated Shields. A way to make good use of the refrigeration available in the escaping vapor is to have it cool a shield suspended between the inner liquid container and the outer warm wall of the vessel. This device can be applied to high-vacuum-insulated vessels as well as vessels utilizing evacuated powder insulation. The openings in the shield required to admit piping and supports or re-entrant irregularities that may be produced by attaching piping to one side of a shield will have little effect when powder insulation is used; but when the shield is in an empty space, these openings and irregularities may somewhat reduce the effective over-all reflectivity of the shield. Moreover in a vessel having sufficient room between the walls to accommodate a shield, the insulation thickness may be great enough to show a substantial improvement when powder is used. Because of the simpler construction and the fact that the ideal is more nearly approached, it is believed that the vapor-cooled shield is more aptly applied to a vessel with evacuated powder insulation.

Some commercial powder-insulated vessels make partial use of the cold escaping vapor by having it flow through several turns of pipe which lie between the inner and outer walls. It is believed, however, that the available refrigeration can be used more effectively if it is made to cool a shield which is located at the optimum position between the inner and outer walls of the insulating space.

The following analysis presents the general method of determining the optimum location of a vapor-cooled shield and the expected gain in performance. The results are applied to the specific case of spherical containers for liquid hydrogen and helium with evacuated perlite insulation.

With evacuated powder insulation filling the entire insulating space the rate at which heat reaches the liquid is

$$W_1 = \frac{4\pi k_1 r_1 r_2 (T_2 - T_1)}{r_2 - r_1} = \dot{m} L_v \tag{7.1}$$

where k_1 is the mean thermal conductivity of the powder in the temperature range T_1 to T_2, r_1 is the radius of the liquid container, r_2 that of the vapor-cooled shield, $\dot{m}$ the mass rate of evaporation, and L_v the heat of vaporization of unit mass of the liquid.

The rate at which heat reaches the shield is

$$W_2 = \frac{4\pi k_2 r_2 r_3 (T_3 - T_2)}{r_3 - r_2} = \dot{m} L_v + \dot{m} \Delta h \tag{7.2}$$

where r_3 is the radius of the outer boundary of the insulation, k_2 is the mean thermal conductivity of the powder in the temperature range T_2 to T_3, and Δh is the change of specific enthalpy of the vapor as it is warmed from T_1 to T_2.

Dividing Equation 7.1 by Equation 7.2 gives

$$\frac{L_v}{L_v + \Delta h} = \frac{k_1}{k_2} \frac{(r_3 - r_2)}{(r_2 - r_1)} \frac{r_1}{r_3} \frac{(T_2 - T_1)}{(T_3 - T_2)}$$

Let $r_3 = ar_1$ and $r_2 = br_1$; then

$$\frac{a(b - 1)}{a - b} = \frac{k_1}{k_2} \frac{L_v + \Delta h}{L_v} \frac{(T_2 - T_1)}{(T_3 - T_2)} = g$$

From Equation 7.1

$$\frac{L_v \dot{m}}{4\pi r_1} = k_1 \frac{b}{b - 1} (T_2 - T_1) \tag{7.3}$$

Since b is a function of a and g only, and g and k are functions of T_2 only, $\dot{m}/r_1$ is a function of a and T_2 only.

For each value of a there is an optimum value of T_2 and a corresponding optimum value of b which will make $\dot{m}/r_1$ a minimum. Since for a given insulation k_1, k_2 and g depend only upon the properties of the liquid and vapor, the fixed boundary temperatures T_1 and T_3, and the variable temperature T_2, we can compute values of g for a series of temperatures T_2 in the range $T_1 < T_2 < T_3$ and use these g's for all subsequent computations dealing with the particular liquid being stored.

Then for a given value of a, values of $\dot{m}/r_1$ can be computed and the minimum can be determined by graphical means. By plotting $\dot{m}/r_1$ versus the position of the shield, $(b - 1)/(a - 1)$, the location of minimum will also yield the optimum value of b, the important design parameter. It will be noted also that for this vessel the rate of evaporation is proportional to the first power of the radius or to (volume)$^{1/3}$, if heat conduction through supports is neglected. Thus this design offers the same premium for large size as that shown in curve C of Figure 7.1.

Liquid Hydrogen Containers. A series of computations was made for values of a ranging from 1.05 to 1.5 for a vessel containing liquid parahydrogen with evacuated perlite insulation. The thermal conductivity of perlite is shown in Figure 7.13, a curve based on two determinations made at NBS— one giving the mean effective conductivity between 304° and 76°K, the other the mean conductivity between 76° and 20°K. These data are admittedly not as complete as they should be for the purpose at hand, but they will serve

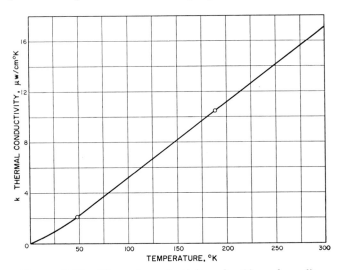

FIGURE 7.13.   Thermal conductivity of −80-mesh perlite.

to demonstrate the usefulness of the vapor-cooled shield in this application. Errors arising from the linear interpolation used in Figure 7.13 are not expected to exceed 20 percent. Additional measurements of the thermal conductivities of powders as functions of temperature are in progress at NBS. The values of Δh were taken from the paper of Woolley et al. [10].

Figure 7.14 shows the results of a representative computation for a liquid-hydrogen container. It is seen that at the optimum position of the shield, about 35 percent of the distance from the cold wall to the warm wall, the shielded vessel will have an evaporation rate of about 38 percent of the unshielded vessel. It is seen also that the optimum location of the shield is not critical; the curve of $\dot{m}/\dot{m}^*$ has a very flat minimum. It was found that the effectiveness of the shield $\dot{m}/\dot{m}^*$ at its optimum location is practically the same for values of a ranging from 1.05 to 1.5.

It will be noted that the shield is somewhat warmer than liquid nitrogen.

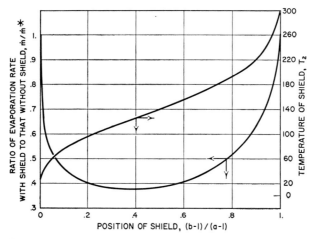

FIGURE 7.14. Optimum position and temperature of a vapor-cooled shield in a powder-insulated vessel for liquid hydrogen.

The rate of evaporation will be lower if a liquid-nitrogen-cooled shield is used. The decision about the use of this method rather than liquid-nitrogen shielding will depend upon the relative costs of liquid nitrogen and liquid hydrogen and the cost of keeping the liquid-nitrogen shield replenished. Also, the complete design study will include heat leaks from piping and supports which cannot be resolved here because they are peculiar to the specific application and mechanical design.

It is remarkable also that the temperature of the shield and its optimum locations, that is its distance from the inner container divided by the distance between the inner and outer walls, $(b - 1)/(a - 1)$, are practically independent of the value of a. This is a consequence of the temperature dependence of the thermal conductivity of the powder and the specific heat of the vapor. As more complete data on the thermal conductivity of powder insulations become available, the optimum position should be recomputed.

To gain an idea of the performance that might be realized in a practical vessel, the results of these computations were applied to a spherical container for liquid hydrogen having an inner shell 2 meters in outside diameter and an outer shell 3 meters in inside diameter. This will have a capacity of slightly more than 4000 liters. The evaporation rate resulting from heat leak through evacuated perlite insulation was found to be sufficient to evaporate 25 liters or 0.62 percent of the contents per day. A vapor-cooled shield reduces this to 0.24 percent per day.

Containers for Liquid Helium. It is quite apparent that the effectiveness of the vapor-cooled shield depends upon the ratio of the heat of vaporization of the liquid being stored to the specific heat of the vapor. Accordingly the application of this device to the storage of liquid helium is very attractive because of the favorable ratio between the specific heat of the vapor and the heat of vaporization.

The results of computations for $a = 1.5$ fully justified this optimism: it was learned that the vapor-cooled shield of a powder-insulated container for liquid helium at its optimum location will have a temperature of 62°K, substantially lower than that of a liquid-nitrogen-cooled shield. The optimum position of such a shield was found to be $(b - 1)/(a - 1) = 0.25$. The designer should again be cautioned against using this value after more data on the thermal conductivity become available. Measurements now in progress will undoubtedly yield more accurate data for this application.

Applying these results to the 4000-liter spherical container described above, it was found that the heat leak through the insulation would cause liquid helium to evaporate at a rate of 7.7 percent per day from the unshielded vessel and 0.7 percent per day from the shielded vessel.

Combining High-Vacuum and Evacuated Powder Insulation. A logical refinement of the foregoing design is to use a high vacuum in the space between the coldest wall and the vapor-cooled shield, and powder insulation in the outer space. If the surfaces bounding the vacuum space have a low emissivity, this arrangement will result in a considerable improvement, an improvement gained at the expense of greater construction costs. The heat leak to the inner vessel, exclusive of solid conduction, can be computed by a method rather similar to that used earlier. In this case, however, the thickness of the high-vacuum space should be made as small as practical, so we can idealize the problem by assuming that the vacuum space has negligible thickness $(r_1 = r_2)$. Then the rate at which heat is transmitted to the inner container by radiation from a shield at the temperature T_2 is

$$\sigma \frac{e}{2 - e} 4\pi r_1^2 (T_2^4 - T_1^4) = \dot{m} L_v \qquad (7.4)$$

where σ is the Stefan-Boltzmann radiation constant, e is the emissivity of the surfaces facing the vacuum space, r_1 is the radius of the inner container and T_2 and T_1 are the temperatures of the shield and inner container respectively, $\dot{m}$ is the mass rate of evaporation of the liquid being stored and L_v is its heat of vaporization. The heat which reaches the shield by conduction through the powder is

$$\frac{k_2 4\pi r_1 r_3 (T_3 - T_2)}{(r_3 - r_1)} = \dot{m} L_v + \dot{m} \Delta h \qquad (7.5)$$

where k_2 is the mean thermal conductivity of the powder, r_3 is the radius of the outer shell at the temperature T_3, and Δh is the change in enthalpy of the vapor as it is warmed from T_1 to T_2. Dividing Equation 7.4 by 7.5 and letting $a = r_3/r_1$ gives

$$\frac{L_v}{L_v + \Delta h} = \frac{\sigma e r_1 (a - 1)(T_2^4 - T_1^4)}{(2 - e) k_2 a (T_3 - T_2)} \qquad (7.6)$$

Since Δh and k_2 are functions of T_2 that are not available from analytic expressions, the simplest method of solving this equation for T_2 is to use successive approximations. A general solution cannot be given. The equation must be solved for specific values of r_1 and a. For this reason the performance of the 4000-liter vessel with an inner diameter of 2 meters and an outer diameter of 3 meters described earlier was computed so that the results can be compared with those resulting from other insulation methods. It was found that with liquid hydrogen the shield temperature will be 129°K and the evaporation rate will be 0.13 percent per day. When this system is used with liquid helium, the temperature of the shield is 86°K and the evaporation rate 0.33 percent per day. These computations assume an emissivity of 0.02 for the surfaces facing the vacuum space and ignore the heat leak through the supporting members.

Discussion. Table 7.2 shows the rates of heat transfer in terms of loss of liquid hydrogen and liquid helium in percent per day for several different types of insulation for a vessel of 4000 liters capacity. These results do not

TABLE 7.2. A COMPARISON OF THE HEAT LEAKS THROUGH VARIOUS INSULATIONS FOR A 4000-LITER SPHERICAL DEWAR[a]

Insulation	Evaporation Rate Caused by the Heat Flow Through the Insulation[b]	
	Liquid Hydrogen, percent per day	Liquid Helium, percent per day
High vacuum[c]	4.0	49.
Evacuated perlite	0.62	7.7
Evacuated perlite *plus* vapor-cooled shield	0.24 (Shield temp. = 124°K)	0.70 (Shield temp. = 62°K)
Evacuated perlite *plus* high vacuum[c] *plus* vapor-cooled shield	0.13 (Shield temp. = 129°K)	0.33 (Shield temp. = 86°K)
High vacuum[c] *plus* liquid N₂ shield (77°K)	0.017	0.21

[a] The outside diameter of the inner vessel is 2 meters and, when powder insulation is used, the outer shell has an inside diameter of 3 meters. For the cases in which no powder is used the diameter of the outer shell will be smaller. The emissivity of the surfaces facing the high-vacuum spaces is taken as 0.02.

[b] Excluding conduction by solid supports and assuming no conduction by residual gas.

[c] These are idealized conditions. The vacuum space is assumed to be negligibly thin and so good that heat conducted by residual gas can be ignored.

take account of heat transfer by conduction through the supports nor heat conduction through the residual gas in a high vacuum. It should be emphasized that the designer and fabricator have a great amount of control over these latter sources of heat leak. The length of thermal path through insulating supports is particularly pliant to the ingenuity of the designer. Figure 7.15 gives a suggestion for increasing the length of supports.

The computations show that the effectiveness of the vapor-cooled shield in powder insulation, $\dot{m}/\dot{m}^*$, is practically independent of the thickness of the insulation, here measured by the constant a. The optimum location of the shield is slightly affected by the thickness of the powder. For the liquid-hydrogen vessel, the optimum position varied from 39 percent of the way from the cold to the warm surface for $a = 1.05$ to 32 percent of the way for $a = 1.5$. The two computations for helium gave 30 percent for $a = 1.2$ and 25

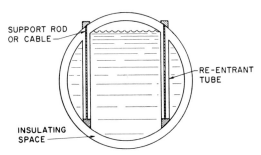

FIGURE 7.15. A way to reduce thermal conduction through supports by increasing their length.

percent for $a = 1.5$. These variations are rather trivial considering the flatness of the minimum in Figure 7.14.

The attainment of a first-rate high vacuum in an insulating space protecting the inner container requires first of all a completely leak-free construction and also a thorough outgassing of all the metal surfaces bounding the high vacuum. The use of an adsorbent cooled to the temperature of the liquid being stored is highly recommended. The attainment of a superior vacuum is more easily accomplished in vessels for liquid-helium storage than in liquid-hydrogen vessels because liquid helium provides a temperature at which all gases except helium have a negligible vapor pressure. Helium is not likely to be found in an insulating vacuum unless there is a leak. It has been observed that commercial containers with liquid-nitrogen-cooled shields have a much smaller heat leak when they are used to store liquid helium than when used with liquid hydrogen, probably because hydrogen gas is very thoroughly condensed when the container holds liquid helium. On the other hand hydrogen is dissolved in, and is slowly released by, nearly all materials used to construct containers for cryogenic liquids; so provision should be made for its disposal if a high vacuum is to be maintained in vessels for other than helium.

A very obvious extension is the use of multiple shields. Since the cold vapor has a substantial refrigerative value after it leaves the shield discussed here, it is apparent that it could be utilized to cool additional shields.

Another source of refrigeration that could be utilized to cool the shield of a container for liquid parahydrogen is the heat absorbed by para-to-ortho conversion. If the proper catalyst is put into the vent tubes which cool the shield the endothermic conversion to a higher ortho concentration will provide extra refrigeration. The cooling produced by converting hydrogen of 99.8 percent para (the equilibrium concentration at the normal boiling temperature) to 38.6 percent para (the equilibrium concentration of $100°K$) is 44 percent of the cooling produced by warming the gas from the hydrogen boiling point to $100°K$.

Finally a word should be said about the storage of liquid oxygen and nitrogen. Since the ratio of the heat of vaporization to the change in enthalpy of the vapor upon being warmed to room temperature is much greater for these materials than it is for hydrogen and helium, it should be expected that the value of a vapor-cooled shield will be correspondingly less. However the principles just discussed are equally valid for this application and should be given adequate consideration in the design of vessels for the long-term storage of liquid oxygen and nitrogen.

7.16. Vapor-Cooled Vent Tube. In those cases in which heat conduction through the supports or fill and vent tubes is a substantial part of the total, it may be worthwhile to use the escaping vapor to intercept part of the heat. This is an important consideration in the vent tubes of some dewars. The escaping vapor maintains good thermal contact with the wall of the tube and absorbs a great deal of the heat that would otherwise enter and cause evaporation of the liquid being stored. The maximum possible saving from this process can be computed upon the assumption that the heat transfer between the vapor and the tube is perfect—that both have the same temperature at each level. Also it is assumed that there is no lateral conduction or radiation to or from the tube. Since, in the temperature regions that are of interest, the thermal conductivity of the tube or support is a function of temperature, the practical solution of the problem can be simplified by assuming that this function is linear, that

$$k = k_0 + a(T - T_0)$$

where k is the thermal conductivity at the variable temperature T, k_0 is the thermal conductivity at the cold end which has the temperature T_0, and a is a constant. Then

$$W = A[k_0 + a(T - T_0)](dT/dx) \tag{7.7}$$

which is the equation for heat conduction where W is the heat current at any point in the tube, A is the cross-sectional area of the tube, and x is the distance from the cold end. Now the issuing vapor will absorb some of the heat traveling down the tube, so that

$$W = W_0 + \dot{m}C_p(T - T_0) \qquad (7.8)$$

where W_0 is the heat current that reaches the cold end of the tube, $\dot{m}$ is the mass rate of flow of the issuing vapor and C_p is its specific heat.

Upon combining Equations 7.7 and 7.8 and integrating, it is found that

$$L/A = \left[\frac{1}{\dot{m}C_p}\right]\left[a\Delta T + \left(k_0 - W_0\frac{a}{\dot{m}C_p}\right)\ln\frac{W_0 + \dot{m}C_p\Delta T}{W_0}\right] \qquad (7.9)$$

where L is the length of the tube and ΔT the temperature difference between the warm and cold ends.

The thermal conductivities of alloys commonly used for vent tubes of metal dewars are rather complex functions of temperature. However, Equation 7.9 can be employed by dividing the total temperature interval into smaller intervals in which the thermal conductivity can be considered to be a linear function of temperature. Then Equation 7.9 is applied to the lowest temperature interval, $\Delta T_1 = T_2 - T_1$, and the dependence of W_0 upon L_1/A for various values of $\dot{m}$ is determined; L_1 is the length of tube lying in the lowest temperature interval. Then values of heat current W'_0 at the bottom of the next higher temperature interval are determined by the relation

$$W'_0 = W_0 + \dot{m}C_p\Delta T_1$$

These values of W'_0 are then used in Equation 7.9 to compute values of L_2/A for the second temperature interval and the process is repeated as required. Finally total values of L/A are obtained by adding the individual values, L_n/A.

For a stainless steel vent tube for hydrogen it is a sufficiently good approximation to use just two temperature intervals; from $20°$ to $80°K$ and from $80°$ to $300°K$. In Figure 7.16 are plotted values of W_0 as a function of L/A for stainless steel vent tubes. It should be remembered that these are limiting values which assume complete heat exchange between the escaping vapor and the vent tube. Thermal conductivities of stainless steel were taken from the data compiled by Powell and Blanpied [11]. In practical vessels it may be necessary to provide baffles or other means for promoting heat transfer between the escaping vapor and the vent tube to approach the thermal equilibrium assumed for these computations. For hydrogen, which has a variable specific heat, $\dot{m}C_p$ can be replaced by $\dot{m}(\Delta h/\Delta T)$ where Δh is the change of specific enthalpy for the temperature interval ΔT.

7.17. Conclusions. The foregoing analyses show quite clearly that important benefits can be realized by utilizing the refrigerative value of the vapor which escapes from an insulated vessel for liquid hydrogen or helium.

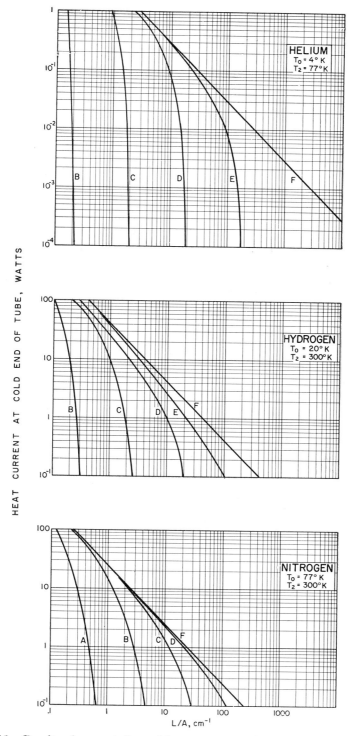

FIGURE 7.16. Results of computations of heat current reaching the cold end of a solid conductor counter to a stream of cold vapor. Curve A, $\dot{m} = 1$ g/sec; B, 10^{-1} g/sec; C, 10^{-2} g/sec: D. 10^{-3} g/sec; E, 10^{-4} g/sec; F, $\dot{m} = 0$.

The problems were idealized in order to make their solution simpler; thus in many practical designs the values given here may be substantially altered by the mechanical requirements. However, there is some definite experimental evidence that these computed values are not unrealistic. A 50-liter commercial container for liquid helium, similar to that illustrated in Figure 7.5, protected with a liquid-nitrogen-cooled shield, showed an evaporation loss of 0.25 liter per day. If all this heat leak is attributed to thermal radiation from the shield at liquid-nitrogen temperature, the emissivities of the surfaces facing the vacuum space (assumed equal) are found to be 0.011, which is an excellent value for copper, much better than the 0.02 assumed in Table 7.2. This result implies that the heat conduction through residual gas and through the supporting neck of the dewar was negligible.

From the dimensions of the dewar neck, 15.9 mm O.D., 0.5 mm thick and 31.8 cm long ($L/A = 130$ cm^{-1}) Figure 7.16 shows that if no vapor were escaping, the heat flow down the neck would be about 0.022 watt, more than twice that required to cause the observed evaporation rate. However, with the observed rate of evaporation, 0.25 liter per day, 3.6×10^{-4} gram per second, an interpolation* of the curves of Figure 7.16 shows that the heat which actually reaches the cold end of the neck is less than 10^{-4} watt, a result consistent with the observations. Thus it appears that a performance very near the ideal has been achieved in a relatively small vessel with a shield cooled with liquid nitrogen. Accordingly it should be entirely practical to approach the ideal in large vessels having either liquid-nitrogen-cooled shields or vapor-cooled shields.

In many applications the neck of the 50-liter helium container described above is inconveniently small. It is possible to increase the neck diameter substantially, keeping the wall thickness the same, without seriously increasing the heat flow to the liquid helium. A value of L/A of 80 cm^{-1} will give a heat current of very nearly 10^{-4} watt, only 1 percent of the total heat leak. Doubling the diameter of the neck, making $L/A = 65$ cm^{-1} will result in a heat current at the bottom of the neck of 2×10^{-3} watt, a 20 percent increase. When the larger neck tubes are used, removable baffles should be provided both to increase heat transfer between the escaping vapor and the tube, and to stop radiation down the tube. Some 25-liter nitrogen-shielded helium containers obtained by the NBS Radio Standards Laboratory have necks 1.75 inches in diameter. However since the necks are long and radiation is stopped by a system of baffles, these containers have a loss rate little different from the usual containers with $\frac{5}{8}$-inch necks.

X. Stratification

7.18. When a container of liquefied gas is closed and its contents allowed

---

* The spacing of the lower parts of the curves of Figure 7.16 indicates that logarithmic interpolation should be satisfactory in the region under consideration.

to warm up, it frequently happens that the temperature of the liquid at the surface rises much more rapidly than that of the bulk of the liquid. Moreover, in the absence of solid conduction, this temperature stratification is a stable condition because the warmer liquid has the lower density and the liquid is a poor thermal conductor. Since the pressure in the vapor space is determined by the temperature of the liquid surface, stratification is accompanied by a corresponding pressure rise, and the length of time that the liquid can be stored without venting vapor is greatly reduced. It has been found that liquid hydrogen which has stratified can be stirred by rocking the dewar. In fact stratification seldom occurs while a liquid-hydrogen dewar is being hauled by truck. Thus it is feasible to keep the vent closed during transit and only allow the vapor to escape after the container is in a safe location.

Stratification can be reduced by providing thermal conductors which offer heat paths of low resistance between the bottom and top of the vessel. In selecting the material for the conductors, care should be taken to obtain a pure metal which has high conductivity at low temperatures, such as electrolytic tough-pitch copper. Sometimes it is convenient to make the walls of the vessel itself of a material of high thermal conductivity such as copper or aluminum.

One liquid-hydrogen container, which was vacuum-insulated and had a shield cooled with liquid nitrogen, was designed so that the greatest heat leak to the hydrogen entered the bottom of the stainless steel inner vessel. It was hoped that this would cause convection stirring and prevent stratification. The results were disappointing. There was no evidence that this design was better than those in which the heat leak is rather uniformly distributed over the surface. It appeared that some of the liquid hydrogen could receive heat near the bottom of the vessel, rise to the surface and collect there, leaving the colder, denser liquid hydrogen below.

Occasionally there is an unstable stratification which occurs in vented dewars. This is the case of liquid becoming superheated in the lower region of a vented dewar of liquid oxygen or nitrogen while the surface, of course, is at saturation temperature. At some stage the superheated liquid starts rising and boils vigorously, producing a geyser. Sometimes this process will eject a liter or more of liquid from a 50-liter container.

XI. Liquid Level Indicators

7.19. Many types of level indicators have been used in dewars and other cryogenic equipment. The simplest is probably a float with a long stem and pointer visible outside the vessel. The float can be used in connection with a mechanical-electrical transducer for remote indication. Another widely used level indicator is the hydrostatic pressure gage. Ordinarily a differential pressure gage is used. One side communicates with the bottom of the vessel and the other with the vapor space above the liquid (Figure 7.17). The connecting tubing should be placed so that liquid which enters the tube will not cause a false reading. Thus in Figure 7.17 the line connecting to the liquid phase has a long horizontal section, and the small heat leak will cause boiling in this horizontal part somewhere between the inner and outer walls of the vessel. Thus the pressure difference indicated by the gage is that corresponding to the hydrostatic head of liquid. An undesirable characteristic of this type of liquid level gage is the tendency for the occurrence of long-period pressure oscillations. These are probably caused by oscillations of the liquid-vapor interface along the lower pressure-transmitting tube. In the extreme cases the differential pressure gage will oscillate from zero to full scale, making readings impossible. Myer [12] has analyzed the use of

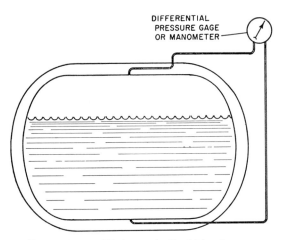

FIGURE 7.17. Hydrostatic liquid-level gage.

pulsation dampers, making computations by electrical analog, and has designed dampers which effectively isolate the pressure gage from the oscillations while still preserving its response to the average pressure.

Figure 7.18 is a practical design of such a pulsation damper which provides an attenuation of 43 decibels at 1 cycle per second when connected to a pressure gage of 0.6 in.^{3} volume. The electrical analog of this damper is the resistance-capacity circuit also shown in Figure 7.18.

The electrical capacitance liquid-level gage has been described in Chapter 2 (page 52). This has the advantage that the output is an electric signal which is readily transmitted to a remote location and can be used to activate a servomechanism. It is accurate, stable, and reliable. However it is more expensive than many other types of liquid level indicators.

A type of level indicator which is relatively inexpensive and simple utilizes the temperature dependence of electrical resistance. A resistor carrying an

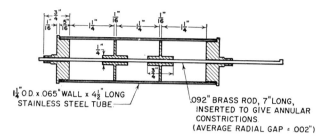

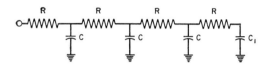

FIGURE 7.18.   Myer pulsation damper.

electric current sufficient to increase its temperature substantially when it is surrounded by gas will have a much lower temperature when it is immersed in liquid because of the greater heat transfer to the liquid. Therefore, if the resistance is temperature dependent, a circuit which includes an instrument which is responsive to changes in the resistance will serve as a liquid-level indicator. Wexler and Cox [13] and Maimoni [14] have used resistors of pure metal wires or strips arranged so that the amount of resistor immersed is proportional to the depth of the liquid. This provides a continuous gage indicating any liquid level within the range.

Figure 7.19 is the circuit diagram for a gage of this type designed by Maimoni. This gage utilizes either a 1-mil platinum wire, or a platinum strip 0.2 mil × 1 mil as the level sensing element. Maimoni presents a theoretical analysis of the performance of this type of liquid level gage as well as data on its observed response. A more common form of liquid level indi-

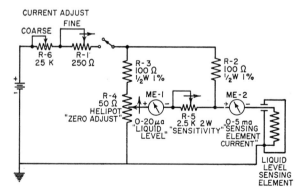

FIGURE 7.19.   Platinum-resistance liquid level gage.

cator or controller uses ordinary carbon resistors of the type manufactured for radio and electronic gear. At liquid hydrogen or helium temperatures these resistors have a much greater temperature coefficient (negative) than that of pure metals, so the response is correspondingly greater (see Clement and Quinnel [15]). It has proved practical to use carbon resistors in a circuit with appropriate relays (no amplification) to activate an automatic mechanism for thermal cycling of test objects at low temperatures.

For many applications a continuous reading of liquid level is not required. Two or three carbon resistors at critical positions will yield the necessary information about the location of the liquid surface. Of course by locating a large number of resistors at slightly different levels the response can be made almost continuous.

Purcell and Johnson [16] have studied the characteristics of several carbon resistors as level indicators and have utilized the data in selecting circuit elements for a very reliable liquid level indicator for hydrogen and helium. The circuit is shown in Figure 7.20. The resistors are $\frac{1}{2}$-watt, carbon-com-

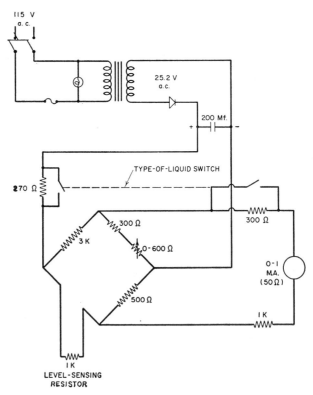

FIGURE 7.20. Liquid level indicator employing commercial carbon-composition resistors. The switch makes it possible to use this instrument for either liquid hydrogen or liquid helium.

position radio resistors. The operation is as follows: The level-sensing resistor is immersed in the liquid and then power is supplied to the circuit. (This sequence is important because the room-temperature resistance of the sensing resistor is so low that the microammeter will not tolerate the unbalance current.) Next the bridge is balanced with the 0–600-ohm rheostat. Now when the sensing resistor is barely withdrawn from the liquid, the unbalance will cause a deflection of approximately half-scale on the microammeter. The ganged type-of-liquid switch is closed for liquid hydrogen, open for liquid helium.

An unusual device for locating the surface of liquid hydrogen or helium depends upon the thermal-acoustic oscillations that are generated in tubes which have one end at room temperature and the other at the temperature of the liquid. The device is shown in Figure 7.21. It consists simply of a length of ⅛-inch thin-wall stainless steel tubing with a brass funnel at the warm end closed with a thin rubber diaphragm [17]. When the open end is inserted into a dewar of liquid hydrogen or helium, acoustical oscillations occur and change abruptly in intensity when the tube touches the liquid surface. The vibrations are detected by feeling or watching the rubber diaphragm. These thermal-acoustical oscillations ordinarily constitute a nuisance to low-temperature investigators because they cause errors in the measurement of pressure and sometimes are responsible for a serious heat leak. Additional information about thermal oscillation is given by Squire [18], Taconis, Beenakker, Nier and Aldrich [19] and Kramers [20].

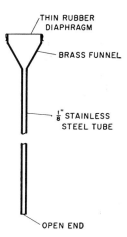

FIGURE 7.21. Thermal-acoustical liquid level indicator.

It is possible to utilize the magnetic susceptibility of liquid oxygen to locate its level. The mutual inductance of a pair of coaxial coils will increase as the coils become filled with liquid oxygen, and this will cause unbalance in a suitable bridge circuit. Likewise the increase in self inductance of a single coil can be utilized.

A method occasionally used to determine the level of liquid in a large container is simply to weigh it. A convenient device for this purpose is the load cell which utilizes a strain gage to measure the applied force. Such a device can be employed to support one end of a horizontal cylindrical vessel and give a continuous reading of the contents.

An optical liquid level finder was described by R. L. Blumberg at the 1954 Cryogenic Engineering Conference at Boulder, Colorado. This device depends for its response on internal reflection of light from the end of a lucite rod. The lower end of the rod is so shaped that when it is in vapor there is total internal reflection of light and when it is in liquid there is light transmission.

REFERENCES FOR CHAPTER 7

[1] W. F. Giauque, *Rev. Sci. Instr.*, **18**, 852 (1947).

[2] W. E. Henry and R. L. Dolecek, *Rev. Sci. Instr.*, **21**, 496 (1950).

[3] A. Wexler, *J. Appl. Phys.*, **22**, 1463 (1951).

[4] H. L. Johnston, O. D. Gonzalez, and D. White, *Rev. Sci. Instr.*, **22**, 915 (1951).

[5] A. Wexler and H. S. Jacket, *Rev. Sci. Instr.*, **22**, 282 (1951).

[6] S. G. Sydoriak and H. S. Sommers, Jr., *Rev. Sci. Instr.*, **22**, 915 (1951).

[7] B. W. Birmingham, E. H. Brown, C. R. Class, and A. F. Schmidt, *J. Research NBS*, **58**, 243 (1957).

[8] B. W. Birmingham, *Ref. Eng.* (July 1957).

[9] D. B. Mann, B. W. Birmingham, and P. C. Vander Arend, *Proc. 1957 Cryogenic Engineering Conf.* (1957).

[10] H. W. Woolley, R. B. Scott, and F. G. Brickwedde, *J. Research NBS*, **41**, 379 (1948) RP 1932.

[11] Robert L. Powell and William A. Blanpied, *NBS Circ. 556* (1954).

[12] C. R. Myer, *Proc. 1954 Cryogenic Engineering Conf.* (1954).

[13] A. E. Wexler and W. S. Cox, *Rev. Sci. Instr.*, **22**, 941 (1951).

[14] Arturo Maimoni, *Rev. Sci. Instr.*, **27**, 1024 (1956).

[15] J. R. Clement and E. H. Quinnel, *Rev. Sci. Instr.*, **23**, 213 (1952).

[16] J. R. Purcell and V. J. Johnson, NBS Boulder Laboratories. Unpublished preliminary measurements (1957).

[17] J. R. Clement, *Proc. 1954 Cryogenic Engineering Conf.* (1954).

[18] C. F. Squire, "Low Temperature Physics," McGraw-Hill Book Co. Inc., N.Y., 1953, p. 23.

[19] K. W. Taconis, J. J. M. Beenakker, A. O. C. Nier, and L. T. Aldrich, *Physica*, **15**, 733 (1949).

[20] H. A. Kramers, *Physica*, **15**, 971 (1949).

Chapter VIII

TRANSFER OF LIQUEFIED GASES

8.1. The transfer of small amounts of liquid nitrogen, oxygen, or hydrogen through short tubes is a common laboratory procedure and usually presents little difficulty. Since the line is short, evaporation losses and pressure drop are not troublesome. However, for large-scale operations, long lines and rapid transfer are often required. In such cases the size of the line and the effectiveness of the insulation become very important. Frequently it is necessary to pump the liquids, and of course, valves are required for control of flow. Also, in many instances it is necessary to provide dismountable couplings or unions that are insulated against heat leak.

This chapter deals with the behavior of cryogenic liquids during transfer and the design of transfer equipment. Some special attention will be devoted to the transfer of liquid helium, because losses of liquid helium during transfer may be serious even in the relatively short transfer lines used in the laboratory.

I. Two-Phase Flow

8.2. Heat flow into a pipe carrying a liquefied gas has two objectionable consequences; first, it wastes liquid by causing evaporation, and second, the vapor thus formed seriously reduces the carrying capacity of the line. The mixture of vapor and liquid, having a lower density than that of the pure liquid, must have a greater velocity in order to maintain a given mass rate of flow of liquid when rapid delivery is desired. The stream velocity in the two-phase region constitutes a serious limitation. The maximum velocity of flow of a fluid in a pipe is equal to the velocity of sound in the fluid. The velocity of sound in cryogenic liquids is quite high: for liquid oxygen, nitrogen and hydrogen of the order of 1000 meters per second, and for liquid helium about 200 meters per second. However, in a two-phase mixture of liquid and vapor the velocity of sound is low because of the high adiabatic compressibility resulting from the presence of vapor.

The problem of two-phase flow has been studied by Silver [1], Lockhart and Martinelli [2], Linning [3], and Rogers [4].

249

For cryogenic fluids the complexities of ordinary two-phase flow are further compounded by the fact that there is mass transition, usually from the liquid phase to the vapor phase. This mass transition depends upon heat influx into the pipe and upon pressure changes. Moreover there is considerable evidence that non-equilibrium between liquid and vapor phases during transfer is a common condition. As a consequence of these and other complexities there is not at present a good analysis of the problem of two-phase, single-component flow. There is in progress at the National Bureau of Standards Cryogenic Engineering Laboratory a study of the problem using both experimental and theoretical methods.

There are three different kinds of two-phase flow: (1) a rather homogeneous mixture of vapor bubbles in the liquid, (2) "slug" flow consisting of alternate regions of pure liquid and pure vapor, each filling the pipe (a condition most common in transfer lines of small diameter) and (3) annular flow, wherein the liquid flows along the annular region next to the wall of the tube and the vapor, moving at a much higher velocity, occupies the central core of the tube.

Fortunately, when high-speed transfer of cryogenic liquid is required, it is usually feasible to control the conditions so that two-phase flow is avoided; all of the fluid in the line is kept in the liquid state so that the ordinary relations between pressure drop, flow velocity, properties of the liquid and dimensions of the pipeline are applicable and high-velocity transfer is readily accomplished. Accordingly, it is much more profitable for the cryogenic engineer to devise means of avoiding two-phase flow than to attempt to design equipment that will accommodate two-phase flow. Of course two-phase flow is often unavoidable, for example during the cool-down of a pipeline; therefore, a solution of the two-phase condition is necessary for the completely reliable design and predictable performance of cryogenic transfer equipment.

II. Cool-Down

8.3. When a cryogenic liquid (somewhat supercooled) is started through a typical transfer line initially at room temperature, at first all the liquid which enters is quickly evaporated and nearly all of the line will contain only gas. As the process continues, a length of the upstream end of the line will be cooled below the saturation temperature and this portion will contain the pure liquid phase. Downstream of this section there will be a region in which both liquid and vapor will be present, and in the remainder of the line, only gas will be flowing. As the line is further cooled by the evaporating liquid and by the resulting cold vapor, the liquid phase will persist farther along the line until finally liquid will be discharged at the exit. This behavior is readily observed in a glass "dewar" siphon (unsilvered) used to transfer liquid hydrogen in the laboratory. It has also been found economical of liquid to watch the start-up behavior of such a siphon and insert the delivery end into apparatus requiring refilling only after liquid hydrogen is seen to wet the entire length of the siphon.   If the warm vapor which precedes the liquid is discharged into the receiver, it evaporates some of the liquid already present.   This evaporation can be largely avoided by making sure that the siphon is ready to discharge liquid before it is inserted into equipment which already contains liquid hydrogen.   With liquid helium this precaution is much more essential because of the very much lower heat of vaporization of helium.

In a long transfer line the vapor may be warmed nearly to the initial temperature of the line during a part of the cool-down process.   This, of course, will be economical of liquid because heat is extracted from the line by both evaporating the liquid and warming the vapor.   The minimum amount of liquid required to cool a long line therefore can be estimated by equating the decrease in enthalpy of the line to the total increase in the enthalpy of the fluid as it is vaporized and the vapor warmed to room temperature.   Such an estimate will be on the optimistic side because it takes no account of the heat leak to the line during cool-down, the frictional energy dissipation or the final cooling of the exit region while cold vapor is discharged.   Obviously there is merit in keeping the mass (and therefore the heat capacity) of the line small.

In the initial stages of the cool-down of a long transfer line a large part of the resistance to flow results from the high-velocity, low-density gas which evaporates from and precedes the liquid during its passage through the line. The warm line may quickly raise the temperature of the gas nearly to the ambient temperature, and at this condition its density may be only about $\frac{1}{1000}$ the density of the liquid.   Accordingly the velocity of the gas will be about 1000 times the velocity of the liquid, since the mass rates of flow are necessarily the same.   The flow resistance associated with the high velocity greatly increases the time required for cooling the transfer line.

In several installations the cool-down of long liquid transfer lines is expedited by providing vapor taps at intervals.   In this way the pressure is relieved and the liquid front moves more rapidly, cooling the line.   The line is cooled most rapidly by leaving a given vapor tap open until liquid arrives. However, this may be wasteful of liquid because the cold vapor preceding the liquid is not completely utilized in refrigerating the line; hence more of the cooling must be done by the evaporating liquid.

Even in short lines, the consequences of cool-down may be very important when liquid helium is being delivered to add to liquid already present in the receiving vessel.   If the warm line is permitted to deliver warm gaseous helium to the receiver during cool-down, a very serious evaporation of liquid may result.   When one considers the fact that the heat of vaporization of a unit mass of helium is sufficient to cool an equal mass of gaseous helium only 4 degrees Kelvin, it is apparent that a little warm helium gas can cause the evaporation of a large quantity of liquid already present in the receiver. The provision of a vapor tap near the exit end of the transfer line can greatly reduce this loss. A transfer line described later in this chapter employs such a vapor tap.

III. The Case of Zero Delivery

8.4. This heading is used to emphasize a condition that can arise if a line is designed without taking account of the effect of heat leak. If the line is perfectly insulated and liquid is continuously introduced into one end, it is only a matter of time before liquid will appear at the discharge end. However, in practical lines there is a heat influx which evaporates liquid; and if the maximum rate of flow is insufficient, it is quite possible that liquid will never reach the exit. Sometimes such a line can be induced to deliver liquid by using vapor bleeding taps as described earlier to effect the initial cool-down. After the line is cold, the greatly increased velocity of flow may cause liquid to be discharged even after part of the liquid has been evaporated by the heat influx.

In some cases it may be profitable to provide occasional gas-liquid separators along the transfer line and allow most of the vapor formed in the line to escape continuously at these places during transfer. This will not avoid two-phase flow, but it will reduce the ratio of the volume of vapor to that of liquid and therefore speed up the rate of delivery of liquid.

IV. Transfer Through Uninsulated Lines

8.5. Liquid air, oxygen, and nitrogen are often transferred through uninsulated metal pipes or tubes. The adjective "uninsulated" may be slightly misleading because even with a line made of a metal with high thermal conductivity, such as copper, there are two mechanisms which automatically provide some resistance to the flow of heat and thus supply a little insulation to the liquid being transferred. These are the so-called *film coefficients*, the coefficient of heat transfer from the ambient air to the outer surface of the tube carrying the cold liquid, and the coefficient of heat transfer from the inner surface of the tube to the liquid flowing within.

In many operations involving only short-time, short-distance transfers of liquid air, oxygen, or nitrogen, the uninsulated line may be economically the most desirable. The cost of insulating the line may exceed the resulting saving. The choice is not always easy to make. For example, when transferring liquid oxygen or nitrogen from a tank truck or railway car to stationary storage through an uninsulated line, two-phase flow is usually present and the transfer may take several hours. Since the flow rate can be substantially increased by insulating the line, thereby reducing the amount of vapor in the line, insulation may pay because of the time and labor saved, even though the saving of liquid may be inconsequential. This is another case in which a reliable solution of the two-phase, single-component, fluid-flow problem would be useful.

It is difficult to imagine a situation in which an uninsulated line for liquid hydrogen would have any merit. The condensation of atmospheric air on the outside of such a line will provide an essentially infinite source of heat for the evaporation of liquid hydrogen. The effectiveness of this heat source may be better appreciated by pointing out that the formation of a unit volume of liquid air will cause the evaporation of more than 10 volumes of liquid hydrogen. The transfer of liquid helium without insulation should not even be considered because, since it has only $\frac{1}{12}$ the heat of vaporization of hydrogen, on a volumetric basis, even the best of insulation is none too good.

V. Transfer Lines Insulated with Porous Materials

8.6. Lines carrying liquid oxygen or nitrogen may be insulated with porous materials. For liquid nitrogen, some extra precautions should be taken because the temperature is such that fractional condensation of air can occur on the nitrogen-cooled surfaces. The air so condensed will be rich in oxygen and will constitute a fire and explosion hazard if the adjacent insulation is combustible. At least one fatal explosion was attributed to a similar circumstance. This danger can be avoided by using non-combustible insulation or by providing a purge flow of gaseous nitrogen through the insulation so as to keep out atmospheric air. The gaseous nitrogen purge is preferred because there will be no condensation as long as the nitrogen pressure is below saturation. The use of non-combustible porous insulators such as Fiberglas®, diatomaceous earth, expanded perlite, vermiculite, etc., without the gaseous nitrogen purge is quite feasible, although the insulating value may be found to be far below that computed because air may condense on the cold line, flow to a warm region, be evaporated and again return to the cold line to be recondensed, thus constituting an additional heat-transfer process. Also when insulation of this type communicates with the atmosphere for long periods of time while it is cold, atmospheric moisture will collect and spoil its insulating properties. The use of gas-filled porous insulation for low-temperature service has been discussed in Chapter 6. It is necessary to prevent the accumulation of moisture in the insulation, and when the line is at a temperature below 83°K, air should be excluded. Thus this type of insulation may be suitable for insulating lines carrying liquid oxygen; and with proper precautions, liquid nitrogen lines may be so insulated.

However, difficulties are almost certain to arise if this type of insulation is used for lines carrying liquid hydrogen. The cold surface can condense air, and the only practical purge gases to prevent this are hydrogen and helium, both of which have very high intrinsic thermal conductivities and therefore will greatly diminish the insulating properties of the porous insulation. Solid impermeable foams such as polystyrene foam may be used if the seams are adequately sealed, but permeable insulations such as powders or fibrous materials are not suitable if they are air-filled. Of course, if the porous insulation is surrounded by a perfectly vacuum-tight enclosure, condensation of the air by the cold surface will produce a good vacuum in the interstices of the insulation and the result will be "evacuated powder" insulation. The discussion of this properly belongs in the section which deals with vacuum insulation.

VI. VACUUM-INSULATED TRANSFER LINES

8.7. For the efficient transfer of liquid hydrogen and helium, and in many cases also liquid oxygen or nitrogen, vacuum-insulated transfer lines appear to be the most appropriate. The literature contains descriptions of several small vacuum-insulated transfer lines intended for use in the laboratory. Some of the more recent of these descriptions are given in references [5] to [13]. The Collins helium cryostat is provided with a vacuum-insulated siphon with a valve at its exit end. Fiske [11] describes vacuum-insulated couplings which permit connections between two or more sections of line.

Herrick L. Johnston and L. E. Cox devised a versatile transfer system consisting of sets of standard vacuum-insulated sections in the form of straight runs, ells, valves, etc., each provided with the appropriate vacuum-insulated couplings so that an assemblage of such components can be readily arranged to make connection between any two points. Lines of Johnston-Cox type have been used extensively in the large-scale transfer of liquid hydrogen. Matheson [12] describes a flexible vacuum-insulated line for liquid hydrogen consisting of coaxial metal hose. The large liquid-hydrogen facility of the National Bureau of Standards has used a similar flexible termination on its transfer lines since the start of operations in 1952.

8.8. Design Considerations. The formulae given in Chapter 6 for the heat transfer across the space between long coaxial cylinders apply very precisely to vacuum-insulated transfer lines. However, there are two items which introduce uncertainties into the computation of heat leak for a practical line. First is the problem of heat flow through the spacers or supports separating the inner, liquid-carrying pipe from the outer pipe which provides the exterior surface of the evacuated annulus. The spacers, commonly constructed of a poorly conducting organic plastic, make rather indeterminate thermal contact with both the inner and outer pipe; hence the heat leak cannot be computed. It was once observed that a transfer line in which the vacuum had deteriorated developed cold spots on the outside at each spacer position. When the vacuum was good there was no external indication of heat conduction through the spacers.

A spacer design frequently used is shown in Figure 8.1A. The central hole fits the inner tube and may make rather good thermal contact. The corners of the square spacers make poor thermal connection with the outer tube.

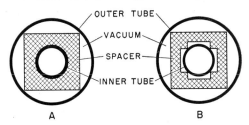

FIGURE 8.1. Insulating spacers for transfer lines.

Figure 8.1B is a suggested design which should greatly decrease heat leak by providing poor thermal contact with the cold tube. It is the opinion of the author that well-designed insulating spacers, used sparingly, will not contribute seriously to transfer-line losses.

The second uncertainty in computing heat leaks for practical lines arises from the difficulty of ensuring low emissivity of the lines after assembly. Transfer lines are usually assembled by soldering with a torch, and unless considerable care is exercised, it is quite likely that oxidation, soldering flux, or carbon deposited from the torch flame will greatly deteriorate the surfaces. (Washing with a 10 percent ammonium persulfate solution after the assembly is almost finished will clean the copper, removing oxide and other corrosion.) Some of the spacers may be overheated during assembly and the resulting products of decomposition may coat the line and spoil its reflectivity. A spacer material that is favored by many cryogenic workers in Teflon®, polytetrafluoroethylene. This plastic is a good insulator, is chemically very stable, has a high decomposition temperature, and does not outgas excessively.

If the insulating space is thick enough, more than two centimeters, evacuated powder may be better than high vacuum alone. There is an increase in the amount of liquid consumed during cool-down because the powder near the inner line must be cooled. On the other hand, the fact that the powder behaves as an adsorbent for residual gas, plus the fact that an extremely good vacuum is not required, strongly favors evacuated powder insulation. Perhaps the greatest objection to powder is the structural-assembly problem. It is not easy to fill the annular space with powder so completely that subsequent shaking during use will not cause the formation of voids. These voids can be serious heat leaks because a small amount of residual gas can conduct heat readily where there is no powder. The pressure required for high-vacuum insulation is two or three orders of magnitude less than that required for evacuated powder insulation.

Thermal contraction complicates the design of vacuum-insulated lines, because the inner pipe is cooled while the outer remains at room temperature.

A copper tube 25 feet long will contract approximately 1 inch upon being cooled from room temperature to liquid hydrogen temperature. There are several ways of designing lines to allow for this contraction: (1) the inner tube may be provided with metal bellows inserts so that these can lengthen as the rest of the tube shortens; (2) the outer tube can have the bellows inserts and be supported in rollers or flexible supports so that it can follow the length changes of the inner tube without much restraint; and (3) for short U-shaped lines, sufficient space may be allowed between the spacers and the inner or outer tube that the contraction will not subject the assembly to undue strain. There is a definite advantage in having the bellows in the outer rather than the inner tubes, because metal bellows constitute a potential vacuum leak. Such leaks are easier to find and repair if they are in the outside tube.

The materials used for transfer lines depend a great deal upon the intended service. Copper is often used for the inner tube because it has a low emissivity and is easy to assemble. The outer tube may very well be copper also except for the ends, which should have low thermal conduction where they provide a heat path from room temperature to the temperature of the cryogenic liquid being transferred. When repeated batch transfers are to be made with the transfer line left in place and warming up between transfers, the ends of the inner line also should be made of poorly conducting material.

The other metals often used are stainless steel and Monel®. These latter have three very desirable characteristics: (1) they are poor conductors of heat, (2) they are available as thin-wall tubing, and (3) they are strong and resist accidental deformation. The thin wall reduces both the longitudinal heat leak and the heat capacity of the inner line. Several of the designs referenced earlier employ Monel® or stainless steel. The principal objection to these alloys is their relatively high emissivity. The radiant heat transfer across a vacuum space bounded by stainless steel or Monel® walls will be several times larger than that across a space bounded by clean copper walls. Seamless flexible tubing can be used to fabricate the terminals of vacuum insulated lines. This makes it convenient to insert the terminal into the filling connection of the receiver.

The Cryogenic Engineering Laboratory now uses bronze or brass flexible tubing because some flexible stainless steel tubing was found to develop vacuum leaks. Perhaps reliable stainless steel flexible tubing is now available. Extraordinary precautions against corrosion must be taken when employing flexible tubing because it is so thin that holes are easily formed. Very thorough removal of soldering flux is mandatory. Also it is usually unwise to join flexible tubing by silver solder because the temperature required will anneal the soldered end and subsequent repeated flexure may cause this part to fail.

Flexible tubing has a very high effective emissivity because the convolutions present recesses that behave as black bodies; incident radiation is almost totally absorbed. In some designs radiant heat transfer has been greatly reduced by wrapping the inner flexible tube with aluminum foil. The writer once constructed a flexible transfer tube with evacuated powder insulation. It was difficult to get the powder in, but the line had good insulating qualities. The Cambridge Corporation devised a flexible line consisting of short metal bellows connecting longer sections (about 15 inches) of rigid tubing. Since the flexible sections are a small fraction of the total length, the radiation loss is greatly decreased. However, this design requires many more soldered joints, all of which must, of course, be vacuum tight.

8.9. Transfer Line for Liquid Hydrogen. The general construction of a transfer line, which delivers liquid from the National Bureau of Standards Cryogenic Engineering Laboratory hydrogen liquefier to the storage vessels located outside the liquefier building, is illustrated in Figure 8.2. It consists for the most part of standard copper tubing and fittings with metal bellows inserts in the outer line to allow for the contraction of the inner line upon cooling. Some special sliding sections on the outside tube are provided to aid in the assembly. The long flexible section is for convenience in connecting the line to the storage or transport container. The relief valve is provided to avoid dangerous pressures in the event valves at each end of the line

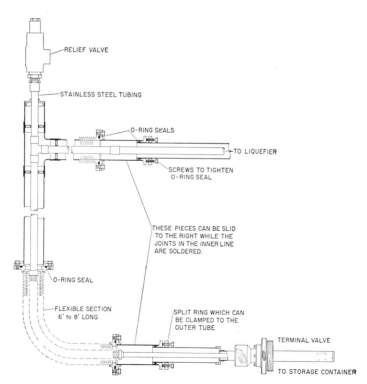

FIGURE 8.2. Vacuum-insulated transfer line (NBS).

are closed while the line contains liquid. The total length of the line is about 75 feet and the losses are about 5 liters per hour during continuous transfer at a rate of about 220 liters per hour. The inner line made of $\frac{3}{8}$-inch (nominal) copper tubing was found to be capable of transferring at a rate of 750 liters per hour with a driving pressure differential of 2.5 psi. The actual diameter of the liquid channel in this line is 0.430 inch. There were also two valves and several short right angle bends which increased resistance to flow.

8.10. Transfer Line for Liquid Helium Protected by a Liquid-Nitrogen-Cooled Shield. Figure 8.3 illustrates a transfer line used at NBS to remove liquid helium from a small liquefier (capacity 15 liters per hour). By surrounding a large part of the line with a shield maintained at the temperature of liquid nitrogen the radiant heat transfer to the liquid helium in this part is reduced by a factor of about 0.004. Porous insulation not shown in the diagram surrounds the part of the line cooled by liquid nitrogen. This line also has another feature designed by Hunter [14] which reduces the loss of liquid when transferring to a storage vessel. The warm helium gas preceding

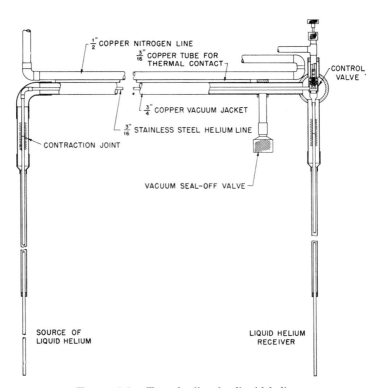

FIGURE 8.3.   Transfer line for liquid helium.

the liquid during cool-down is bypassed back to the compressor through the valve. After the line is cold, this valve is turned so that the liquid helium enters the receiving vessel. Without this feature the first warm gas arriving at the receiver will evaporate a considerable amount of the liquid already present.

Most cryogenic workers have found it advantageous to transfer liquid helium from the liquefier in batches, allowing the transfer line to warm up between transfers. Spoendlin [15] has pointed out that there is a very great advantage in making a helium transfer line so large that the contents of the liquefier can be transferred to the receiver in a few seconds. Spoendlin has used this method to minimize his transfer losses. Of course the heat capacity of the inner tube of the transfer line also must be kept small by using thin tubing.

8.11. Unions for Transfer Lines. A union for connecting vacuum-insulated transfer lines was originally designed by H. L. Johnston and L. E. Cox. Several modifications have been made by various workers, but all employ the Johnston principle of mating vacuum-insulated sections sealed at the warm exterior by an O-ring between flanges. Figure 8.4 is a diagram of such a union. The principal modification in this case from the original Johnston-Cox design is provision of a Teflon O-ring near the cold end of the union, which prevents liquid hydrogen from flowing to the warm seal. This is necessary if the union is to be used with the cold end higher

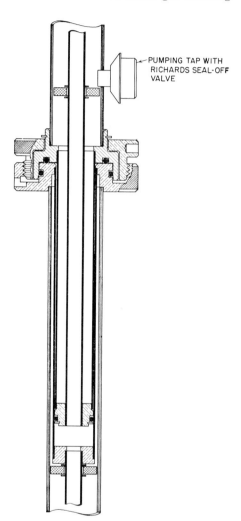

PUMPING TAP WITH
RICHARDS SEAL-OFF
VALVE

FIGURE 8.4. Johnston-Cox type transfer-line coupling.

than the warm end. If the male portion of the union is directed so that the cold end is lower than the warm end, there is no need for such a seal; gaseous hydrogen will prevent liquid from flowing to the warm parts.

VII. Valves for Cryogenic Liquids

8.12. In the foregoing discussion of transfer lines it was indicated that valves are used to direct and control the flow. Some desirable characteristics of a satisfactory valve for this service are (1) low heat leak, (2) reliable operation at the required temperature, (3) small heat capacity, (4) small resistance to flow, (5) simplicity and economy of construction, and (6) adaptability for insertion into ordinary vacuum-insulated lines. None of the valves thus far designed can be given high ratings in all these respects. The following discussion is devoted to descriptions of some of the valves that have been used in vacuum-insulated transfer lines and some comments on their characteristics.

A design frequently employed consists of extending the stem of an ordinary commercial valve so as to reduce heat leak and surrounding the assembly in the vacuum enclosure which is a part of the insulating vacuum of the line. Such a

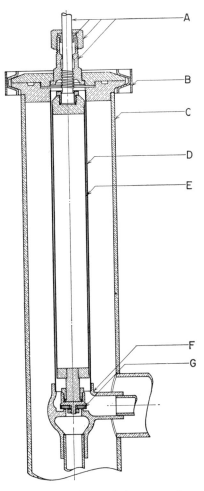

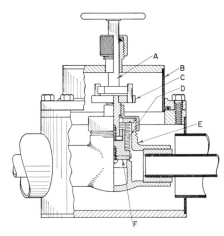

Figure 8.5. Extended stem valve. A, commercial valve stem and packing for gas seal; B, Marman V-band coupling; C, outer wall of vacuum jacket; D, valve stem; E, fluid line and inner wall of vacuum jacket; F, commercial valve; G, closing element.

Figure 8.6. Broken-stem valve. A, valve stem; B, outer wall of vacuum jacket; C, valve wheel; D, bellows seal between liquid line and vacuum jacket; E, modified commercial valve; F, closing element.

valve is illustrated in Figure 8.5. A valve of this type is probably the most economical in first cost because the principal parts are stock items, commercially available. It is common practice to replace the closing disk, usually made of

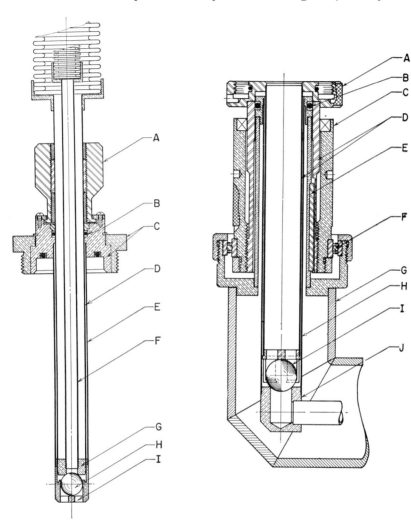

FIGURE 8.7. Terminal valve. A, valve handle; B, neoprene O-ring gas seal; C, coupling for transfer line; D, outer wall of vacuum jacket and valve stem; E, ball supporting sheath; F, liquid line; G, valve seat; H, closing element; I, valve ports.

FIGURE 8.8. Dewar inlet valve. A, coupling for transfer line; B, neoprene O-ring gas seal; C, valve handle; D, valve stem; E, key to hold valve stem from turning; F, bearing; G, outer wall of vacuum jacket; H, fluid line and inner wall of vacuum jacket; I, closing element; J, valve seat.

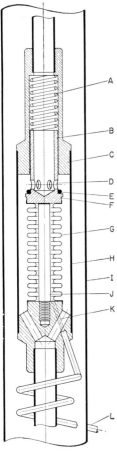

FIGURE 8.9. Helium-operated valve. A, spring which opens valve; B, valve guide; C, valve body; D, valve ports; E, Teflon® O ring; F, part which forms one side of O-ring seal; G, operating bellows; H, fluid lines; I, outer wall of vacuum jacket; J, valve stop; K, helium inlet port; L, stainless steel helium line.

fiber, with a disk of Teflon which gives a better seal at low temperatures. There is some heat leak through the extended stem but this can be made small by employing thin-wall alloy tubing for this part of the stem. The valve may have an objectionably high heat capacity because the commercial valve body was intended for use at room temperature, hence there was no incentive to minimize heat capacity.

Figure 8.6 illustrates a valve in which metallic heat conduction from the exterior is eliminated except while the valve is being adjusted. In this valve the actuating stem can be withdrawn after the valve is turned so that there is no metallic contact. Valves of a somewhat similar principle have been devised in which the actuating device operates through a metal bellows. These latter have the advantage of a positive, soldered, vacuum seal rather than the O-ring seal indicated in Figure 8.6.

A special-purpose but still very useful valve is the terminal valve illustrated in Figure 8.7. This valve is used at the end of a transfer line and makes it possible to close the transfer line at the very end before it is removed from a vessel being filled. This end closure prevents contaminants such as solid air or ice from entering the line.

A somewhat similar valve is illustrated in Figure 8.8. This valve was designed for use in the fill-and-empty fixture of a large transport container for liquid hydrogen. Both this valve and the preceding one have an advantage that is not always appreciated. The stainless steel ball closing member is self-centering so that minor machining errors do not prevent tight closure. It has been found desirable to prepare the seat in the shape of a sharp edged cylinder of deformable metal (e.g., brass); then when the truly spherical ball is pressed against the seat the deformation provides an accurate match and a good seal.

A valve that has been found quite convenient for controlling the transfer of liquid hydrogen is the helium-operated valve shown in Figure 8.9. In this valve gaseous helium admitted through a small, poorly conducting tube into the interior of the metal bellows provides the force required to close the valve. The principal advantage of this valve is that it is readily controlled from a remote location. Valves operated by electromagnets and permanent magnets have been designed. These also avoid any metallic conduction to the inner part of a transfer line. However, thus far such valves have not been widely used.

VIII. Pumping Cryogenic Liquids

8.13. There is very little published information about pumps for cryogenic liquids, although some reciprocating piston pumps for this purpose are in regular use as adjuncts to air liquefaction and separation columns. The pumps, operating directly upon the high-density liquid, force the liquid oxygen or nitrogen through a heat exchanger where it is vaporized, still at high pressure, and is delivered to high-pressure gas cylinders. This method is not only more economical of power than the old method of pumping the gas, but since the part of the pump handling the liquid is non-lubricated, the gas is delivered to the cylinders without contamination by lubricating oil or water.

Recently, high-capacity rotary pumps have been designed to deliver liquid oxygen for use in rocketry. Some of these pumps transfer liquid oxygen from the storage vessel to the rocket tank and others are in the rockets themselves, pumping oxygen from the rocket tank to the engine. However, a brief search of the published literature failed to yield information concerning the characteristics of such pumps.

In 1955 the NBS Cryogenic Engineering Laboratory undertook the task of examining the characteristics of some available rotary pumps when pumping liquid nitrogen or liquid hydrogen. This task was in support of a project being pursued at the Los Alamos Scientific Laboratory in which liquid hydrogen was being used to cool the copper coils of an electromagnet. These efforts resulted in the adaptation of a commercial water pump so that it was suitable for the specific job, and in the course of the investigations, certain information was acquired which appears to be generally applicable to the problems of pumping cryogenic liquids. The results of this investigation have not yet been published, although a report was prepared by the investigators, R. B. Jacobs, K. B. Martin, Gordon J. Van Wylen, and B. W. Birmingham. The following is an account of some of the highlights of this report

The experimental arrangement is shown schematically in Figure 8.10. By immersing the pump in the liquid being circulated the need for insulating the pump was avoided. During the pump tests the electromagnet was not used; the liquid from the pump passed through a regulating valve and was returned to the bath. Thus the loss of liquid was only that resulting from heat leak and energy introduced by the pump. The rate of flow was measured with an orifice meter calibrated with water and corrected for liquid nitrogen or hydrogen by means of the density ratios. Three pumps were tested: (1) a two-stage turbine pump rated for water 11 gpm at a 200-foot discharge head at 1725 rpm, (2) a ten-stage centrifugal pump rated at 9.7 gpm, 100-foot dis-

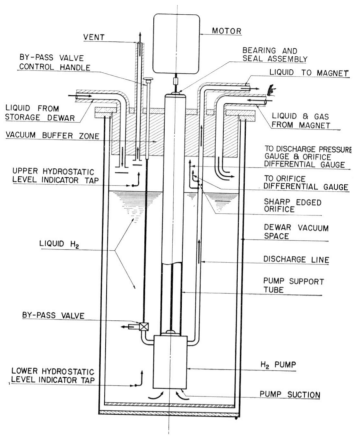

VENT — MOTOR
BY-PASS VALVE CONTROL HANDLE — BEARING AND SEAL ASSEMBLY
LIQUID TO MAGNET
LIQUID FROM STORAGE DEWAR — LIQUID & GAS FROM MAGNET
VACUUM BUFFER ZONE
TO DISCHARGE PRESSURE GAUGE & ORIFICE DIFFERENTIAL GAUGE
UPPER HYDROSTATIC LEVEL INDICATOR TAP — TO ORIFICE DIFFERENTIAL GAUGE
SHARP EDGED ORIFICE
DEWAR VACUUM SPACE
LIQUID H₂ — DISCHARGE LINE
PUMP SUPPORT TUBE
BY-PASS VALVE
LOWER HYDROSTATIC LEVEL INDICATOR TAP — H₂ PUMP
PUMP SUCTION

FIGURE 8.10. Schematic diagram of pump testing equipment.

charge head at 3450 rpm, and (3) a four-stage centrifugal pump rated at 95 gpm at 200-foot discharge head at 3450 rpm.

The principal results of these tests can be very briefly summarized:

(1) It was found that when sufficiently supercooled liquid nitrogen or liquid hydrogen entered the intake of the pump, its performance characteristics were not substantially different from those for water. As a rule the cryogenic liquid capacity for a given head was 5 to 10 percent lower than the capacity for water and the maximum head at zero delivery was approximately the same amount lower. These differences were attributed to the lower viscosity of the cryogenic liquid.

(2) As was anticipated, when the liquid was not sufficiently supercooled, cavitation in the pump caused a marked decrease in the mass delivery rate.

(3) The hydrostatic head of liquid above saturation pressure, net positive

suction head (NPSH), required to suppress cavitation when liquid hydrogen was being pumped was only a few inches, while for liquid nitrogen several feet were required. Figure 8.11 illustrates some performance curves of the four-stage centrifugal pump.

(4) The pump efficiencies of these off-the-shelf water pumps was disappointingly low when pumping liquid hydrogen (about 15 percent maximum). However, some pump design experts have expressed the opinion that it should be possible to design a pump specifically for liquid hydrogen that will have good efficiency.

Because it is often desirable to operate the pump totally immersed in the cryogenic liquid the NBS Cryogenic Engineering Laboratory has started a study of bearings operating at low temperature. This project is still in its early stages, but it may be of interest to report that a ball bearing of commercial design with reinforced plastic retainers ran continuously at 3300 rpm in liquid nitrogen for 3700 hours before there was a noticeable increase of friction. A torque meter was incorporated in the test setup so that any increase in rotational resistance was immediately evident.

Figure 8.11 shows the data obtained with the four-stage centrifugal pump with liquid hydrogen.

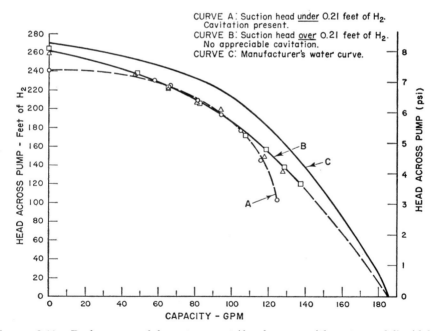

FIGURE 8.11. Performance of four-stage centrifugal pump with water and liquid hydrogen.

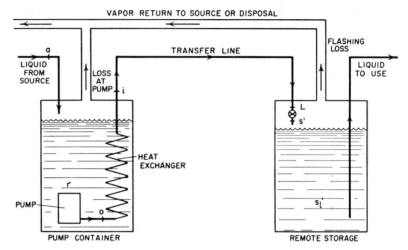

FIGURE 8.12. Liquefied gas transfer system.

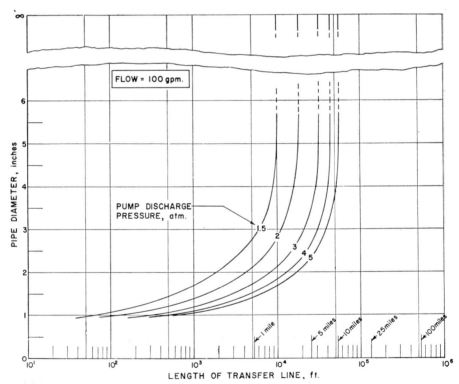

FIGURE 8.13. Transfer characteristics for a line carrying liquid hydrogen. This line consists of coaxial pipes of diameter ratios = 5 with the annulus filled with evacuated silica aerogel (pressure less than 10^{-5} mm Hg). The properties of liquid hydrogen used for the computations were taken as those of the saturated liquid at 20.4 °K.

IX. Long-Distance Transfer

8.14. A detailed mathematical analysis of steady-state, single-phase transfer of liquefied gases through insulated pipes has been made by Jacobs [16]. The system he analyzed is shown in Figure 8.12. Here liquid at saturation conditions at a pressure of about 1 atmosphere is compressed to a predetermined higher pressure in the pump. The heat introduced by the pump is delivered to the low-pressure liquid through the heat exchanger, and the pumped liquid, now at a pressure well above saturation, is forced into the transfer line. The problem was solved for the condition that liquid reach the valve L at saturation conditions. Numerous examples were computed for various rates of flow, pump discharge pressures, pipe diameters and lengths of transfer line. Figure 8.13 is one of these examples for a transfer line carrying liquid hydrogen.

REFERENCES FOR CHAPTER 8

[1] R. S. Silver, *Proc. Roy. Soc.*, **A194**, 464 (1948).
[2] R. W. Lockhart and R. C. Martinelli, *Chem. Eng. Prog.*, **45-1**, 39 (1949).
[3] D. L. Linning, *Inst. Mech. Eng. Proc.*, **1B**, 64 (1952).
[4] John D. Rogers, *Am. Inst. Chem. Eng. J.*, **2**, 536 (1956).
[5] H. A. Fairbank, *Rev. Sci. Instr.*, **17**, 473 (1946).
[6] W. F. Giauque, *Rev. Sci. Instr.*, **18**, 852 (1947).
[7] R. B. Scott and J. W. Cook, *Rev. Sci. Instr.*, **19**, 889 (1948).
[8] J. C. Daunt and H. L. Johnston, *Rev. Sci. Instr.*, **20**, 122 (1949).
[9] Aaron Wexler, *Rev. Sci. Instr.*, **25**, 442 (1954).
[10] J. W. Stout, *Rev. Sci. Instr.*, **25**, 929 (1954).
[11] M. D. Fiske, *Rev. Sci. Instr.*, **26**, 90 (1955).
[12] R. C. Matheson, *Rev. Sci. Instr.*, **26**, 616 (1955).
[13] Robert B. Jacobs and Robert R. Richards, *Rev. Sci. Instr.*, **28**, 291 (1957).
[14] B. J. Hunter, NBS-CEL. Unpublished (1957).
[15] Rudolf Spoendlin, Laboratoires du C.N.R.S., Bellevue, France. Private communication.
[16] R. B. Jacobs, NBS. *NBS Circular* 596 (1958).

Chapter IX

PROPERTIES OF CRYOGENIC FLUIDS

9.1. This chapter provides a convenient collection of data on some cryogenic fluids and refers to additional information.

A brief survey of a large number of elements and compounds with low melting temperatures is presented in Table 9.1, which lists triple points (or

TABLE 9.1. TEMPERATURES OF FUSION AND NORMAL
BOILING POINTS OF SOME CRYOGENIC FLUIDS[a]

Substance	Fusion Temperature, °K	Boiling Point, °K
He	—	4.216
H_2	13.96	20.39
Ne	24.57	27.1
O_2	54.40	90.19
F_2	55.20	85.24
N_2	63.15	77.34
NF_3	64.7	144.1
CO	68.10	81.66
A	83.85	87.29
SiH_4	88.5	161.8
CF_4	89.47	145.14
C_2H_6	89.89	184.53
CH_4	90.68	111.67
CF_3Cl	91.6	192.0
C_2H_4	103.97	169.45
B_2H_6	107.7	180.63
NO	109.51	121.39
CHF_3	113.	189.0
CHF_2Cl	113.	232.4
C_2F_3Cl	115.7	245.3
Kr	115.95	119.93
CF_2Cl_2	118.	242.7
C_2F_4	130.7	197.
CHFCl	138.	282.1
$C_2F_2Cl_2$[b]	142.7	294.3
SF_4	149.	233.

TABLE 9.1. (*continued*)

Substance	Fusion Temperature, °K	Boiling Point, °K
$C_2F_2Cl_2{}^c$	158.	292.
HCl	158.94	188.11
Xe	161.3	165.1
$CFCl_3$	162.68	296.8
$C_2F_2Cl_2{}^d$	162.9	295.2
Cl_2	172.16	239.10
C_2F_6	173.10	194.9
CH_3Cl	175.44	248.94
CH_2Cl_2	176.	313.
CO_2		194.68
		(normal sublimation temperature)

ᵃ The fusion temperature listed is the triple point temperature in most cases, although for some of the less volatile materials the melting point temperature (under 1 atmosphere of air) is given. This list was selected from data given in *NBS Circular 500* [4] with the exception of the neon boiling point, which is taken from a compilation by Hoge [5]. It is not intended that this list be complete or constitute a critical survey of fixed temperatures; it merely gives an idea of what fluids might be used for low-temperature research.

ᵇ *cis*-1,2 Difluoro-1,2 dichloroethene.

ᶜ 1-1, Difluoro-2,2-dichloroethene.

ᵈ *trans*-1,2-Difluoro-1,2-dichloroethene.

fusion temperatures) and boiling temperatures. The fluids most commonly used in cryogenic research and development—oxygen, nitrogen, air, hydrogen, and helium—are considered in much more detail. Tables of viscosity and thermal conductivity of the gas and temperature-entropy diagrams for these are presented, as well as tables, equations, and graphs of the properties of the condensed state. Complete tables of thermodynamic properties of the gaseous state have deliberately been omitted because such tables are readily available elsewhere. Of course the temperature-entropy charts will provide approximate values of *p-v-t* relations and several other thermodynamic properties.

Thermodynamic properties of several industrial gases are presented in great detail in two recent publications. The first [1] lists the thermodynamic and transport properties of air, argon, carbon dioxide, carbon monoxide, hydrogen, nitrogen, oxygen, and steam. The other, by Din [2], deals with ammonia, carbon dioxide, carbon monoxide, air, acetylene, ethylene, propane, and argon. The properties of helium are thoroughly discussed by Keesom [3].

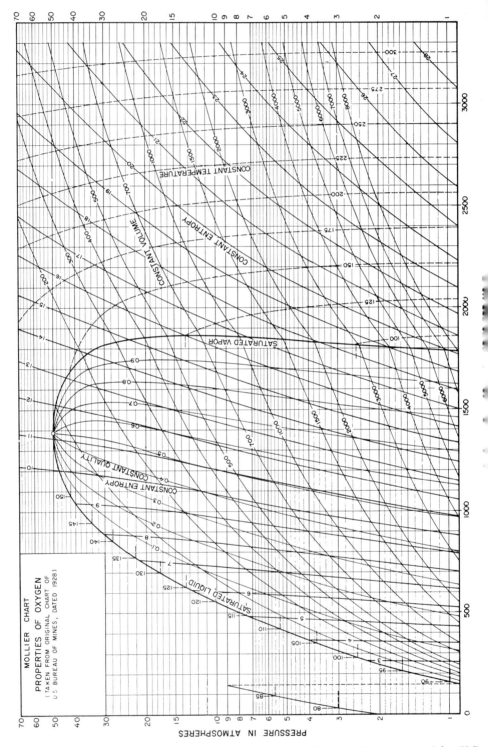

FIGURE 9.1. Mollier chart: The properties of oxygen. From a chart prepared by U.S. Bureau of Mines to accompany *Technical Paper* 424 [7]. Volumes are in cm³ mole⁻¹, temperatures in °K, entropies in cal mole⁻¹ °K⁻¹.

I. OXYGEN

9.2. Oxygen is the base used for chemical atomic weights, being assigned the atomic weight 16.000. Naturally occurring oxygen consists of three stable isotopes of atomic mass numbers 16, 17, and 18, having abundances in the proportion 10,000 : 4 : 20. Since the isotopes of oxygen are difficult to separate, it is unlikely that the cryogenic engineer will encounter oxygen of isotopic composition that differs appreciably from the above proportion. Accordingly the data presented in this section are from measurements on naturally occurring oxygen. Also the data refer to diatomic, molecular oxygen O_2, except that in the condensed state there is some weak transient association of oxygen molecules forming the polymer O_4, which is said to be responsible for the blue color of liquid and solid oxygen. There appears to be little or no molecular association in the gaseous state. The metastable molecule O_3, ozone, is not included in this discussion.

Oxygen is a normal fluid in most respects, its outstanding difference from most other fluids being its strong paramagnetism. The paramagnetic property has been exploited in an instrument for detecting small amounts of oxygen in other gases. Because of its chemical activity the handling of oxygen is attended by some hazards. For example, ordinary hydrocarbon lubricants are dangerous to use in oxygen compressors and vacuum pumps exhausting oxygen. Also valves, fittings and lines used with oil-pumped gases should never be used

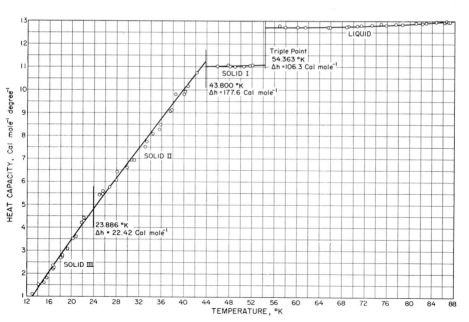

FIGURE 9.2. Heat capacity of oxygen in the solid and liquid states [11].

with oxygen. Serious explosions have resulted from the combination of oxygen with the lubricant. Combustible materials soaked in liquid oxygen are used as inexpensive commercial explosives.

Liquid oxygen is manufactured in large quantities by the liquefaction and distillation of air. For most industrial applications it is used in the gaseous state, but when oxygen is shipped in large quantities it is much less expensive to ship it in the liquid state than in high-pressure gas cylinders.

TABLE 9.2. BOILING POINT, TRIPLE POINT, AND CRITICAL CONSTANTS OF OXYGEN

Normal boiling point, °K	90.19	[1]
Critical temperature, °K	154.7$_8$	[1]
Critical pressure, atm	50.1$_4$	[1]
Critical density, g cm^{-3}	0.430	[6]
Triple point temperature, °K	54.363	[1]
Triple point pressure, atm	0.00150	[1]

TABLE 9.3. THERMAL CONDUCTIVITY OF GASEOUS OXYGEN AT ATMOSPHERIC PRESSURE [1]

Temp., °K	k, watt cm^{-1} °K^{-1} $\times 10^4$	Temp., °R
80	0.719	144
90	0.813	162
100	0.903	180
110	0.997	198
120	1.090	216
130	1.183	234
140	1.277	252
150	1.367	270
160	1.461	288
170	1.552	306
180	1.642	324
190	1.733	342
200	1.824	360
210	1.912	378
220	2.001	396
230	2.087	414
240	2.173	432
250	2.259	450
260	2.342	468
270	2.428	486
280	2.51	504
290	2.60	522
300	2.68	540

TABLE 9.4. VISCOSITY OF GASEOUS OXYGEN
AT ATMOSPHERIC PRESSURE [1]

Temp., °K	η, Poise $\times$ 10^4	Temp., °R
100	0.7773	180
110	0.8546	198
120	0.9306	216
130	1.0055	234
140	1.0786	252
150	1.1502	270
160	1.2204	288
170	1.2893	306
180	1.3567	324
190	1.4221	342
200	1.4860	360
210	1.5490	378
220	1.6106	396
230	1.6710	414
240	1.7304	432
250	1.7887	450
260	1.8457	468
270	1.9017	486
280	1.9564	504
290	2.0104	522
300	2.0633	540

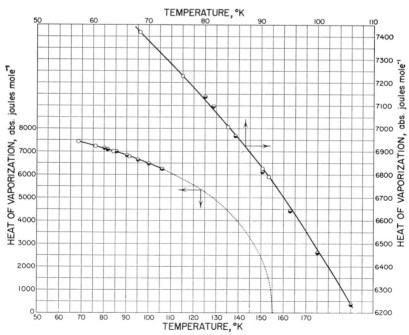

FIGURE 9.3. The heat of vaporization of oxygen: ○ Furukawa and McCoskey [12].
◑ Alekhanov [13]. - - - Computed from an equation given by Alekhanov [13].

TABLE 9.5. VAPOR PRESSURE OF OXYGEN [1]

| Temp., °K | Pressure | | | Temp., °R |
	mm Hg	atm	psia	
55	1.38	.00182	.027	99
60	5.44	.00716	.105	108
65	17.4	.0229	.34	117
70	46.8	.0616	.90	126
75	108.7	.1430	2.10	135
80	225.3	.2964	4.36	144
85	425.4	.5597	8.23	153
90	745.0	.9803	14.41	162
95	1223.3	1.6096	23.65	171
100	1905.0	2.5066	36.84	180
105	2838.2	3.7345	54.88	189
110	4072.9	5.3591	78.76	198
115	5661.6	7.4495	109.48	207
120	7658.6	10.077	148.09	216
125	10120	13.316	195.7	225
130	13102	17.239	253.4	234
135	16670	21.934	322.3	243
140	20892	27.489	404.0	252
145	25843	34.004	499.7	261
150	31631	41.620	611.6	270

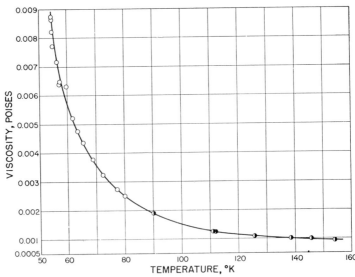

FIGURE 9.4. Viscosity of liquid oxygen: ○ Rudenko and Shubnikov [14]. ◑ Rudenko [15].

TABLE 9.6. DENSITY OF LIQUID OXYGEN
(SATURATED)

Temp., °K	ρ, g cm^{-3}	
61	1.282	[8]
62.7	1.2746	[9]
65	1.263	
70	1.239	
75	1.215	[8]
80	1.191	
85	1.167	
90	1.142	
91.1	1.1415	
118.6	.9758	
132.9	.8742	
143.2	.7781	[9]
149.8	.6779	
152.7	.6032	
154.3 (crit.)	.4299	

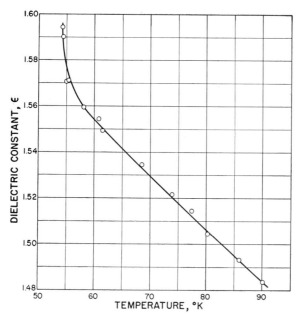

FIGURE 9.5. The dielectric constant of liquid oxygen [19].

TABLE 9.7. LIQUID OXYGEN: VELOCITY OF SOUND AND COMPRESSIBILITY COEFFICIENTS [8]

Temp., °K	Velocity of Sound, m sec⁻¹	Density, g cm⁻³	Adiabatic Compressibility (Calculated), cm² dyne⁻¹ × 10¹²	$\dfrac{C_p}{C_v}$	Isothermal Compressibility (Calculated), cm² dyne⁻¹ × 10¹²	Isothermal Compressibility (Observed), cm² dyne⁻¹ × 10¹²
90.0	913	1.142	105			
85.0	951	1.167	95			
80.0	989	1.191	86	1.69	145	169 [10]
75.0	1027	1.215	78			
70.0	1065	1.239	71			
65.0	1103	1.263	66			
61.0	1133	1.282	61			

The thermal conductivity of liquid oxygen, nitrogen, and several mixtures of the two were measured by Hammann [16], who obtained values of approximately 5×10^{-4} cal sec⁻¹ °K⁻¹ cm⁻¹ for both liquid oxygen and nitrogen and slightly lower values for the mixtures. There was little variation with temperature. However, Powers, Mattox and Johnston [17] measured the thermal conductivity of liquid nitrogen and obtained values which ranged from 3×10^{-4} to 3.6×10^{-4} cal sec⁻¹ °K⁻¹ (see properties of nitrogen, pp. 277-286). The fact that these later data on nitrogen show a good internal consistency and differ so much from those of Hammann throws doubt upon Hammann's values for liquid oxygen and the mixtures. Table 9.8 lists values of thermal conductivity of liquid and gaseous oxygen at several pressures and temperatures.

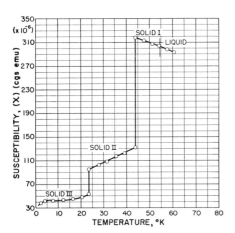

FIGURE 9.6. The paramagnetic susceptibility of solid and liquid oxygen [20].

TABLE 9.8. THERMAL CONDUCTIVITY OF OXYGEN (WATT CM^{-1} $^{\circ}$K^{-1} $\times$ 10^4) [18]
(The horizontal bars separate the values for the liquid and gaseous phases)

Temp., °K \ Pressure, atm	1	20	40	60	80	100
73.16	0.6507	17.1976	17.1976	17.1976	17.3133	17.4300
93.16	0.8366	14.6412	14.6412	14.7574	14.8736	14.8736
113.16	1.0226	11.9686	12.0848	12.3172	12.4334	12.5496
133.16	1.2085	1.5338	9.5284	9.7608	9.9932	10.1094
153.16	1.3944	1.6384	2.23104	6.1586	6.6234	7.0882
173.16	1.5803	1.7546	2.0800	2.6958	3.5557	4.6131
193.16	1.7662	1.9057	2.1381	2.4634	2.8934	3.4860
213.16	1.9405	2.0684	2.2543	2.4867	2.7888	3.1606
233.16	2.1148	2.2427	2.3821	2.5680	2.8237	3.0677
253.16	2.2775	2.3821	2.5099	2.6610	2.8818	2.0909
273.16	2.4402	2.5332	2.6494	2.7888	2.9631	3.1374
293.16	2.6029	2.6958	2.8004	2.9282	3.0793	3.2420
313.16	2.7656	2.8585	2.9631	3.0793	3.2071	3.3466

II. NITROGEN

9.3. Nitrogen (atomic weight 14.008) has two stable isotopes of mass numbers 14 and 15 with a relative abundance of 10,000 to 38. Liquid nitrogen is of considerable importance to the cryogenic engineer because it is a safe refrigerant. It is rather inactive chemically and is neither explosive nor toxic. It is commonly used in hydrogen and helium liquefaction cycles as a precoolant. It is widely available commercially, being prepared by the fractionation of liquid air.

TABLE 9.9. BOILING POINT, TRIPLE POINT,
AND CRITICAL CONSTANTS OF NITROGEN

Normal boiling point, °K	77.395	[1]
Critical temperature, °K	126.1$_{35}$	[1]
Critical pressure, atm	33.49	[1]
Critical density, g cm^{-3}	0.31096	[13]
Triple point temperature, °K	63.156	[1]
Triple point pressure, atm	0.1237	[1]

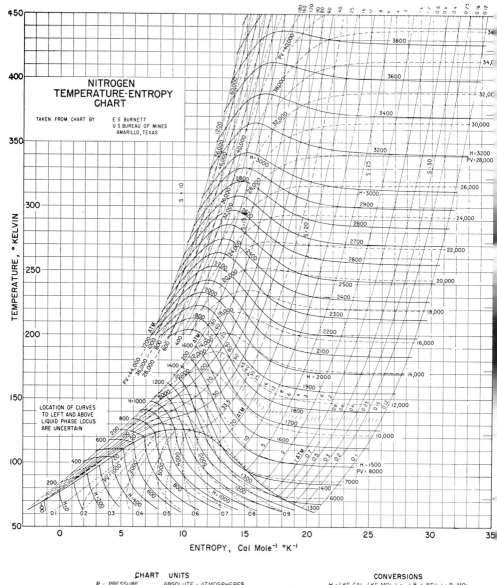

CHART UNITS

P - PRESSURE — ABSOLUTE - ATMOSPHERES
T - TEMPERATURE — ABSOLUTE -°K (KELVIN)
V - VOLUME — LITERS PER KG MOL
PV - PRODUCTS — (LTR-ATM) / KG MOL
H - ENTHALPY — KG CAL / KG MOL
S - ENTROPY — (KG CAL / KG MOL)/°K
NOTE ZERO OF ENTHALPY AND OF ENTROPY
TAKEN AT BOILING POINT OF LIQUID NITROGEN
P = I ATM T = 77 35°K (-195 8°C)

PV/J = PV/41 3 ≡ PV IN ENTHALPY UNITS
U - " INTERNAL ENERGY = H-PV/J KG CAL / KG MOL
PV/P = VOLUME IN (LITER-ATM)/ KG MOL

CONVERSIONS

H - (KG CAL / KG MOL) x I 8 = BTU / LB MOL
PV/J " " " " x I 8 = " "
U " " " " x I 8 = " "
S - (KG CAL / KG MOL)/°K x I O = (BTU / LB MOL)/°R
V - (LITERS / KG MOL) x O 0I60₂ = (CU FT / LB MOL)
PV - (LITER - ATM) / KG MOL x 33 9 = (FT LBS / LB MOl

DIVIDE VALUES "PER MOL" BY 28.0I6, THE MOLECU
WEIGHT OF NITROGEN, TO GET CORRESPONDING VA
PER KG OR PER POUND OF NITROGEN

FIGURE 9.7. Temperature-entropy chart for nitrogen. Pressure is in atmospheres, volume in liters per kg mol, pv products in liter atm per kg mol, enthalpy (H) in cal mole^{-1}, °K^{-1}.

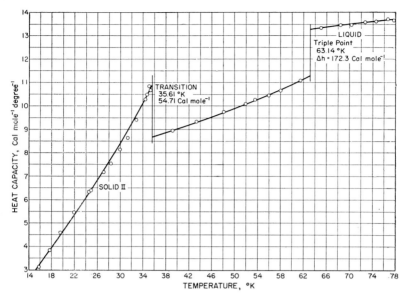

FIGURE 9.8. Heat capacity and heats of transition of solid and liquid nitrogen [22].

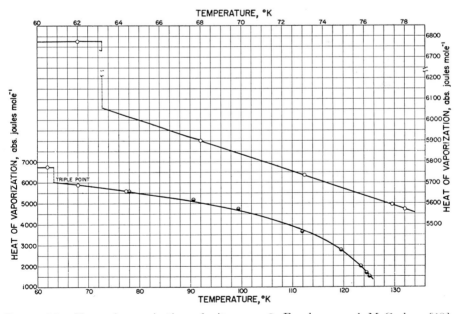

FIGURE 9.9. Heat of vaporization of nitrogen: ○ Furukawa and McCoskey [12]. ◑ Computed by means of the Clausius-Clapeyron relation using the density data of Mathias, Onnes and Crommelin [21] and the vapor pressure data given by Hilsenrath et al. [1].

Temp., °K	k, watt cm^{-1} °K^{-1} × 10^4	Temp., °R
100	0.9399	180
110	1.029	198
120	1.121	216
130	1.210	234
140	1.296	252
150	1.388	270
160	1.475	288
170	1.562	306
180	1.648	324
190	1.733	342
200	1.815	360
210	1.901	378
220	1.983	396
230	2.065	414
240	2.150	432
250	2.227	450
260	2.306	468
270	2.386	486
280	2.461	504
290	2.533	522
300	2.605	540

TABLE 9.11.   VISCOSITY OF GASEOUS NITROGEN
AT ATMOSPHERIC PRESSURE [1]

Temp., °K	η, Poise × 10^4	Temp., °R
100	0.6866	180
150	1.009	270
200	1.295	360
250	1.553	450
300	1.785	540

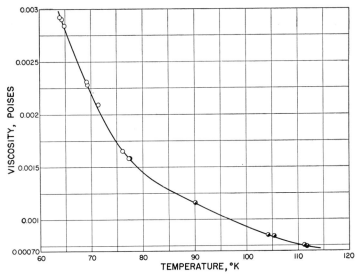

FIGURE 9.10. Viscosity of liquid nitrogen: ○ Rudenko and Shubnikov [14]. ◗ Rudenko [15].

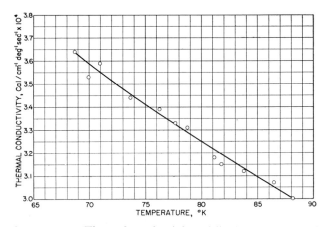

FIGURE 9.11. Thermal conductivity of liquid nitrogen [23].

TABLE 9.12. VAPOR PRESSURE OF NITROGEN [1]

	Temp., °K	Pressure			Temp., °R
		mm Hg	atm	psia	
Solid	52	5.7	.0075	.110	93.6
	54	10.2	.0134	.197	97.2
	56	17.6	.0232	.341	100.8
	58	29.4	.0386	.568	104.4
	60	47.2	.0621	.913	108.0
	62	73.6	.0969	1.424	111.6
Liquid	64	109.4	.1439	2.115	115.2
	66	154.1	.2028	2.980	118.8
	68	212.6	.2797	4.110	122.4
	70	287.6	.3785	5.56	126.0
	72	382.5	.503	7.40	129.6
	74	500.0	.658	9.67	133.2
	76	643.0	.847	12.44	136.8
	78	815.0	1.073	15.76	140.4
	80	1019.0	1.341	19.71	144.0
	82	1259.0	1.657	24.35	147.6
	84	1539.0	2.026	29.77	151.2
	86	1869.0	2.460	36.15	154.8
	88	2255.0	2.967	43.60	158.4
	90	2697.0	3.548	52.1	162.0
	92	3194.0	4.203	61.8	165.6
	94	3752.0	4.937	72.5	169.2
	96	4377.0	5.76	84.6	172.8
	98	5076.0	6.68	98.1	176.4
	100	5851.0	7.70	113.1	180.0
	102	6708.0	8.83	129.7	183.6
	104	7650.0	10.07	147.9	187.2
	106	8682.0	11.42	167.9	190.8
	108	9808.0	12.91	189.7	194.4
	110	11033.0	14.52	213.3	198.0
	112	12360.0	16.26	239.0	201.6
	114	13797.0	18.15	266.8	205.2
	116	15351.0	20.20	296.8	208.8
	118	17033.0	22.41	329.4	212.4
	120	18854.0	24.81	364.6	216.0
	122	20823.0	27.40	402.7	219.6
	124	22960.0	30.21	444.0	223.2
	126	25287.0	33.27	489.0	226.8

TABLE 9.13. THE DENSITY OF LIQUID NITROGEN (SATURATED) [21]

Temp., °K	Density, g cm^{-3}
64.8	0.8622
67.71	0.8499
73.13	0.8265
78.07	0.8043
90.65	0.7433
99.43	0.6922
111.96	0.6071
119.51	0.5332
123.41	0.4799
124.55	0.4504
125.08	0.4314
126.03[a]	0.31096 (critical)

[a] Reference [1] gives 126.1$_{25}$°K as the critical temperature.

TABLE 9.14. LIQUID NITROGEN: VELOCITY OF SOUND AND COMPRESSIBILITY COEFFICIENTS [8]

Temp., °K	Velocity of Sound, m sec^{-1}	Density, g cm^{-3}	Adiabatic Compressibility (Calculated), cm^2 dyne^{-1} × 10^{12}	$\dfrac{C_p}{C_v}$	Isothermal Compressibility (Calculated), cm^2 dyne^{-1} × 10^{12}	Isothermal Compressibility (Observed), cm^2 dyne^{-1} × 10^{12}
77.0	880	0.811	159			
74.0	910	0.825	146	2.02	295	247 [10]
71.0	940	0.839	135			
68.0	970	0.854	124			
65.0	1005	0.868	114			

TABLE 9.15. THE DIELECTRIC CONSTANT OF SOLID AND LIQUID NITROGEN AT SATURATION PRESSURE [24]

(The horizontal bars separate the values for the liquid and solid phases)

Temp., °K	ϵ
56	1.516
58	1.515
60	1.515
62	1.514
—	—
64	1.475
66	1.466
68	1.460
70	1.456
72	1.448
74	1.442
76	1.438
77.4	1.433$_5$

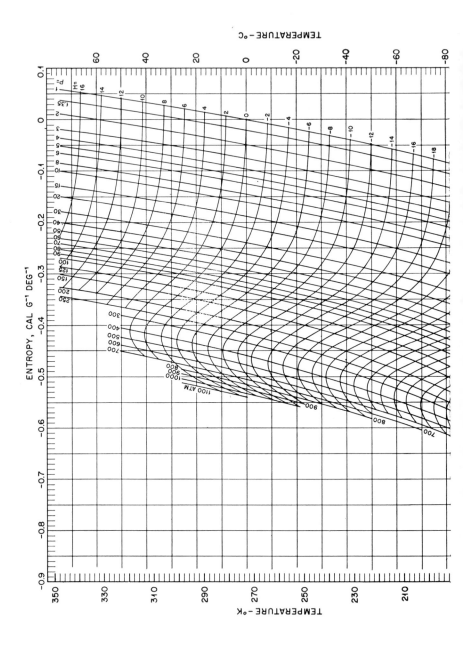

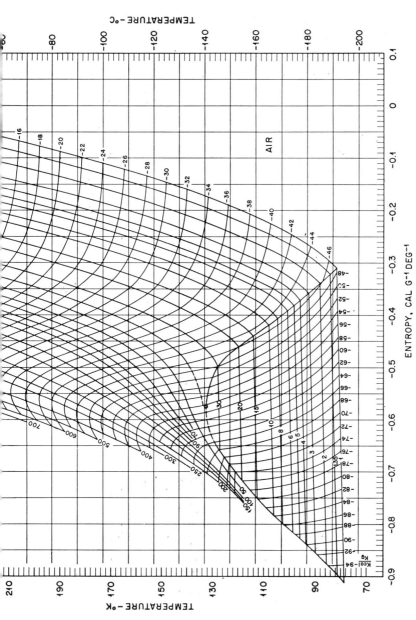

FIGURE 9.12. Temperature entropy diagram for air. This diagram combines the high-pressure measurements of Michels, Wassenaar, and Wolkers [26] with the lower-pressure region according to the data of Claitor and Crawford [27]. Pressures are in atmospheres, entropy in cal g^{-1} deg^{-1}, and the enthalpy in cal g^{-1}.

III. Air: Mixtures of Oxygen and Nitrogen

9.4. Dry air is a mixture consisting principally of nitrogen, oxygen and argon with traces of other gases as shown in Table 9.16.

TABLE 9.16. COMPOSITION OF THE AIR NEAR GROUND LEVEL [25]

Gas	Molecular Weight	Percent by Volume
Nitrogen	28	78.09
Oxygen	32	20.95
Argon	40	.93
Carbon dioxide	44	.02-.04
Neon	20.2	18×10^{-4}
Helium	4	5.3×10^{-4}
Krypton	83	1.1×10^{-4}
Hydrogen	2	$.5 \times 10^{-4}$
Xenon	130	$.08 \times 10^{-4}$
Ozone	48	$.02 \times 10^{-4}$
Radon	222	7×10^{-18}

When air is liquefied, the carbon dioxide is usually removed, so for practical purposes, liquid air can be considered to consist of 78 percent nitrogen, 21 percent oxygen, and 1 percent argon, the other constituents being present in

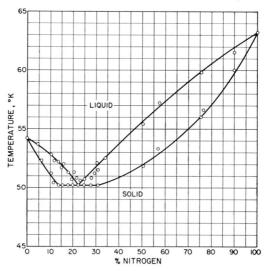

FIGURE 9.13. Solid-liquid equilibrium phase diagram for mixtures of oxygen and nitrogen [28].

negligible amounts. Sometimes the presence of argon is ignored and liquid air is considered to be a binary mixture of 21 percent oxygen and 79 percent nitrogen. Since argon has a vapor pressure between those of oxygen and nitrogen, this assumption is a rather good approximation for some purposes.

The principal interest in liquid air is in the preparation of pure nitrogen, oxygen, and rare gases. This is discussed in the chapter on separation of gases. Liquid air is often used as a refrigerant but of course it is not as safe as liquid nitrogen for this purpose. Because of the lower solidification temperature, liquid air is sometimes preferred for obtaining low temperatures by reducing the pressure over the surface of the liquid. There is a hazard associated with this process because the evaporation will increase the concentration of oxygen in the liquid which remains. This has caused explosions in the vacuum pumps used to reduce the pressure.

TABLE 9.17. THERMAL CONDUCTIVITY OF GASEOUS AIR
AT ATMOSPHERIC PRESSURE [1]

Temp., °K	k, watts cm^{-1} °K^{-1} $\times$ 10^4	Temp., °R
80	0.746	144
90	0.835	162
100	0.925	180
110	1.015	198
120	1.105	216
130	1.194	234
140	1.284	252
150	1.373	270
160	1.461	288
170	1.549	306
180	1.637	324
190	1.723	342
200	1.809	360
210	1.894	378
220	1.978	396
230	2.062	414
240	2.145	432
250	2.227	450
260	2.308	468
270	2.388	486
280	2.467	504
290	2.547	522
300	2.624	540

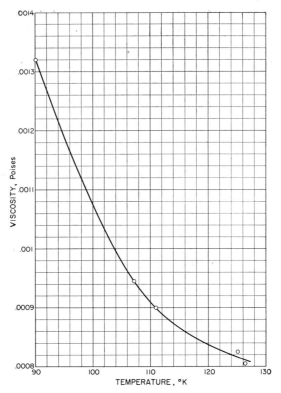

FIGURE 9.14.   Viscosity of liquid air [15].

TABLE 9.18.   VISCOSITY OF GASEOUS AIR
AT ATMOSPHERIC PRESSURE [1]

Temp., °K	η, Poise $\times 10^4$	Temp., °R
100	0.6929	180
110	0.7633	198
120	0.8319	216
130	0.8990	234
140	0.9646	252
150	1.028	270
160	1.091	288
170	1.152	306
180	1.212	324
190	1.271	342
200	1.328	360
210	1.385	378
220	1.440	396
230	1.494	414

TABLE 9.18. (*continued*)

Temp., °K	η,Poise $\times$ 10^4	Temp., °R
240	1.547	432
250	1.599	450
260	1.650	468
270	1.700	486
280	1.750	504
290	1.798	522
300	1.846	540

IV. HYDROGEN

9.5. Natural hydrogen of atomic weight 1.008 is a mixture of two stable isotopes; hydrogen, of atomic mass 1; and deuterium, of mass 2.   The abundance ratio is about 6400 to 1, although slight variations occur, depending on the source of the hydrogen.   Actually, since molecular hydrogen is diatomic, nearly all the deuterium atoms in natural hydrogen are in combination with hydrogen atoms; molecular deuterium is highly improbable in such a mixture. Accordingly, ordinary hydrogen is a mixture of H_2 and HD molecules in the ratio 3200 to 1.   There is also a very rare radioactive isotope of hydrogen of atomic mass 3, called *tritium*, which is now available in small quantities. However, this section will be restricted to a discussion of the properties of the more abundant compounds—hydrogen, deuterium, and hydrogen deuteride.

Different relative orientations of the two nuclear spins in the diatomic molecules H_2 and D_2 give rise to the molecular modifications designated by the prefixes *ortho* and *para*.   The equilibrium ortho-para composition is temperature dependent.   The high-temperature equilibrium concentration of hydrogen, closely approached at room temperatures and known as "normal" hydrogen, is 75 percent orthohydrogen (nuclear spins in the same direction) and 25 percent parahydrogen (nuclear spins in opposite directions).   At the boiling point of liquid hydrogen, 20.4°K, the equilibrium ortho and para concentrations are 0.21 and 99.79 percent respectively.   The high-temperature equilibrium composition of deuterium is two-thirds ortho, and one-third para, while at 20.4°K it is about 98 percent orthodeuterium.

Most of the physical properties of hydrogen and deuterium, such as vapor pressure, density of the liquid, triple point temperature and pressure, etc., are mildly dependent upon the ortho-para composition.   Most important, however, is the large energy difference between the two varieties.   This results in a considerable difference between the specific heats and thermal conductivities of normal and parahydrogen in certain temperature ranges.   The spontaneous conversion to the equilibrium ortho-para composition characteristic of a given temperature is rather slow at moderate and low temperatures, so it is quite feasible to have a composition that differs greatly from the equilibrium value. However, very effective catalysts for the ortho-para conversion have been found and it is relatively easy to achieve the equilibrium composition at any temperature.

The ortho-to-para conversion of liquid hydrogen in the absence of a catalyst is attributed to the magnetic interactions between ortho molecules. Since this is a bimolecular reaction, the rate of decrease of orthohydrogen concentration $(-dx/dt)$ is proportional to the square of the concentration;

$$-dx/dt = kx^2 \tag{9.1}$$

Scott, Brickwedde, Urey, and Wahl [29] measured the rate of uncatalyzed conversion and obtained a value for k of 0.0114 per hour. The rate of loss of hydrogen from a storage vessel caused by the heat generated by the ortho-para conversion can be computed from this reaction constant k, the heat of conversion, and the heat of vaporization, if it is assumed that the vapor leaving has the same composition as the liquid remaining. Weitzel [30] has made this computation and prepared a graph, Figure 9.15, which gives the para concentration and the fraction of the original amount of liquid remaining, M/M_0, in a perfectly insulated vessel originally filled with a mass M_0 of liquid normal hydrogen.

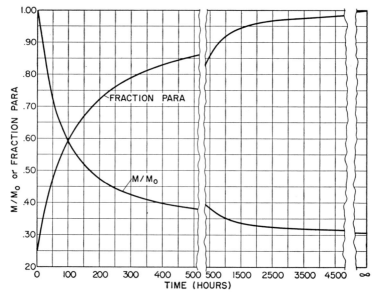

FIGURE 9.15. Storage loss of uncatalyzed liquid hydrogen.

TABLE 9.19. TRIPLE POINTS, BOILING POINTS, AND CRITICAL CONSTANTS OF HYDROGEN

	Normal Hydrogen, 75 per cent $o\text{-}H_2$	20.4°K Equilibrium Hydrogen, 0.21 percent $o\text{-}H_2$	Normal Deuterium, 66.67 percent $o\text{-}D_2$	20.4°K Equilibrium Deuterium, 97.8 percent $o\text{-}D_2$	Hydrogen Deuteride
Triple point temperature, °K	13.95_7 [31]	13.81_3 [31]	18.72_3 [31]	18.69_1 [31]	16.60_4 [31]
Triple point pressure, atm	0.07105 [31]	0.0694_7 [31]	0.1690_8 [31]	0.1690_8 [31]	0.122_1 [31]
Normal boiling point, °K	20.39_0 [31]	20.27_3 [31]	23.57_3 [31]	23.52_7 [31]	22.13_3 [31]
Critical temperature, °K	33.19 [31]	32.9_{94} [32]		38.2_{62} [32]	35.9_{08} [32]
Critical pressure, atm	12.98 [31]	12.7_{70} [32]		16.2_{82} [32]	14.6_{45} [32]
Critical volume, cm³/mole	66.95 [31]	65.5 [32]		60.3 [32]	62.8 [32]

The thermal conductivity of gaseous normal hydrogen is given in Table 9.20. Parahydrogen has a higher thermal conductivity at moderate to low temperatures because of its higher specific heat. Table 9.21 gives the ratio of the thermal conductivity of parahydrogen to that of normal hydrogen as a function of temperature.

TABLE 9.20. THERMAL CONDUCTIVITY OF GASEOUS NORMAL HYDROGEN AT ATMOSPHERIC PRESSURE [1]

Temp., °K	k, watts cm^{-1} °K^{-1} × 10³	Temp., °R
10	0.074	18
20	0.155	36
30	0.229	54
40	0.298	72
50	0.362	90
60	0.422	108
70	0.481	126
80	0.542	144
90	0.602	162
100	0.664	180
110	0.727	198

TABLE 9.20. (*continued*)

Temp., °K	k, watts cm^{-1} °K^{-1} × 10^3	Temp., °R
120	0.790	216
130	0.854	234
140	0.918	252
150	0.981	270
160	1.043	288
170	1.103	306
180	1.165	324
190	1.224	342
200	1.282	360
210	1.340	378
220	1.398	396
230	1.452	414
240	1.507	432
250	1.561	450
260	1.613	468
270	1.665	486
280	1.717	504
290	1.768	522
300	1.816	540

TABLE 9.21. RATIO OF THE THERMAL CONDUCTIVITY OF PARAHYDROGEN TO THAT OF NORMAL HYDROGEN [33] (These values apply at low pressures, 1 atm or less, where the hydrogen approximates an ideal gas behavior)

Temp., °K	k_{para}/k_{normal}
10	1.000
20	1.000
20.39	1.000
30	1.000
33.1	1.000
40	1.000$_5$
50	1.004
60	1.015
70	1.036
80	1.065
90	1.100
100	1.135
120	1.187
150	1.203
200	1.136
250	1.066
298.16	1.028
300	1.028$_8$

TABLE 9.22. VISCOSITY OF GASEOUS HYDROGEN
AT ATMOSPHERIC PRESSURE [1]

Temp., °K	η, Poise $\times$ 10^5	Temp., °R
10	0.510	18
20	1.092	36
30	1.606	54
40	2.067	72
50	2.489	90
60	2.876	108
70	3.237	126
80	3.579	144
90	3.903	162
100	4.210	180
110	4.507	198
120	4.792	216
130	5.069	234
140	5.338	252
150	5.598	270
160	5.852	288
170	6.100	306
180	6.343	324
190	6.580	342
200	6.813	360
210	7.042	378
220	7.268	396
230	7.489	414
240	7.708	432
250	7.923	450
260	8.135	468
270	8.345	486
280	8.552	504
290	8.757	522
300	8.959	540

The vapor pressures of the hydrogens can be represented by equations of the form

$$\log_{10} P(\text{mm Hg}) = A + B/T + CT. \qquad (9.2)$$

Table 9.23 gives values of A, B, and C for hydrogen, deuterium, and hydrogen deuteride.

For convenience, vapor-pressure tables are given also, although for greater accuracy Equation 9.2 with the appropriate constants should be used. Measurements of the vapor-pressure of hydrogen agree with the equation to within the accuracy of the experiments over almost the entire liquid range, to temperatures approaching the critical. No data have been found for deuterium and hydrogen deuteride at high pressures.

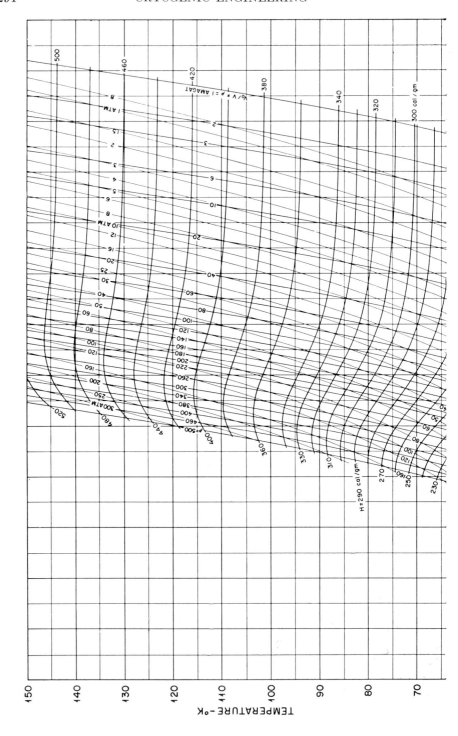

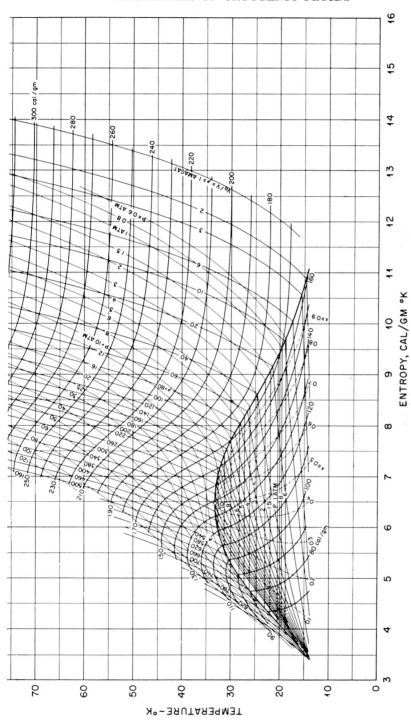

FIGURE 9.16. Temperature-entropy diagram for hydrogen [31].

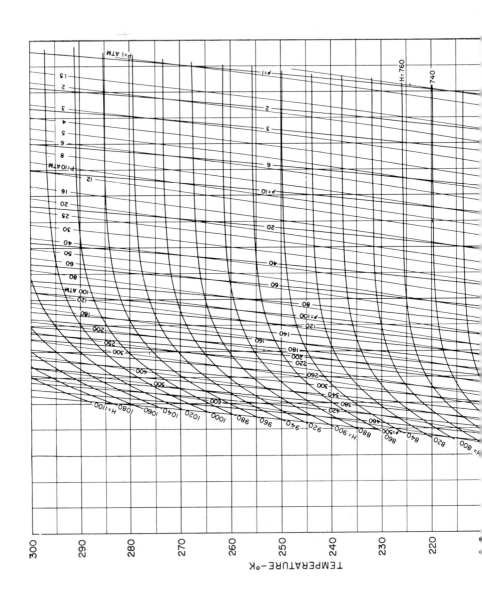

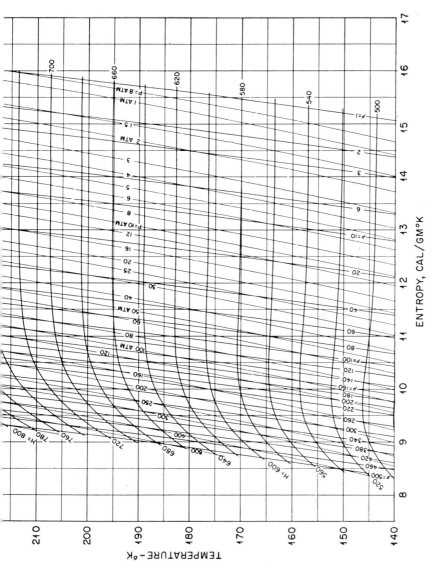

FIGURE 9.16. (Continued)

TABLE 9.23. VALUES OF THE CONSTANTS IN THE VAPOR-PRESSURE EQUATION,
$\log P$ (mm Hg) $= A + B/T + CT$ [31]

Material	State	A	B	C
Normal hydrogen, 75 percent	Liquid	4.66687	−44.9569	0.020537
o-H$_2$	Solid	4.56488	−47.2059	0.03939
20.4°K Equilibrium hydrogen,	Liquid	4.64392	−44.3450	0.02093
0.21 percent o-H$_2$	Solid	4.62438	−47.0172	0.03635
Normal deuterium, 66.67 per-	Liquid	4.7312	−58.4619	0.02671
cent o-D$_2$	Solid	5.1626	−68.0782	0.03110
20.4° Equilibrium deuterium,	Liquid	4.7367	−58.4440	0.02670
97.8 percent o-D$_2$	Solid	5.1625	−67.9119	0.03102
Hydrogen deuteride	Solid	5.04964	−55.2495	0.01479
	Liquid	4.70260	−56.7154	0.04101

TABLE 9.24. VAPOR PRESSURE OF e-H$_2$ (.21% ORTHO
AND 99.79% PARA AT 20.4°K) [1]

		Pressure			
	Temp., °K	mm Hg	atm	psia	Temp., °R
Solid	10	1.93	.00254	.0373	18.0
	11	5.62	.00739	.109	19.8
	12	13.9	.0183	.269	21.6
	13	30.2	.0397	.584	23.4
Liquid	14	58.8	.0774	1.137	25.2
	15	100.3	.1320	1.939	27.0
	16	161.1	.2120	3.115	28.8
	17	246.0	.3237	4.757	30.6
	18	360.3	.4741	6.967	32.4
	19	509.5	.6704	9.852	34.2
	20	699.2	.9200	13.520	36.0
	21	935.3	1.2307	18.086	37.8
	22	1223.7	1.6101	23.663	39.6
	23	1570.5	2.0664	30.369	41.4
	24	1981.8	2.6076	38.322	43.2
	25	2463.8	3.2418	47.642	45.0
	26	3022.9	3.9775	58.45	46.8
	27	3665.1	4.8225	70.87	48.6
	28	4396.8	5.785	85.02	50.4
	29	5227.	6.877	101.07	52.2
	30	6162.	8.108	119.16	54.0
	31	7210.	9.486	139.41	55.8
	32	8383.	11.031	162.10	57.6

TABLE 9.25. VAPOR PRESSURES OF SEVERAL ISOTOPIC
AND ORTHO-PARA VARIETIES OF HYDROGEN [31]
(The horizontal bars separate the solid and liquid ranges)

Temp., °K	20.4°K Equilibrium Hydrogen, mm Hg	Normal Hydrogen, mm Hg	Normal Deuterium, mm Hg	Hydrogen Deuteride, mm Hg
10	1.93	1.7_3	0.05	0.28
11	5.62	5.0_9	.20	.99
12	13.9	12.7	.73	2.94
13	30.2	27.9	2.14	7.46
14	58.8	55.4	5.44	16.8
15	100.4	95.0	12.3	34.4
16	161.2	153.5	25.4	65.2
17	246.2	235.2	48.6	112.5
18	360.6	345.9	87.2	176.4
19	510.1	490.8	145.1	264.7
20	700.3	675.7	219.9	382.8
21	937.0	906.4	322.2	536.2
22	1226.6	1189.0	458.5	730.5
23	1574.9	1529.6	636.2	972.0

TABLE 9.26. MOLAR VOLUMES OF NORMAL HYDROGEN, PARAHYDROGEN,
NORMAL DEUTERIUM, AND HYDROGEN DEUTERIDE IN THE LIQUID STATE [31]

Temp., °K	Volume of the liquid at saturation pressure			
	n-H_2, cm³ mole⁻¹	p-H_2, cm³ mole⁻¹	n-D_2, cm³ mole⁻¹	HD, cm³ mole⁻¹
13.813		26.176 (Trp.)		
13.96	26.108 (Trp.)			
14	26.119	26.227		
15	26.407	26.518		
16	26.712	26.836		
16.604				24.487 (Trp.)
17	27.061	27.179		24.594
18	27.426	27.549		24.885
18.723			23.162 (Trp.)	
19	27.816	27.945	23.237	25.211
20	28.232	28.368	23.525	25.572
20.39	28.401 (N.B.P.)			
22	29.233			
24	30.451			
26	31.995			
28	34.059			
30	37.138			
32	43.211			
33.19	66.95 (Crit.)			

(Trp.) indicates the triple point, (N.B.P.) the normal boiling point, and (Crit.) the critical point.

The differences between vapor pressures of several orthoparahydrogen mixtures are shown in Figures 9.17 and 9.18.

Molar volumes of normal and parahydrogen, normal deuterium and hydrogen deuteride in the saturated liquid state are given in Table 9.26. Figure 9.19 is a graphical representation of the molar volumes of the several hydrogens.

The pvt relations for liquid hydrogen given as compressibility factor, $Z = PV/RT$, in Table 9.27 are from an unpublished correlation by A. S. Friedman of data of Bartholomé [34] and Johnston, Keller, and Friedman [35].

The compressibility factors for liquid deuterium in Table 9.28 are from another unpublished correlation by Friedman of data of Bartholomé [34] and Friedman, Trzeciak, and Johnston [36].

TABLE 9.27. COMPRESSIBILITY FACTOR Z FOR LIQUID HYDROGEN
$$Z = PV/RT$$

Temp., °K \ Pressure, atm	10	20	30	40	60	80	100	120
16.0	.2022	.3999	.5941	.7851	1.159			
17.0	.1923	.3798	.5637	.7444	1.097	1.444	1.787	
18.0	.1835	.3624	.5370	.7087	1.044	1.371	1.695	2.002
19.0	.1760	.3471	.5140	.6773	.9960	1.306	1.612	1.906
20.0	.1693	.3337	.4936	.6498	.9542	1.250	1.539	1.821
21.0	.1636	.3218	.4756	.6256	.9168	1.199	1.474	1.746
22.0	.1587	.3113	.4595	.6036	.8838	1.154	1.416	1.676
23.0	.1545	.3023	.4456	.5850	.8552	1.114	1.366	1.615
24.0	.1510	.2944	.4332	.5685	.8290	1.079	1.321	1.559
25.0	.1480	.2880	.4229	.5538	.8052	1.046	1.280	1.509
26.0	.1457	.2828	.4137	.5403	.7841	1.017	1.243	1.464
27.0	.1440	.2782	.4057	.5286	.7645	.9908	1.210	1.421
28.0	.1431	.2744	.3988	.5185	.7471	.9666	1.179	1.382
29.0	.1437	.2718	.3932	.5095	.7317	.9450	1.151	1.347
30.0	.1456	.2708	.3890	.5026	.7185	.9255	1.124	1.316
31.0	.1498	.2712	.3864	.4969	.7069	.9076	1.101	1.287
32.0		.2732	.3848	.4919	.6965	.8912	1.079	1.261
33.0		.2781	.3845	.4876	.6869	.8757	1.058	1.235

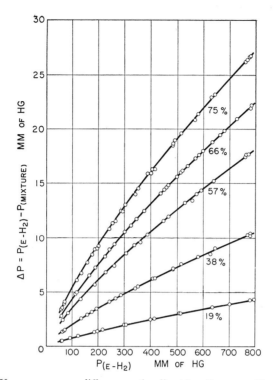

FIGURE 9.17. Vapor-pressure differences for liquid ortho-para H_2 mixtures [31].

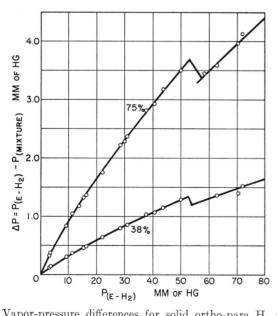

FIGURE 9.18. Vapor-pressure differences for solid ortho-para H_2 mixtures [31].

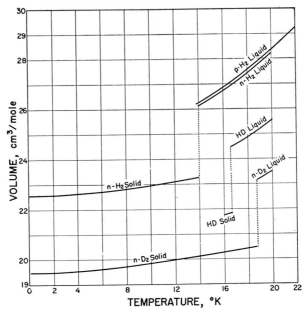

FIGURE 9.19. Molecular volumes of solid and liquid hydrogen, deuterium, and hydrogen deuteride under saturation conditions [31].

TABLE 9.28. COMPRESSIBILITY FACTOR Z FOR LIQUID DEUTERIUM

$$Z = PV/RT$$

Temp., °K \ Pressure, atm	10	20	30	40	60	80	100	120
20.0	.1415	.2815	.4194	.5550				
21.0	.1363	.2709	.4030	.5325	.7873	1.035	1.273	
22.0	.1318	.2616	.3889	.5132	.7585	.9967	1.226	1.454
23.0	.1278	.2534	.3766	.4968	.7336	.9633	1.184	1.403
24.0	.1244	.2462	.3656	.4824	.7115	.9335	1.147	1.358
25.0	.1214	.2400	.3560	.4697	.6919	.9071	1.113	1.317
26.0	.1188	.2345	.3474	.4581	.6738	.8829	1.083	1.281
27.0	.1166	.2296	.3397	.4477	.6575	.8605	1.056	1.248
28.0	.1147	.2255	.3332	.4382	.6431	.8405	1.031	1.217
29.0	.1133	.2221	.3277	.4300	.6299	.8223	1.009	1.190
30.0	.1121	.2194	.3228	.4232	.6181	.8055	.9877	1.164
31.0	.1117	.2173	.3187	.4172	.6072	.7902	.9682	1.139
32.0	.1119	.2162	.3152	.4123	.5980	.7761	.9502	1.117
33.0	.1129	.2158	.3128	.4081	.5898	.7634	.9332	1.096
34.0	.1143	.2162	.3112	.4047	.5826	.7519	.9176	1.076
35.0		.2169	.3113	.4021	.5762	.7422	.9034	1.057
36.0		.2206	.3126	.4001	.5703	.7338	.8907	1.040
37.0		.2251	.3157	.3997	.5658	.7263	.8793	1.023
38.0		.2302	.3209	.4007	.5625	.7198	.8691	1.008

TABLE 9.29. LIQUID HYDROGEN: VELOCITY OF SOUND
AND COMPRESSIBILITY COEFFICIENTS [8]

Temp., °K	Velocity of Sound, m sec^{-1}	Density, g cm^{-3}	Adiabatic Compressibility (Calculated), cm^2 dyne^{-1} $\times 10^{12}$	$\dfrac{C_p}{C_v}$	Isothermal Compressibility (Calculated), cm^2 dyne^{-1} $\times 10^{12}$
20	1199	0.0712	977	1.57	1534
19	1224	0.0722	924		
18	1250	0.0732	874		
17	1276	0.0742	828		
16	1302	0.0752	784		

V. Specific Heats

9.6. Specific heats of condensed hydrogen at saturation condition are shown in Figures 9.20, 9.21, 9.22, and 9.23.   Figure 9.20 gives the specific heats of several varieties of hydrogen in the temperature range 10° to 22°K.   Figures 9.21 and 9.22 illustrate the anomalous specific heats of solid hydrogen containing various concentration of orthohydrogen.   Figure 9.23 shows the specific heat of parahydrogen over a range extending from the solid region through the liquid range to nearly the critical temperature.   It will be noted that there is good agreement between the values for liquid normal hydrogen given in Figure 9.20 and those for liquid parahydrogen in Figure 9.23.

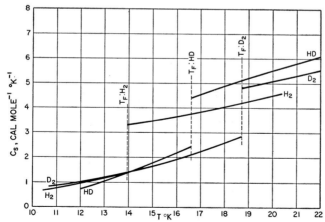

FIGURE 9.20.   Specific heats at saturation pressure of normal hydrogen, deuterium and hydrogen deuteride [31].

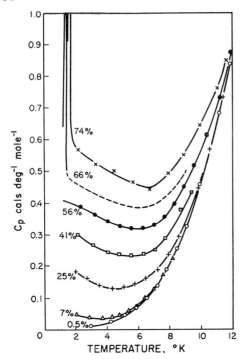

FIGURE 9.21. Specific heat of solid hydrogen. The dotted curve is extrapolated. The percent orthohydrogen is indicated. From Hill and Ricketson [37].

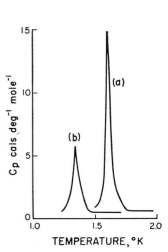

FIGURE 9.22. λ-Anomalies in solid hydrogen: (a) 74% orthohydrogen, (b) 66% orthohydrogen. From Hill and Ricketson [37].

TABLE 9.30. LATENT HEATS OF FUSION [31]

Substance	Heat of Fusion, cal mole^{-1}	Temp., °K	Pressure, mm Hg
Normal hydrogen	28.0	13.95$_7$	54.0
Parahydrogen	28.0$_3$	13.81$_3$	52.8
Normal deuterium	47.0	18.72$_3$	128.5
Hydrogen deuteride	38.1	16.60$_4$	92.8

The heat of vaporization of liquid hydrogen having different ortho concentrations can be represented by the equation

$$L_v = 217.0 - 0.27(T - 16.6)^2 + 1.4x + 2.9x^2 \ [31] \qquad (9.3)$$

where L_v is the heat of vaporization in cal mole^{-1}, x is the orthohydrogen mole fraction, and T is the Kelvin temperature.

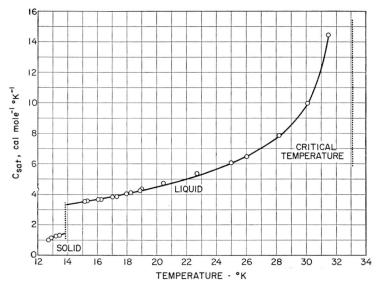

FIGURE 9.23. Heat capacity of saturated liquid and solid parahydrogen. Data below 20°K are by Smith, Hallett, and Johnston [38] and those above 20°K are by Johnston, Clark, Rifkin, and Kerr [39].

The heat of vaporization of normal deuterium was measured by Clusius and Bartholomé [40]. They obtained the value 302.3 cal mole^{-1} at 19.70°K. The heat of vaporization of hydrogen deuteride [30] was found to be 257 cal mole^{-1} at 22.54°K.

TABLE 9.31. THE HEAT OF CONVERSION, ORTHOHYDROGEN TO PARAHYDROGEN [31]

Temp., °K	Δh, cal mole^{-1}
10	338.648
20	338.649
20.39	338.648
30	338.648
33.1	338.648
40	338.634
50	338.460
60	337.616
70	335.200
80	330.164
90	321.700
100	309.440
120	274.475
150	207.175
200	105.20
250	45.31
298.16	18.35
300	17.71

TABLE 9.32. THE VISCOSITY OF LIQUID HYDROGEN AND DEUTERIUM
(From the data of van Itterbeek and van Paemal [41]).

Viscosity

Temp., °K	Hydrogen Micropoise	Deuterium Micropoise
15	234	
16	209	
17	188	
18	170	
19	155	488
20	142	420
21	131	374
22		340
23		310
24		284

TABLE 9.33. THERMAL CONDUCTIVITIES OF LIQUID
HYDROGEN AND DEUTERIUM
(From the data of Mattox, Powers and Johnston [42].
The authors estimated that the maximum error is 3.5 percent for hydrogen, 2.5 percent for deuterium. Within
the experimental precision the values were independent
of the ortho-para composition.)

Temp., °K	Thermal Conductivity, watts cm^{-1} °K^{-1} × 10^4	
	Hydrogen	Deuterium
16	10.85	
18	11.32	
20	11.79	12.61
22	12.25	13.03
24	12.72	13.44
26	13.18	13.85
28	13.65	14.27
30	14.12	14.69

TABLE 9.34. THE DIELECTRIC CONSTANT OF LIQUID
HYDROGEN AND DEUTERIUM
(From an unpublished correlation by A. S. Friedman of
data of Wolfke and Onnes [43], van Itterbeek and
Spaeden [44].)

Dielectric Constant

Temp., °K	Hydrogen	Deuterium
14	1.248	
15	1.244	
16	1.241	
17	1.237	
18	1.234	
19	1.230	1.281
20	1.227	1.277
21	1.224	1.273
22	1.220	1.269
23	1.217	1.265
24	1.214	1.261
25		1.257

VI. HELIUM

9.7. It is somewhat paradoxical that although helium is a rare gas and is
the most difficult of all to liquefy, the properties of liquid helium have been
investigated more extensively than those of any other fluid with the possible
exception of water. The unique properties of liquid helium are responsible for
the great attention given it. One of the first properties to attract attention
was the absence of a solid-liquid-vapor triple point. Helium can be solidified
by applying high pressure to the liquid, but not by cooling it under its own
vapor pressure. The most striking properties, however, are those exhibited
by liquid helium at temperatures below 2.19°K. Liquid helium undergoes a
second-order transformation at this temperature, and the low-temperature
liquid phase, called liquid helium II, has properties exhibited by no other
liquid. The transition point between the two forms of liquid helium, I and
II, is called the λ-point because of the resemblance of the specific heat curve
to the Greek letter lambda.

One unique property of liquid helium II is its so-called *superfluidity*. Liquid
helium II flows so rapidly through fine capillary channels that it appears to
have almost zero viscosity. Another strange property is the formation of a
thin film of helium II on surfaces with which it has contact. The film mi-
grates rather rapidly over the solid surface and readily overcomes the gravita-
tional forces opposing the motion. This phenomenon of "creep" makes it
difficult to achieve a very low pressure when pumping the vapor from a vessel
of liquid helium. The thin liquid film forms on the walls of the vessel or
pumping tube and creeps up until it reaches a warmer region, where it evaporates and increases the amount of vapor that the pump must handle.

A class of unique phenomena involves the mechanism of heat transport in liquid helium II. Simple heat-flow experiments yield results that show helium II as having a thermal conductivity greater than that of copper instead of the low value usually exhibited by liquids. Also when a heat pulse of short duration is generated at one point in a bath of helium II, it is found that a temperature wave is propagated through the liquid with a finite velocity, leaving the temperature of the liquid through which it has passed at the initial value. This is highly analogous to the passage of a mechanical disturbance, or sound wave, through an elastic medium. For this reason the phenomenon of heat transmission in liquid helium II has been named *second sound*. Second sound can be detected with a device sensitive to temperature oscillations but not with an ordinary microphone which is sensitive only to pressure variations. Second sound can be reflected, and standing waves can be set up in a resonating tube.

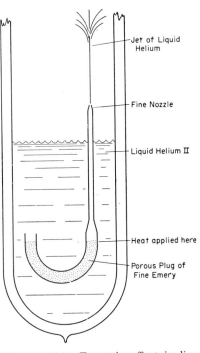

FIGURE 9.24. Fountain effect in liquid helium II.

Another phenomenon which depends upon the mechanism of heat transport in helium II is the *fountain effect*, illustrated in Figure 9.24. A tube containing a porous plug and having a nozzle projecting above the bath of liquid helium II will produce a fountain of liquid helium at the nozzle when the part of the plug nearest the nozzle is heated.

The two-fluid theory has been very successful in providing an explanation for many of the unique properties of liquid helium II. In this theory liquid helium II is considered to be a homogeneous mixture of a superfluid component having very small energy and a normal component possessing nearly all of the thermal energy of the mixture. The concentration of the superfluid component depends upon the temperature, being 100 percent at absolute zero and zero at the λ point. It is further postulated that the superfluid atoms can move about without transferring momentum either to or from the normal atoms. The fountain effect just described can be explained on the basis of this two-fluid model as follows:

Warming the liquid helium increases the concentration of the normal atoms in the right-hand arm of the U tube. Immediately superfluid atoms flow through the porous plug to maintain uniform concentration. Since the normal fluid in the right-hand arm is prevented by its viscosity from flowing out through the porous plug, helium accumulates in the right-hand arm until it is expelled through the nozzle with considerable force. Jets many centimeters high have been observed.

The phenomenon of second sound has a further analogy with ordinary sound. In ordinary sound the propagation of a disturbance consisting of abnormal or subnormal density is accomplished by the restoring effect due to the elasticity of the medium. In second sound the disturbance consists of an abnormal or subnormal concentration of superfluid atoms (more or less than in the surrounding liquid) and the restoring force is the tendency towards uniform concentration.

It has been remarked that an ordinary microphone will not respond to second sound. This is because there is no net motion of the bulk liquid associated with second sound; motion of superfluid atoms in one direction is balanced by motion of normal atoms in the opposite direction. However, Pellam [45] has used a mechanical device to measure second sound in some very interesting experiments. He took note of the fact that the Rayleigh disk, which consists of a disk suspended at 45 degrees to the direction of propagation of sound, always tends to rotate towards a position at right angles to the direction of wave propagation. He reasoned that the opposing directions of flow of the normal and superfluid atoms in second sound would not cancel each other in their effect upon the disk; hence the Rayleigh disk could be used as a detector for second sound. He showed that both the normal and superfluid components of liquid helium II contribute to the torque experienced by the disk when subjected to a beam of second sound.

Most of the data presented in this section have been taken from two sources, "Helium" by Keesom [3] and "Progress in Low-Temperature Physics" edited by Gorter [46]. The reader is referred to these books for additional information.

Helium has two stable isotopes of mass numbers 4 and 3. In helium obtained from natural gas the ratio of He^3 to He^4 is about 10^{-7}. Helium separated from atmospheric air has a concentration of the He^3 isotope about ten times larger, 1 in 10^6. Recently the U.S. Atomic Energy Commission has made available sufficient quantities of pure He^3 to permit the condensation and the determination of some of the properties of the condensed phase. As might be expected from its smaller atomic mass, He^3 is considerably more volatile than He^4. The He^3 experiments of greatest interest had to do with superfluidity. Thus far experiments with pure liquid He^3 have shown no evidence of superfluidity down to temperatures as low as $0.25°K$. Two survey articles dealing with helium three are included in "Progress in Low Temperature Physics" [46]. The first, by E. F. Hammel, is entitled "The low temperature properties of helium three." The other, by J. J. M. Beenakker and K. W. Taconis, is entitled "Liquid mixtures of helium three and four."

The most complete temperature-entropy diagram for helium was prepared by the Kamerlingh Onnes Laboratory of the University of Leiden for the Inter-

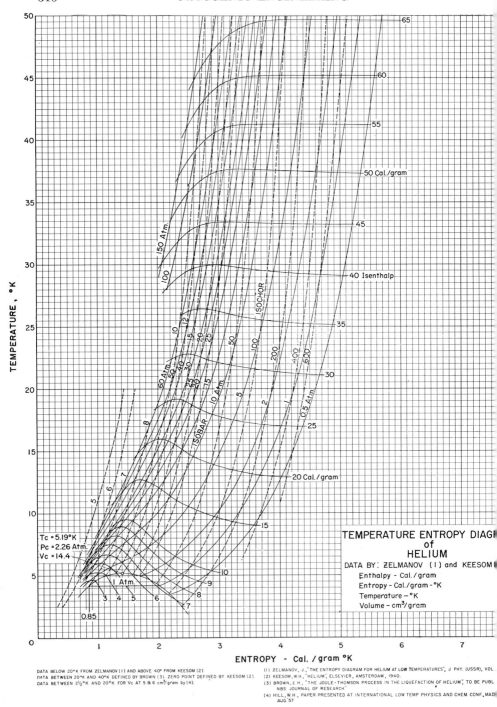

DATA BELOW 20°K FROM ZELMANOV (1) AND ABOVE 40° FROM KEESOM (2)
DATA BETWEEN 20°K AND 40°K DEFINED BY BROWN (3). ZERO POINT DEFINED BY KEESOM (2).
DATA BETWEEN 2½°K AND 20°K FOR Vc AT 5 & 6 cm³/gram by (4).

(1) ZELMANOV, J., "THE ENTROPY DIAGRAM FOR HELIUM AT LOW TEMPERATURES", J PHY. (USSR), VOL.
(2) KEESOM, W.H., "HELIUM", ELSEVIER, AMSTERDAM, 1940.
(3) BROWN, E.H., "THE JOULE-THOMSON PROCESS IN THE LIQUEFACTION OF HELIUM", TO BE PUBL
NBS JOURNAL OF RESEARCH"
(4) HILL, W.H., PAPER PRESENTED AT INTERNATIONAL LOW TEMP PHYSICS AND CHEM CONF, MADI
AUG.'57

FIGURE 9.25. Temperature-entropy diagram for liquid helium.

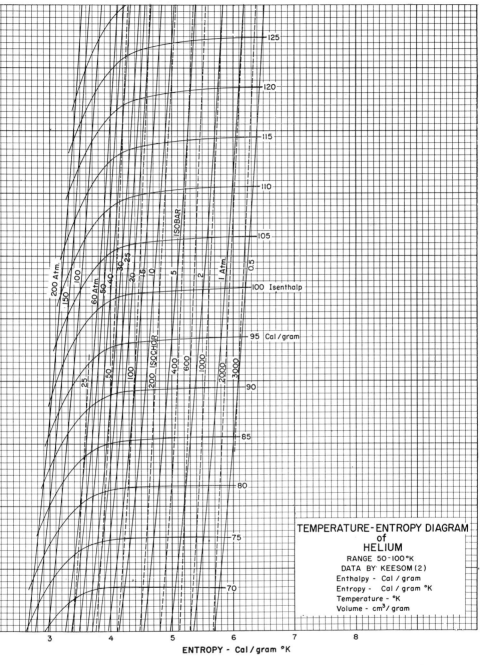

TEMPERATURE-ENTROPY DIAGRAM
of
HELIUM
RANGE 50-100°K
DATA BY KEESOM (2)
Enthalpy - Cal / gram
Entropy - Cal / gram °K
Temperature - °K
Volume - cm³/ gram

ENTROPY - Cal / gram °K

(2) KEESOM, W.H., "HELIUM", ELSEVIER, AMSTERDAM, 1940

JULY 1, 1957

FIGURE 9.25. (*continued*)

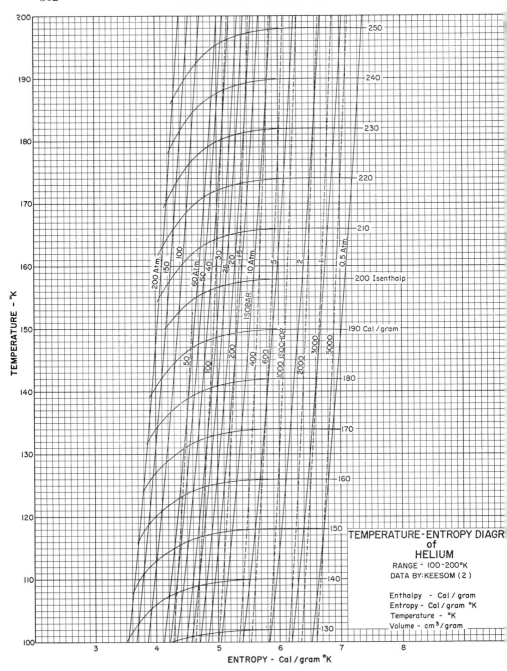

FIGURE 9.25. (*continued*)

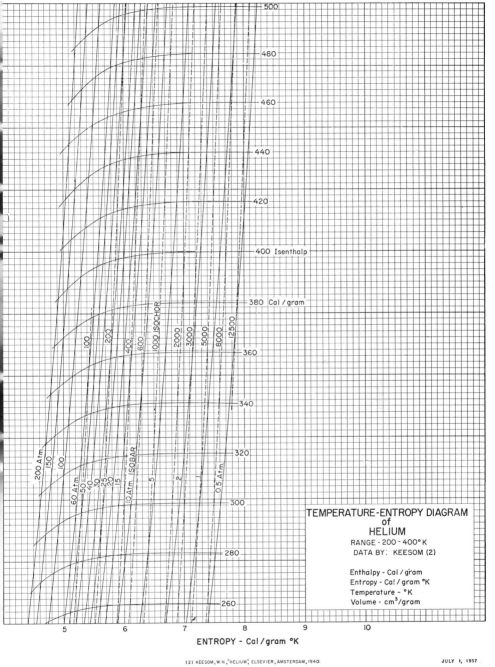

TEMPERATURE-ENTROPY DIAGRAM
of
HELIUM
RANGE - 200 - 400° K
DATA BY: KEESOM (2)

Enthalpy - Cal / gram
Entropy - Cal / gram °K
Temperature - °K
Volume - cm³/gram

ENTROPY - Cal / gram °K

(2) KEESOM, W.H., "HELIUM", ELSEVIER, AMSTERDAM, 1940.

JULY 1, 1957

FIGURE 9.25. (continued)

TABLE 9.35. BOILING POINT, λ POINT,
AND CRITICAL CONSTANTS OF HELIUM [3]

Normal boiling point, °K	4.216
Critical temperature, °K	5.20
Critical pressure, atm	2.26
Critical density, g cm⁻³	0.0693
λ-point temperature, °K	2.18
λ-point pressure, atm	0.050

TABLE 9.36. THE THERMAL CONDUCTIVITY
OF GASEOUS HELIUM [3]

Temp., °K	Thermal conductivity, milliwatts cm^{-1} °K^{-1}
20	0.21
60	.48
100	.70
140	.90
180	1.08
220	1.24
260	1.39
273	1.43
323	1.60
373	1.76

national Institute of Refrigeration. This covers the temperature range 1° to 500°K. A somewhat more recent chart by Zelmanov [47] covers only the range 3° to 21°K. Brown [48] found the Zelmanov chart in its limited temperature span to be the more reliable of the two at high pressures. The chart presented here is a combination of the two prepared by D. B. Mann. It agrees with the Zelmanov diagram below 20°K and with the Leiden diagram above 40°K. The transition range 20° to 40°K was plotted according to a method proposed by Brown [48]. Hill and Lounasma [49] have recently measured the thermal properties of helium from 4° to 20°K at pressures up to 100 atmospheres.

Keesom shows that the experimental data on *the viscosity of gaseous helium* in the temperature range 4° to 1100°K can be represented with an accuracy better than 1 percent by the formula

$$\eta = 5.023T^{0.647} \text{ [3]} \tag{9.4}$$

where T is in degrees Kelvin and η in micropoise. Figure 9.26 is a graph of Equation 9.4 with temperatures plotted on a logarithmic scale. It is seen that the equation fits the observed measurements.

The vapor pressure-temperature relation for helium has been investigated very thoroughly because of its importance in thermometry. The helium vapor-pressure scale has been accepted by low-temperature workers as the standard temperature scale to which their measurements will be referred (see Chapter 5, Low-Temperature Thermometry).

Van Dijk and Durieux [50] have published a table of the vapor pressure of

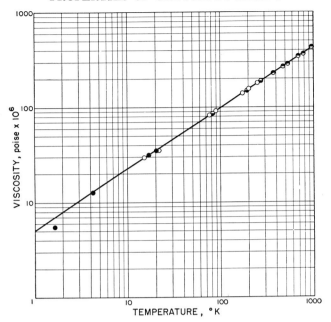

FIGURE 9.26. The viscosity of gaseous helium at pressures near one atmosphere [3]. The differently marked circles indicate data from four independent sources.

helium at temperature intervals of 0.01°K from 0.9° to 5.2°K. Table 9.37 is a reproduction of the entries in this table at 0.1 degree intervals.

TABLE 9.37. VAPOR PRESSURE OF HELIUM [50]

Temp., °K	Pressure, mm Hg	Temp., °K	Pressure, mm Hg	Temp., °K	Pressure, mm Hg
0.9	0.04224	2.5	77.7884	4.0	614.680
1.0	0.12170	2.6	94.0407	4.1	679.152
1.1	0.29597	2.7	112.474	4.2	748.459
1.2	0.63253	2.8	133.227	4.3	822.418
1.3	1.22196	2.9	156.437	4.4	901.013
1.4	2.17762				
		3.0	182.242	4.5	984.366
1.5	3.63354	3.1	210.782	4.6	1072.60
1.6	5.74065	3.2	242.192	4.7	1165.82
1.7	8.66124	3.3	276.610	4.8	1264.15
1.8	12.5614	3.4	314.174	4.9	1367.71
1.9	17.6010				
		3.5	355.030	5.0	1476.60
2.0	23.9199	3.6	399.334	5.1	1590.94
2.1	31.6106	3.7	447.258	5.2	1710.84
2.2	40.6754	3.8	498.988		
2.3	51.2531	3.9	554.723		
2.4	63.5739				

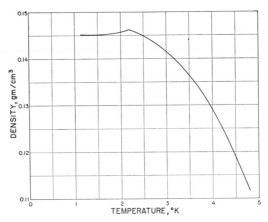

FIGURE 9.27.　Density of liquid helium at saturation [3].

The density of liquid helium at saturation is given in Figure 9.27.　Table 9.38 is a correlation by Keesom [3] of the dependence of the density of liquid helium upon pressure and temperature.　The horizontal bars separate the data above and below the λ point.

TABLE 9.38.　DENSITIES OF LIQUID HELIUM IN G/CM³

Pressure, atm \ Temp., °K	1	5	10	15	20	25	30	35
1.25	0.1462	0.1522	0.1584	0.1636	0.1681	0.1722		
1.50	0.1463	0.1524	0.1585	0.1638	0.1685	0.1727		
1.75	0.1465	0.1526	0.1590	0.1645	0.1694	0.1741		
1.80	0.1465	0.1527	0.1592	0.1647	0.1702	0.1747	0.1796	
1.90	0.1466	0.1530	0.1596	0.1653	0.1708	0.1757	0.1795	
2.00	0.1468	0.1533	0.1603	0.1666	0.1713	0.1756	0.1794	0.1829
2.10	0.1470	0.1539	0.1609	0.1665	0.1712	0.1755	0.1793	0.1828
2.20	0.1472	0.1540	0.1608	0.1663	0.1710	0.1753	0.1790	0.1826
2.25	0.1471	0.1539	0.1606	0.1662	0.1709	0.1752	0.1789	0.1824
2.50	0.1460	0.1530	0.1600	0.1655	0.1703	0.1745	0.1783	0.1818
3.00	0.1425	0.1506	0.1579	0.1637	0.1687	0.1730	0.1768	0.1803
3.50	0.1373	0.1471	0.1552	0.1615	0.1667	0.1712	0.1751	0.1786
4.00	0.1293	0.1422	0.1519	0.1588	0.1644	0.1691	0.1732	0.1768
4.20	0.1251	0.1399	0.1502	0.1575	0.1634	0.1682	0.1724	0.1761

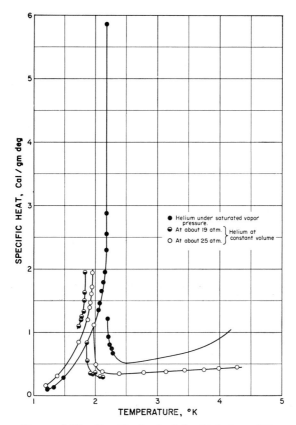

FIGURE 9.28. Specific heat of liquid helium [3].

The heat of vaporization of liquid helium was calculated from other thermal properties by Van Dijk and Durieux [50] and compared with a table compiled by averaging and smoothing all the existing experimental data on the heat of vaporization. The greatest difference was only 0.4 percent. The values in Table 9.39 are selected entries from the smoothed experimental table of Van Dijk and Durieux.

The thermal conductivity of liquid helium at 3.6°K is given by Keesom [3] as 6×10^{-5} cal cm^{-1} deg^{-1} sec^{-1}. This is approximately 2.5×10^{-4} watt cm^{-1} deg^{-1} or about the same as that of air at room temperature. Heat transport through liquid helium II was discussed briefly in the introduction to this chapter. Because of the peculiar nature of this heat transport, a value of thermal conductivity cannot be assigned. However, since heat is transmitted so very rapidly, the designer can usually assume that temperature differences will not persist in a bath of liquid helium II.

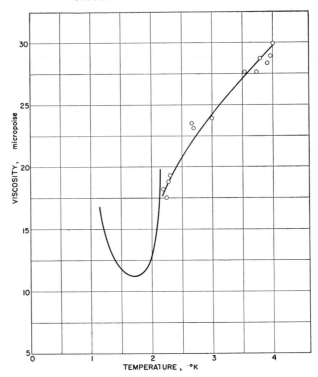

FIGURE 9.29. The viscosity of liquid helium at saturation pressure. The data above 2.2°K, open circles, are from Keesom and McWood [51]. Those below 2.2°K are for the normal component of helium II, Hollis Hallett [52].

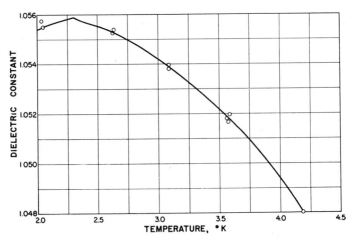

FIGURE 9.30. Dielectric constant of liquid helium at saturation condition [3].

TABLE 9.39. HEAT OF VAPORIZATION OF HELIUM

Temp., °K	L_v, joules mole^{-1}	Temp., °K	L_v, joules mole^{-1}
1.5	89.70	2.9	93.81
1.6	90.86	3.0	93.90
1.7	91.92	3.1	93.90
1.8	92.72	3.2	93.78
1.9	93.13	3.3	93.50
2.0	93.01	3.4	93.06
2.1	92.03	3.5	92.46
2.2	90.77	3.6	91.67
2.3	91.34	3.7	90.71
2.4	91.91	3.8	89.55
2.5	92.46	3.9	88.22
2.6	92.95	4.0	86.62
2.7	93.31	4.1	84.76
2.8	93.59	4.2	82.46

The viscosity of liquid helium I as determined by Keesom and MacWood [51] from the damping of an oscillating disk is shown in Figure 9.29. It will be noted that the viscosity increases with rising temperature instead of decreasing as does the viscosity of nearly all other liquids.

Although liquid helium II will flow through fine capillaries so rapidly that its viscosity appears to be less than 10^{-5} micropoise, when the viscosity is determined by observing the damping of the vibrations of an oscillating disk or cylinder suspended in the liquid, values a million times larger are obtained.

The viscosity and flow behavior of liquid helium II is discussed by Hollis Hallett in "Progress in Low Temperature Physics" [46]. The viscosity of the normal component of helium II represented by the lower curve of Figure 9.29 was derived from data given by Hollis Hallett [52].

The superfluidity of helium II is responsible for the phenomenon known as a *superleak*—the sudden loss of insulating vacuum surrounding a vessel when its liquid helium contents are cooled below the λ point. The leak which is undetectable with a helium leak detector at ordinary temperatures becomes very serious at temperatures below 2.19°K.

REFERENCES FOR CHAPTER 9

[1] Joseph Hilsenrath, Charles W. Beckett, William S. Benedict, Lilla Fano, Harold J. Hoge, Joseph F. Masi, Ralph L. Nuttall, Yeram S. Touloukian, Harold W. Woolley, "Tables of Thermal Properties of Gases," *NBS Circ. 564* (1955).

[2] F. Din, "Thermodynamic Functions of Gases," Butterworth's Scientific Publications, London, (1956).

[3] W. H. Keesom, "Helium," Elsevier, Princeton, N.J., 1942.

[4] Frederick D. Rossini, Donald D. Wagman, William H. Evans, Samuel Levine, and Irvine Jaffe, *NBS Circ. 500* (1952).

[5] H. J. Hoge, "Temperature, Its Measurement and Control in Science and Industry," Reinhold Publishing Corp., N.Y., 1941, Vol. 1, p. 141.

[6] *J. Phys. Soc. Japan*, **9**, 74 (1954).
[7] Russell W. Millar and John D. Sullivan, *Bur. Mines Tech. Paper* 424 (1928).
[8] A. van Itterbeek, in C. J. Gorter (Ed.), "Progress in Low Temperature Physics," International Publishers, Inc., N.Y.; North Holland Publishing Company, Amsterdam, 1955, Vol. 1, p. 366.
[9] E. Mathias and H. K. Onnes, *Leiden Comm.* No. **117** (1911).
[10] F. Simon and F. Kippert *Zt. Phys. Chem.*, **35**, 113 (1928).
[11] W. F. Giauque and H. L. Johnston, *J. Amer. Chem. Soc.*, **51**, 2300 (1929).
[12] G. Furukawa and R. E. McCoskey, *National Advisory Committee for Aeronautics Technical Note* 2969 (1953).
[13] R. A. Alekhanov, *J. Exp. Theor. Phys. U.S.S.R.*, **2**, 771 (1956).
[14] N. S. Rudenko and L. V. Shubnikov, *Phys. Z. Sowjetunion*, **6**, 470 (1934).
[15] N. S. Rudenko, *J. Exp. Theor. Phys. U.S.S.R.*, **9**, 1078 (1939).
[16] Gunther Hammann, *Ann. d. Phys.*, **32**, 595 (1938).
[17] R. W. Powers, R. W. Mattox, and H. L. Johnston, *J. Amer. Chem. Soc.*, **76**, 5968 (1954).
[18] N. V. Tsederberg and D. L. Timrot, *Zhurnal Tek. Fiz.*, **26**, 1849-56 (1956).
[19] Warlaw Werner and W. H. Keesom, *Leiden Comm.* No. **178C** (1926).
[20] E. Kandra, T. Haseda, and A. Otsubo, *Sci. Repts. Research Inst. Tohuku Univ.*, **A7**, 1 (1955).
[21] E. Mathias, H. Kamerlingh Onnes, and C. A. Crommelin, *Leiden Comm.* **14**, No. **145C** (1914).
[22] W. F. Giauque and J. O. Clayton, *J. Amer. Chem. Soc.*, **55**, 4875 (1933).
[23] R. W. Powers, R. W. Mattox, and H. L. Johnston, *J. Amer. Chem. Soc.*, **76**, 5968 (1954).
[24] Robert Guillien, *J. physique*, **(8) 1**, 29 (1940).
[25] E. Regener, "The Structure and Composition of the Stratosphere," No. 509, Headquarters Air Material Command, Wright-Patterson Air Force Base (1946). Also Forsythe, "Smithsonian Physical Tables," 9th rev. ed., 1954, p. 592.
[26] A. Michels, T. Wassenaar, and G. J. Wolkers, *Appl. Sci. Res.* **A5**, 121 (1954).
[27] L. C. Claitor and D. B. Crawford, *Trans. Amer. Soc. Mech. Engr.*, **71**, 885 (1949).
[28] M. and B. Ruhemann, "Low Temperature Physics," Cambridge University Press, London, 1937, p. 100.
[29] R. B. Scott, F. G. Brickwedde, Harold C. Urey, and M. H. Wahl, *J. Chem. Phys.*, **2**, 454 (1934).
[30] D. H. Weitzel, NBS. Unpublished work.
[31] H. W. Woolley, R. B. Scott, and F. G. Brickwedde, *J. Research NBS*, **41**, 379 (1948) RP 1932.
[32] H. G. Hoge and J. W. Lassiter, *J. Research NBS*, **47**, 75 (1951) RP 2229.
[33] A. Farkas, "Orthohydrogen, Parahydrogen, and Heavy Hydrogen," Cambridge University Press, London, 1955, p. 21.
[34] E. Bartholomé, *Z. Physik Chem.* **B33**, 387 (1936).
[35] H. L. Johnston, W. E. Keller, and A. S. Friedman, *J. Amer. Chem. Soc.*, **76**, 1482 (1954).
[36] A. S. Friedman, M. Trzeciak, and H. L. Johnston, *J. Amer. Chem. Soc.*, **76**, 155?? (1954).
[37] R. W. Hill and B. W. A. Ricketson, *Phil. Mag.*, **45**, 277 (1954).
[38] A. L. Smith, N. C. Hallet, and H. L. Johnston, *J. Amer. Chem. Soc.*, **76**, 1486 (1954).
[39] H. L. Johnston, J. T. Clarke, E. B. Rifkin, and E. C. Kerr, *J. Amer. Chem.*

Soc., **72**, 3933 (1950).
[40] K. Clusius and E. Bartholomé, *Z. Physik Chem.*, **B30**, 237 (1935).
[41] A. van Itterbeek and O. van Paemal, *Physica*, **7**, 208 (1940); *ibid.* **8**, 133 (1941).
[42] R. W. Mattox, R. W. Powers, and H. L. Johnston, *Ohio State University Technical Reports*, TR **264-10** and TR **436-1** (1951).
[43] M. Wolfke and H. Kammerlingh Onnes, *Leiden Comm.* No. **171a.**
[44] A. van Itterbeek and J. Spaeden, *Physica*, **9**, 339 (1942).
[45] J. R. Pellam, Rayleigh disks in liquid helium II, in C. J. Gorter (Ed.), "Progress in Low Temperature Physics," Interscience Publishers, Inc., N.Y.; North Holland Publishing Co., Amsterdam, 1955, Vol. 1, p. 54.
[46] C. J. Gorter (Ed.), "Progress in Low Temperature Physics," Interscience Publishers, Inc., N.Y.; North Holland Publishing Company, Amsterdam, Vol. 1 (1955) and Vol. 2 (1957).
[47] J. Zelmanov, *J. Phys. U.S.S.R.*, **8**, 135 (1944).
[48] E. H. Brown and J. W. Dean, *J. Research NBS*, **60**, 161 (1958) RP 2834.
[49] R. W. Hill and O. V. Lounasma, *Proc. Fifth Int. Conf. Low Temp. Phys. and Chem.*, 1957.
[50] H. van Dijk and M. Durieux, in C. J. Gorter (Ed.), "Progress in Low Temperature Physics," North Holland Publishing Co., Amsterdam, Vol. 2 (1957) p. 431.
[51] W. H. Keesom and G. E. MacWood, *Leiden Comm.* **254a**, *Physica*, **5**, 737 (1938).
[52] A. C. Hollis Hallett, *Proc. Camb. Phil. Soc.*, **49**, 717 (1953).

Chapter X

LOW-TEMPERATURE PROPERTIES
OF STRUCTURAL MATERIALS

10.1. This chapter presents brief general discussions of various low-temperature properties of structural materials most likely to be of interest to the cryogenic engineer. Selected data on some of the more widely used materials are included, but there is no intention of offering a handbook of low-temperature properties. There are numerous references to compilations and review articles which will supply additional data when needed. It is hoped that the information given here will be helpful in making preliminary plans and estimates of the feasibility of a scheme, and guide the designer in his search for the data needed for the final design.

A recent review article by Corruccini [1] dealing with thermal and mechanical properties at low temperatures is particularly useful because it treats the subjects from basic considerations and presents methods of estimating values of properties where experimental data are lacking.

I. Mechanical Properties

10.2. In general, lowering the temperature of a solid will increase its yield strength, tensile strength, hardness and resistance to fatigue. A few materials undergo solid-solid transitions which may or may not be reversible, and such a transition can be accompanied by an abrupt change of either sign in mechanical properties. A well-known result of such a transition is the low-temperature embrittlement exhibited by some steels and by several plastics.

10.3. Metals. In the mechanical properties of metals at quite low temperatures, one of the most conspicuous shortcomings is the brittle behavior of ordinary carbon steel. Several disastrous failures of large structures have been attributed to this cause. Actually this notoriety should properly be considered something of a coincidence. It just happens that carbon steels are our most widely used structural materials; and while their low-temperature embrittlement is unfortunate, it is not a general characteristic of common metals and alloys. Most other ordinary structural metals such as

borosilicate glass down to 20°K with various constant rates of loading. Table 10.2 is a summary of their results.

TABLE 10.2. BREAKING STRESS OF A BOROSILICATE GLASS (BSC-2, CORNING 8370)

Condition	Rate of Stress Increase, lb in^{-2} sec^{-1}	Breaking Stress, lb in^{-2}			
		296°K	194°K	76°K	20°K
Abraded	800	7500	9500	10,400	10,400
Abraded	10	5500	7500	10,400	10,600
Abraded	1	5000	6400	10,400	10,200
Unabraded	800	10,400		18,000	

The average strength of unabraded specimens is considerably higher than that of the abraded specimens. However, it was found that the statistical scatter of the values for the unabraded specimens was much greater. It appears that an accidental (and often invisible) surface defect can greatly reduce strength. Consequently for design purposes one should use values for abraded specimens.

II. SPECIFIC HEAT

10.6. The design problems of the cryogenic engineer seldom call for extremely precise data on specific heats of structural materials. Nearly all the needs can be met with a general knowledge of the temperature dependence of specific heat and approximate estimates of the specific heats of those materials most likely to be of use. The specific heats of simple crystalline solids are well represented by the Debye relation. Actually the Debye equation is a general relationship, applicable to many elements and compounds, being expressed as the heat capacity per gram mole of the solid. Figure 10.2 shows a graph of the Debye equation,

$$C_v = 9R(T/\theta)^3 \int_0^{(\theta/T)} \frac{x^4 e^x}{(e^x - 1)^2}\, dx = 3RD(\theta/T)$$

C_v is the heat capacity per gram mole, R is the universal gas constant, θ is a constant of the material having the dimensions of temperature and called the Debye characteristic temperature, or simply the Debye theta. $D(\theta/T)$ is the Debye function. Tables of Debye values of C_v and the corresponding internal energy function, $E - E_0$ are given by Beattie [15]. The graphs of these functions as shown in Figure 10.2 are suitable for approximate computations, when the value of θ for the material is known. The principal shortcoming of this approach is that only rather simple isotropic crystalline solids are well represented. However, Corruccini [1] has studied the problem carefully with the objective of making estimates of the specific heats of alloys and

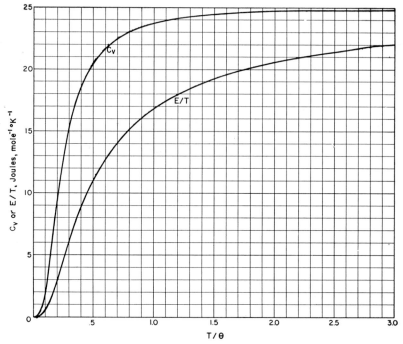

FIGURE 10.2.   Debye specific heat (C_v) and internal energy (E) functions.

TABLE 10.3.   DEBYE CONSTANTS

Substance	$\theta(°K)$	Substance	$\theta(°K)$
Li	430	Ta	245
Na	160	Cr	440
K	100	Mo	375
Be	980	W	315
Mg	320	Mn	350
Ca	230	Re	300
Sr	170	α-Fe	430
Al	390	γ-Fe	320
Diamond	1850	Co	385
Graphite	1500	Ni	375
Si	625	Ru	400
Ge	290	Rh	370
Sn (white)	165	Pd	275
Sn (gray)	240	Os	250
Pb	86	Ir	280
Sb	140	Pt	225
Bi	110	La	150
I	106	LiF	650
Ne	63	NaCl	275
A	85	KCl	230

TABLE 10.3. (*continued*)

Substance	$\theta(°K)$	Substance	$\theta(°K)$
Cu	310	KBr	180
Ag	220	KI	175
Au	180	RbBr	130
Zn	240	RbI	115
Cd	165	CaF_2	475
Hg	95	AgCl	183
Ga	125	AgBr	144
In	100	MgO	800
Tl	96	ZnS	270
Ti	350	FeS_2	645
Zr	280		
Hf	213		

compounds in the absence of experimental data. He also gives recommendations for reducing the C_v values to values of C_p which are commonly needed. It is noted that the difference, $C_p - C_v$, is usually so small that it may be overshadowed by the error inherent in the estimation.

Table 10.3 lists values of the Debye θ for several elements and simple compounds according to Corruccini. The value of θ may vary 10 percent or more for many of the materials according to the temperature range being fitted. The values given in Table 10.3 were selected to favor the region 100° to 300°K. Table 10.4, also from Corruccini [1], lists the specific heats of several of the materials of construction likely to be used by cryogenic engineers. Available data on elements and inorganic compounds have been compiled by Kelley [16] and Shiffman [17].

At very low temperatures, 4°K and lower, the specific heat which arises from the thermal energy of the conduction electrons in a metal becomes significant. At ordinary and moderately low temperatures the contribution of the electrons to the total specific heat is altogether trivial. At very low temperatures the ordinary specific heat of a metal arising from thermal vibrations of the crystal lattice is proportional to T^3 while that of the electrons is proportional to T. Thus when the temperature becomes low enough, the electronic specific heat predominates.

III. THERMAL EXPANSION

10.7. Tables 10.5 and 10.6 list the linear thermal expansion at low temperatures of a number of materials as given in the literature survey by Laquer [18] and the measurements of plastics by Laquer and Head [19]. In their discussion Laquer and Head point out that while the expansion of the reinforced plastics is low, it is dependent upon the ratio of plastic to reinforcing materials. Moreover, the reinforced plastics exhibit a large anisotropy. Variation between different non-reinforced specimens of nominally identical composition was as large as 5 percent. The materials included in Table 10.5 show

TABLE 10.4. SPECIFIC HEATS OF SOME SELECTED SUBSTANCES

C_p, cal/g-deg K

Temp., °K	Al	Mg	Cu	Ni	α-Mn	α-Fe	γ-Fe	Cr	18-8 Stainless[a]	Monel[b]	Fused Silica	Pyrex[c]	Teflon
20 (H₂ b. pt.)	.0024	.0040	.0019	.0012	.0025	.0011	.0014	.0006	.0011	.0014	.006	.0055	.0183
50	.0337	.0580	.0236	.0164	.0211	.0129	.0218	.0090	.016	.0186	.0272	.0264	.0491
77 (N₂ b. pt.)	.0815	.119	.0471	.0392	.0473	.0343	.0487	.0277	.038	.0417	.0470	.047	.0739
90 (O₂ b. pt.)	.102	.141	.0554	.0488	.0574	.0441	.0604	.0381	.050	.0509	.0570	.0575	.0851
100	.116	.155	.0607	.0555	.0641	.0516	.0684	.0459	.057	.0571	.0643	.065	.0931
150	.164	.202	.0774	.0785	.0872	.0775	.0975	.0757	.085	.0782	.0982	.101	.132
200	.191	.221	.0854	.0915	.1003	.0918	.1118	.0925	.099	.0897	.129	.132	.166
298	.215	.235	.0924	.1060	.1146	.1070	.1251	.1073	.114	.1019	.177	.182	(.248 at 280°K)

[a] Calculated on basis 18 Cr 8 Ni balance γ-Fe, then adjusted for agreement with experimental values near room temperature.
[b] Calculated.
[c] Calculated from data for SiO_2 and B_2O_3.

TABLE 10.5. MEAN LINEAR THERMAL EXPANSION OF VARIOUS PLASTICS [19]

Material Temp., °K	Molded Polyester Rod Reinforced with Glass Fiber	Cast Phenolic Rod	Cast Epoxy Polymer	Nylon Rod	Fluorothene	Polystyrene[a]	Polytetrafluoroethylene[a]	Pyrex[b]
				Expansion, $\Delta L/L_i \times 10^5$				
0	0	0	0	0	0	0	0	0
20	3	14	10	10	21	27	45	−1
40	11	38	39	37	65	82	115	−2
60	21	70	78	81	116	152	200	−1.5
80	34	109	126	142	173	235	300	+1
100	49	154	181	217	235	329	410	4.5
120	67	205	242	301	301	432	525	8.5
140	88	261	310	393	372	542	650	13
160	110	321	385	493	444	658	785	17.5
180	134	385	467	600	531	778	940	22.5
200	159	452	556	716	618	900	1130	27.5
220	184	524	651	841	711	1024	1370	33
240	210	602	753	977	811	1152	1620	39
260	237	688	862	1124	921	1284	1875	44.5
273.2	255	749	939	1228	1001	1374	2045	—
280	264	782	980	1282	1045	1422	2130	50.5
300	291	889	1107	1450	1187	1566	2695	57

[a] Specimen taken parallel to the rod extrusion direction.
[b] Calculated from data for SiO_2 and B_2O_3.

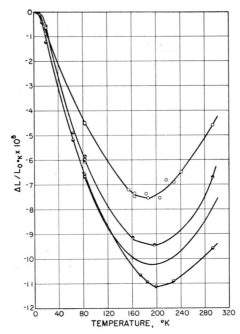

FIGURE 10.3. Thermal expansion of fused silica. The three curves with the experimental points indicated are by Scott [20]. The other curve represents smoothed data of Scheel and Heuse [21]. The extrapolation to absolute zero is very uncertain. The coefficient of expansion (slope of curve) must be zero at absolute zero, but the experimental data do not extend to a sufficiently low temperature to indicate this trend.

the wide range of expansivities exhibited by plastics. Those of high expansivity are apt to show damage when subjected to thermal "shock." That is, a thick piece cooled rapidly on one side is likely to crack because of the stress induced by the non-homogeneous contraction.

Figure 10.3 shows the thermal expansion of several samples of fused silica. Fused silica has a very low expansivity; therefore it is often used as the reference material in apparatus for measuring expansion. It is seen that the expansion varies somewhat from sample to sample, although it is quite small in every case.

IV. ELECTRICAL RESISTANCE

10.8. In regard to the ability to conduct electricity, nearly all solids and liquids fall into five distinct categories: (1) *insulators* which offer extremely high resistance to the flow of current, (2) *semiconductors* which have resistivities much smaller than those of insulators and much greater than those of most metallic conductors, (3) *ionic conductors* (usually liquid) which conduct by virtue of the migration of charged ions, (4) *metallic conductors* whose low

TABLE 10.6. MEAN LINEAR THERMAL EXPANSION OF VARIOUS MATERIALS [18]

Expansion, $\Delta L/L_0 \times 10^5$

Material Temp., °K	Cu	Ni	Al	Mg	Zn	Ti	1020 Low-Carbon Steel	304 Stainless Steel	Monel	Inconel	Free-Machining Yellow Brass
0	0	0	0	0	0	0	0	0	0	0	0
20	0	0	0	1	1	0	0	-1.1	0	0	0
40	2	1	2	5	9	1	1	-1.5	-1.5	1	4
60	10	4	10	12	28	2	4	+2.8	6	5	15
80	25	12	24	29	57	6	10	14	15	12	34
100	44	23	46	55	93	14	20	30	29	24	57
120	67	38	72	87	133	24	32	50	45	38	85
140	92	55	104	124	176	35	47	73	64	55	115
160	119	74	138	164	221	47	63	97	85	74	146
180	148	95	175	208	267	60	81	124	107	95	180
200	178	117	214	254	314	74	101	151	130	117	214
220	209	140	255	303	363	89	121	180	155	140	249
240	240	164	297	353	413	105	142	210	180	163	285
260	272	188	341	403	465	121	164	241	207	187	322
280	305	213	385	453	518	138	187	272	234	212	359
300	339	239	431	503	572	155	210	304	261	238	397

resistance to the flow of electricity is attributed to "free" electrons which can traverse the metallic lattice without interference except that offered by lattice imperfections and by the disturbances caused by the thermal agitation of the atoms of the lattice, and (5) *superconductors* which have zero electrical resistance. All the superconductors thus far discovered enter their superconducting state at temperatures lower than 20°K.

10.9. Insulators. Solid electrical insulators do not present any special problems at low temperatures. In fact, their insulating quality usually improves as the temperature is lowered, probably because accidental surface films of moisture become less conducting. All the common cryogenic fluids are good electrical insulators.

10.10. Semiconductors. Chapter 5 on resistance thermometry (pp. 131–134) described the general behavior of semiconductors. According to the theory of semiconductors their conduction of electricity is achieved by *carriers* which may be either occasional excess electrons loosely bonded to lattice positions, or *holes*, the absences of electrons at scattered lattice spaces. In the presence of an electric field these holes or electrons can migrate through the lattice and conduct an electric current. The temperature coefficient of resistance of semiconductors is negative (the resistance decreasing with increasing temperature) because the increased thermal vibrations accompanying an increase in temperature promote the transition of a carrier from one lattice point to the next.

Semiconductors with excess electrons are called n-type (negative) and those with holes are called p-type (positive). The two types are readily distinguishable by Hall-effect experiments. Among the semiconductors which have been studied are germanium and silicon, with minute traces of impurities to provide carriers, and several metallic oxides and mixtures of oxides in which carriers are present because the oxides are not prepared with exact stoichiometric proportions. The commercial Thermistors® are usually of the latter composition. Another class of semiconductors consists of intermetallic compounds. A recent review article [22] treats these materials exclusively.

Ordinary carbon and pure polycrystalline graphite having small crystallites have negative temperature coefficients of resistance (semiconductor), while single crystals of graphite have positive temperature coefficients [23] [24]. The resistance-temperature relations for ordinary carbon resistors widely used in radio circuitry are of particular interest to the low-temperature worker because of their usefulness as thermometers and liquid level sensing devices. Clement, Dolecek, and Logan [25] have studied the behavior of Allen-Bradley carbon-composition resistors at temperatures ranging from 0.3° to 300°K. They find that resistors of nominal values 2.7 to 270 ohms have rather similar behaviors. By the proper choice of two scaling parameters, R_0 and T_0, the resistance R can be related to the absolute temperature T by a universal

TABLE 10.7. REDUCED TEMPERATURE-RESISTANCE FUNCTION [25]

T/T_0	R/R_0	T/T_0	R/R_0	T/T_0	R/R_0
0.70	8.37×10^6	1.83	1.24×10^4	21.5	107
0.78	2.96×10^6	2.37	4.49×10^3	38.0	76.3
0.89	9.55×10^5	3.28	1.63×10^3	67.0	60.5
1.02	3.38×10^5	4.85	653	120	51.2
1.21	1.08×10^5	7.50	311	215	45.7
1.46	3.69×10^4	12.5	168	375	42.2
				700	39.7

function, $R/R_0 = f(T/T_0)$. Table 10.7, taken from the paper of Clement, Dolecek, and Logan [25] gives values of this function. It is stated that except for a few points at room temperature and liquid nitrogen temperature this function represents the observed resistances to within 1 or 2 percent. Table 10.8 gives typical values of scaling factors for resistors of various nominal resistances.

TABLE 10.8. TYPICAL SCALING FACTORS [26]

Nominal Resistance, ohms	R_0, ohms	T_0, °K
2.7	0.108	0.433
10	0.308	0.650
15	0.380	0.807
22	0.663	0.855
33	1.00	1.00
56	1.55	1.11
82	2.20	1.32
150	5.20	1.43
270	9.5	1.62

It will be noted that the reduced temperature-resistance function gives values higher than the nominal resistances of the resistors at room temperature. This is caused by the method of preparing the resistors for use as thermometers. The insulating covering is ground off, and with it a little of the carbon, thus increasing the resistance. An empirical resistance-temperature relation for quite low temperatures developed by Clement and Quinnel was given in Chapter 5 (p. 133).

10.11. Electrolytes. Electrolytes are of interest to the cryogenist only because electrolytic conduction is greatly reduced at very low temperatures. Thus hygroscopic materials, which are poor insulators in the ordinary atmospheric environment, may become good insulators when cooled to low temperatures. Also, the experimenter may observe electrolytic conduction through an insulating varnish that is not completely dry. This has sometimes caused unnecessary concern during the testing of low-temperature apparatus. A low resistance to ground may be only electrolytic conduction through the wet insulating varnish. An electrolytic "leak" of this type can be identified by the polarization that occurs; the apparent resistance to a direct current rises rapidly during the first few moments after the potential is applied.

10.12. Metallic Conductors. The electrical resistivity of most pure metallic elements at ordinary and moderately low temperatures is approximately proportional to the absolute temperature. It is postulated that the microscopic mechanism responsible for the temperature dependence is the interference to the flow of electrons caused by the thermal agitation of the crystal lattice. At very low temperatures, however, the resistivity approaches a residual value almost independent of temperature. This residual resistance is attributed to lattice imperfections and impurities. A small impurity has the effect of adding a temperature-independent increment to the resistivity. The residual resistance of ordinary copper wire, electrolytic tough pitch, is about 0.002 to 0.01 of its room temperature resistance. However, a special, very pure, carefully-annealed copper specimen had a residual resistance of only 0.0006 the room temperature value. The residual value is closely approached at liquid-hydrogen temperature.

The small resistivity of copper at the hydrogen boiling point has been exploited in the liquid-hydrogen-cooled electromagnet [27]. The power consumed by such a magnet is less than 1 percent of that required for a comparable electromagnet operating at room temperature. Of course this advantage is paid for by the cost of producing liquid hydrogen. This method of producing high magnetic fields has somewhat of the attributes of a storage battery, or accumulator; the hydrogen liquefier can be operated for a day or more to provide the cooling needed by the magnet for about an hour. This greatly reduces the peak power demand and also makes the magnet controls cheaper and more convenient.

Alloys, as a rule, have resistivities much higher than those of their constituent elements and resistance-temperature coefficients that are quite low. For example, the alloy, 60 parts copper, 40 nickel (constantan), has a room-temperature resistivity of about 44 micro-ohm cm while copper and nickel separately have resistivities of 1.7 and 6 micro-ohm cm respectively. Also, while the residual resistances of the pure metallic elements at very low temperatures are very small, that of constantan is about 95 percent of the room-temperature value.

Table 10.9 shows the temperature dependence of resistance of several common elements.

Park, Fulk and Reynolds [29] measured the resistance of several commercial alloys at 20°, 76°, 195° and 273.2°K. Their results are given in Table 10.10.

TABLE 10.9.   EFFECT OF TEMPERATURE ON THE ELECTRICAL RESISTANCE
OF SEVERAL PURE[a] ELEMENTS [28]

(Values are given as R/R_0, where R is the resistance of a specimen
at the indicated temperature and R_0 is its resistance at 0°C.)

Material Temp., °C	R/R_0						
	Al	Cu	Fe	Mg	Ni	Pb	Zn
−80	0.641	0.649	0.569	0.674	0.605	0.683	0.678
−100	.552	.557	.473	.590	.518	.606	.597
−120	.464	.465	.381	.505	.437	.530	.516
−140	.377	.373	.292	.419	.361	.455	.435
−160	.289	.286	.207	.332	.287	.380	.353
−180	.202	.201	.131	.244	.217	.306	.271
−200	.120	.117	.062		.156	.232	.188
−220	.071	.047	.027		.112	.157	.108
−240	.049	.012	.014$_5$		.089	.075$_4$	.041
−253	.0427	.00629	.011$_3$		.085	.0303	.014

[a] Small amounts of impurity will have little influence upon the resistance at the higher
temperatures. However, the resistance at −253°C and lower may be greatly increased by a
minor impurity or by lattice imperfections caused by strain or work hardening.

TABLE 10.10.   ELECTRICAL RESISTIVITY OF SOME COMMERCIAL ALLOYS
AT LOW TEMPERATURES

(Values are in ohms per foot for a cross-sectional area of 1 circular mil.)

Material	Resistivity (ohms circular-mil foot^{-1})[a]			
	20°K	76°K	195°K	273.2°K
Manganin	255	267	282	284.8
Cupron	259	275	283	285.2
Advance	262	278	284.5	286.5
Stainless Steel type 304	332	337	425	616.5
Chromel A	613	617	627.5	632.5
Tophet A	653	655	665.5	670.5
Evanohm	797		803	803.0

[a] The values of resistivity may be somewhat in error because they were
computed by accepting the nominal wire size as correct. However the
fractional change with temperature is reliable.

Table 10.11 lists the compositions of the alloys listed in Table 10.10 and manufacturers as given by Woldman [30].

TABLE 10.11. COMPOSITIONS AND MANUFACTURERS OF ALLOYS REPORTED IN TABLE 10.10

Alloy	Composition	Manufacturer
Manganin	84 Cu, 12 Mn, 4 Ni	Wilbur B. Driver Co., Newark, N.J.
	10.5-13.5 Mn, 1-2 Ni, bal. Cu	Driver Harris Co., Harrison, N.J.
Cupron	55 Cu, 45 Ni	Wilbur B. Driver Co., Newark, N.J.
Advance	54-55 Cu, 44-46 Ni	Driver Harris Co., Harrison, N.J.
Stainless steel, type 304	0.11 max. C, 17-19 Cr, 7-11 Ni, bal. Fe	Several
Chromel A	80 Ni, 20 Cr	Hoskins Mfg. Co., Detroit, Mich.
Tophet A	80 Ni, 20 Cr	Wilbur B. Driver Co., Newark, N.J.
Evanohm	20 Cr, 75 Ni, 2.75 Al, 2.75 Cu	Wilbur B. Driver Co., Newark, N.J.

10.13. Superconductivity. Superconductivity was discovered by H. Kammerlingh Onnes in 1911 when he observed the sudden disappearance of the resistance of mercury at about 4°K. This discovery inaugurated an entirely new field of basic research and gave promise of yielding important new understanding of the basic nature of electrical conduction. The results of many of the subsequent experiments have been almost as unexpected as the original discovery; hence it is not surprising that superconductivity has been the subject of a great number of experimental and theoretical studies. This discussion will be limited to bare descriptions of a few of the more basic facts about superconductivity. The reader who is interested in details and interpretation of the phenomena and theories of superconductivity is referred to the extensive journal literature and particularly to the recent review articles [31] [32] [33].

The absence of electrical resistance was, of course, the phenomenon observed when superconductivity was discovered. For a time there was speculation as to whether a superconductor was really a perfect conductor or whether there remained a "micro-residual" resistance which might be detected by more sensitive experimental methods. The evidence at the present time strongly supports the conclusion that the electrical resistance of a superconductor is mathematically zero; *that an electric current in a closed superconducting circuit will continue, undiminished, forever.*

The absence of resistance naturally suggested the utilization of superconducting coils in powerful electromagnets. Such a device was tried and it was found that normal resistance reappeared when the magnetic field reached a moderate value. External magnetic fields also were found to destroy the superconducting state. Moreover it was found that a straight superconducting wire regained its normal resistance when the electric current it carried reached a certain critical value. Silsbee [34] correlated the data on these seemingly independent experiments and arrived at the conclusion that superconductivity disappeared when the magnetic field reached a certain critical value, which depended upon the temperature. The critical field could be applied externally or arise from the current in the conductor. This is called the *Silsbee hypothesis.*

The temperature dependence of the critical magnetic field, the field required to suppress superconductivity in a material, has been well explored. It has been found that the curve, temperature versus H_c (*critical field*), approximates a parabola (Figure 10.4).

For many years it was thought that the absence of electrical resistance would account for all the phenomena

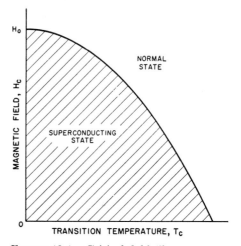

FIGURE 10.4. Critical field of a superconductor.

exhibited by superconductors. Thus it was believed that when an external magnetic field of less than the critical value is applied to an object (e.g., a sphere) in the superconducting state, penetration of the field into the superconductor will be prevented by persistent currents which are set up in the surface of the superconductor. Conversely it was believed that if the magnetic field is applied when the sphere is in its normally resistive state, the field will be frozen in when the sphere is cooled to the superconducting state. In 1933 Meissner and Ochsenfeld [35] performed such an experiment and found, surprisingly, that a specimen expels the magnetic field when it becomes superconducting. This is the *Meissner effect.* Thus the superconducting state exhibits zero magnetic induction as well as zero electrical resistivity (or zero electric field).

The first assumption, that a field applied to a body in the superconducting state will set up persistent currents that prevent the penetration of the field, has been well substantiated. A very striking demonstration of this has been

Figure 10.5. Floating magnet.

devised. If a small permanent bar magnet is lowered into a superconducting saucer, it will float above the saucer, repelled and supported by the persisten currents induced by the near approach of the magnet. Figure 10.5 is a photo graph of this phenomenon. The magnitude and distribution of the persisten currents are such as to simulate a virtual image of the magnet below the actua magnet. This phenomenon may have a practical application because in a high vacuum it could constitute a frictionless support or bearing. The per manent magnet may be replaced by a superconductor carrying a persisten current.

Another attribute of superconductors which presents some intriguing com plexities is the intermediate state. It might very well be assumed that a material must be either superconducting or resistive, there is no obvious inter mediate ground if it is agreed that superconducting material has zero resis tivity. However the existence of a critical magnetic field complicates th picture.

Consider the superconducting sphere of Figure 10.6 in an external field tha would be uniform if it were not for the diamagnetic superconductor in it path. Let us assume that the applied magnetic field is increased until th crowding of the lines of force at the equator of the superconducting spher causes the field at this region to exceed the critical value. It can be show that this occurs when the ambient field is two-thirds the critical value. Ob viously, at this threshold, the applied magnetic field must penetrate the spher but if it becomes uniformly distributed throughout the sphere it would b below the critical value and, by the Meissner effect, be expelled. This im

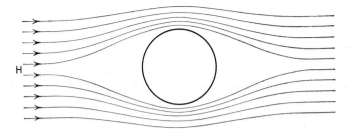

FIGURE 10.6. A superconducting sphere in a magnetic field, H.

passe is avoided if it is postulated that although the magnetic field penetrates
the specimen, it does not remain uniform. It causes the specimen to break
up into small needle-like or laminar domains of alternately normal and superconducting material. The magnetic field penetrates only the normal domains.
In this way the average magnetic field can be maintained and still there can
be sharp discontinuities between regions of normal and superconducting material. This behavior has been verified experimentally [36]. There is at least
one common configuration in which the intermediate state does not appear:
the long cylinder in a magnetic field parallel to the axis of the cylinder. In
this case the transition from the superconducting to the normal state is abrupt
when the applied field becomes critical.

The transition from the superconducting to the normal state takes place
in a very small temperature interval for pure monocrystalline specimens. For
a single crystal of pure tin the transition occupied about 0.001°K. Polycrystalline and impure specimens have broader transitions. It was found
that a hard-drawn specimen of tantalum wire had a broad S-shaped transition
curve (resistance versus temperature) that was well represented by the probability integral.

Table 10.12 lists the transition temperatures and the critical fields at 0°K,
H_0, for superconducting elements. Since the temperature dependence of critical fields is approximated by

$$H_c = H_0[1 - (T/T_c)^2]$$

the value H_0 can be used to estimate the magnetic field required to restore
resistance at any temperature. H_c is the critical field at the temperature T,
and T_c is the superconducting transition temperature in zero magnetic field.

A large number of superconducting compounds have been discovered.
These are of theoretical importance because of the correlation of superconductivity with crystal lattice and electronic structure [38]. Their chief interest to the engineer probably is the fact that many of them have quite high
transition temperatures, permitting the utilization of superconductivity at temperatures attainable with liquid hydrogen. The highest transition tempera-

TABLE 10.12. TRANSITION TEMPERATURES AND CRITICAL FIELDS
AT 0°K FOR SUPERCONDUCTING ELEMENTS [37]

Element	Transition Temperature, °K	Critical Field H_0, oersted
Al	1.175	106
Cd	0.56-0.65	27-28.8
Ga	1.103	47-50.3
Hf	0.37	
Hg	4.160	400-419
In	3.374-3.432	269-275
La	4.8, 5.8	
Nb	8.7-8.9	1960
Os	0.71	65
Pb	7.22	800
Re	1.70	188
Rh	0.9	
Ru	0.47	46
Sn	3.74	304-310
Ta	4.38	860
Tc	11.2	
Th	1.388-1.40	131
Ti	0.39	100
Tl	2.392	171
U	1.1	
V	4.89	1340
Zn	0.93	42-52.5
Zr	0.55	46.6

ture thus far observed is that of the intermetallic compound, Nb_3Sn, 18°K. The compounds listed in Table 10.13 were selected because they have the highest transition temperatures of those thus far studied.

TABLE 10.13. SOME SUPERCONDUCTING COMPOUNDS
WITH HIGH TRANSITION TEMPERATURES

Compound	T_c, °K
MoC	9.76
$MoGa_2$	9.5
MoN	12.0
Nb_3Au	11.6
NbC	6.
NbN	15.
Nb_3Sn	18.0
V_3Ga	16.8
V_3Ge	6.
V_3Si	17.
V_3Sn	6.

V. Thermal Conductivity

10.14. Thermal conductivity in pure metals (particularly at low temperatures) is due principally to the "free" conduction electrons, those which are so loosely bound to the atoms that they wander readily throughout the crystal lattice and thus transfer thermal energy. In nonmetallic crystals and some intermetallic compounds, the principal mechanism of heat conduction is by the mechanical interaction between molecules. For single crystals at quite low temperatures this mode of heat conduction can be very effective, equaling or exceeding the conduction by pure metals. Lattice imperfections introduce resistance to heat flow. Accordingly the disordered dielectrics such as glass and polymeric plastics are the poorest solid conductors of heat.

Powell and Blanpied [39] have published the most complete and authoritative review of the literature and compilation of existing data on thermal conductivity available at the present time. This document of 68 pages is a review of the literature from 1900 to 1954 and presents the data in a large number of graphs and tables. It also lists 198 references to original articles on the subject.

This section presents data for a few of the materials commonly used by low-temperature workers. Much of the data is from the review of Powell and Blanpied but some more recent data are included. The thermal conductivities of insulating materials are given in Chapter 6 on insulation (page 142).

Figure 10.7 gives the low-temperature thermal conductivities of several metals usually considered to be good conductors. It will be noted that the metals of high purity exhibit a maximum of conductivity at low temperatures which in some cases is many times the room-temperature value. Moreover the conductivities of these metals approach a room-temperature value that is almost temperature independent. The height (or existence) of the maximum is quite sensitive to certain slight impurities, although it will be noted that some of the commercial coppers and aluminums exhibit maxima.

Of special importance to the low-temperature worker is the behavior of the commercial coppers. Copper is often chosen for its high thermal conductivity. One of the common commercial coppers is "phosphorus deoxidized," commonly used for fabricating tubing and sheet. The conductivity of this material is given by Curve I, Figure 10.7. It is quite apparent that this particular variety of copper should not be chosen for good thermal conductivity, particularly when it is noted that two other commercial coppers "electrolytic tough pitch" and free-machining tellurium copper, Curves D and F, are much better conductors at low temperature. Copper wire is nearly all electrolytic tough pitch, and some sheet stock is made of the same material. The free-machining tellurium copper can be obtained as bar and plate stock.

There is also commercially available a free-machining leaded copper which

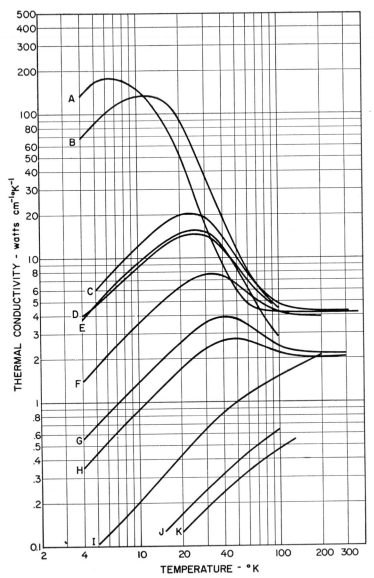

FIGURE 10.7. Low-temperature thermal conductivities of some metals having relatively high conductivities. A, silver 99.999% pure [39]; B, high purity copper [42]; C, coalesced copper [42]; D, copper, electrolytic tough pitch [42]; E, aluminum single crystal [43]; F, free-machining tellurium copper [42]; G, aluminum, 1100 F [43]; H, aluminum, 6063-T5 [43]; I, copper, phosphorus deoxidized [42]; J, aluminum, 2024-T4 [43]; K, free-machining leaded brass [42].

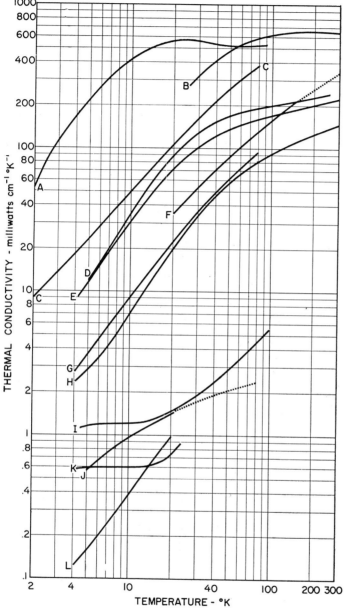

FIGURE 10.8. Low-temperature thermal conductivities of some solids with relatively ow conductivities. A, 50-50 lead-tin solder [44]; B, steel, SAE 1020 [39]; C, beryl-um copper [44]; D, constantan [39]; E, Monel ® [39]; F, silicon bronze [42]; G, nconel ® [39]; H, type 347 stainless steel [39]; I, fused quartz [39]; J, polytetra-uoroethylene (Teflon®) [41]; K, polymethylmethacrylate (perspex) [39]; L, nylon [44].

has a slightly higher conductivity maximum [40] than that of the tellurium copper. These free-machining copper alloys have rather large additions of the alloying element, approximately 1 percent. However, it appears that the additives are segregated at the copper crystallite boundaries and do not interfere greatly with heat conduction.

Figure 10.8 shows the low-temperature thermal conductivities of some solids that are poor heat conductors. Many of these are often used as supporting elements in cryogenic equipment because of their low conductivity.

VI. Emissivity, Reflectivity, and Absorptivity

10.15. The computation of radiant heat transfer across an insulating vacuum calls for data on the emissivity, absorptivity and/or reflectivity of the bounding surfaces. These properties are commonly designated and defined as follows.

$\epsilon_n = total\ normal\ emissivity:$ rate of radiant energy emission normal to the surface, divided by the corresponding rate from a black body.

$\epsilon_h = total\ hemispherical\ emissivity:$ rate of radiant energy emission into a hemisphere (centered on the normal to the emitting surface), divided by the corresponding rate from a black body.

$a = total\ adsorptivity:$ fraction of energy incident upon a surface that is absorbed. Quantities a_n and a_h analogous to ϵ_n and ϵ_h may be distinguished.

$r = reflectivity:$ fraction of incident energy which is reflected; $r = 1 - a$. The value of the reflectivity also depends upon the angle of incidence.

$\sigma =$ Stefan-Boltzmann black-body radiation constant, the rate of energy emission from a "black" body at the temperature T; $Q = \sigma T^4$, where Q is the rate of energy emission, T is the Kelvin temperature and σ the Stefan-Boltzmann constant. Emissivities are increased by roughening the surface, and in the case of metals emissivities are increased by work-hardening, impurities, and contaminating surface films such as oxides or films of oil or grease.

Table 10.14 gives values of emissivity selected from a more complete table by M. M. Fulk and M. M. Reynolds in the *American Institute of Physics "Handbook"* [45].

It will be noted that the emissivity (or absorptivity) of metals decreases with decreasing temperature. At a fixed temperature the emissivity must equal the absorptivity. (If these differed, there could be a net transfer of heat between two surfaces at the same temperature—a violation of the second law of thermodynamics.) The rate of radiant heat transfer between two surfaces at different temperatures, where the geometry permits multiple reflections, depends in a complicated way upon the emissivities of both surfaces and their absorptivities of the radiant energy emitted by the opposite surface as well as upon the geometric configuration. Fortunately, in the region

TABLE 10.14. EMISSIVITY OF VARIOUS MATERIALS [45]

(An emissivity value followed by a temperature denotes absorptivity at that temperature for black-body radiation of the temperature listed in the "temperature" column. An asterisk denotes a total hemispherical absorptivity.)

Material	Temp., °K	Emissivity (Total Normal) ϵ_n
Aluminum-annealed (electropolished)	300	0.03
	300	.018 (76°K)*
	300	.011 (4°K)
Aluminum with oxide layer		
0.25 μ thick	311	.06
1.0 μ thick	311	.30
7.0 μ thick	311	.75
Aluminum with lacquer layer		
0.5 μ thick	311	.05
2.0 μ thick	311	.30
8.0 μ thick	311	.57
Aluminum vaporized on $\frac{1}{2}$-mil Mylar plastic (both sides)	300	.04 (76°K)*
Brass, polished	373	.03
rolled plate	300	.06
shim stock, 65 Cu and 35 Zn	295	.029 (76°K)*
shim stock, 65 Cu and 35 Zn	295	.018 (4°K)
oxidized	373	.60
Cadmium, electroplate (mossy)	295	.03 (76°K)*
Chromium-plated on copper	300	.08
Copper, black oxidized	300	0.78
scraped	300	.07
commercial polish	300	.03
electrolytic, careful polish	295	.015 (76°K)*
chromic acid dip	295	.017 (76°K)*
polished	295	.019 (76°K)*
liquid honed (a commercial liquid "sandblast")	295	.088 (76°K)*
electrolytic polish	295	.0062 (4°K)
mechanical polish	295	.015 (4°K)
carefully prepared surface of pure Cu	295	.0082 (90°K)
Gold, 0.0015″ foil (on glass or Lucite plastic)	295	.01 (76°K)*
0.0005″ foil (on glass or Lucite plastic)	295	.016 (76°K)*
0.000,010″ leaf (on glass or Lucite plastic)	295	.063 (76°K)*
Au vaporized onto both sides of $\frac{1}{2}$-mil Mylar plastic	295	.02 (76°K)*
Au plate .0002″ on stainless steel (1% Ag in Au)	295	.025 (76°K)*
Au plate .00005″ on stainless steel (1% Ag in Au)	295	.027 (76°K)*

TABLE 10.14. (CONTINUED)

Material	Temp., °K	Emissivity (Total Normal) ϵ_n
Iron, electrolytic	450-500	.05-.065
cast iron, polished	311	0.21
cast iron, oxidized	311	0.63
galvanized iron	365	0.07
stainless steel, polished	373	0.08
stainless steel, type (302)	300	.048 (76°K)*
Lead, 0.004 inch foil	295	.011 (4°K)
Lead, gray oxidized	295	0.28
Magnesium	295	.07
Mercury	273-373	.09-.12
Nickel, electrolytic	295	.04
.004 inch foil	295	.022 (76°K)*
electroplated on copper	300	.03 (76°K)*
Platinum	290	.016 (85°K)
Rhodium, plated on stainless steel	295	.078 (76°K)*
Silver	295	.022
	295	.01 (76°K)*
	295	.008 (76°K)*
	295	.006 (85°K)*
Tin, 0.001 inch foil	295	.013 (76°K)*
	295	.012 (4°K)
Tin with 1% indium	295	.0125 (4°K)
Tin with 5% indium	295	.0174 (4°K)
Solder, 50-50 solder on copper	295	.032 (76°K)*
Stellite	293	0.11
Monel, smooth, not polished	366	0.16
Copper-nickel	373	.059
Ice, smooth, H_2O	273	.96
Glass	293	.94
Lacquer, white	373	.925
black matte	373	.97
Oil paints, all colors	273-373	.92-.96
Candle soot	273-373	.952
Paper	373	.92
Quartz (fused)	295	.932

of the electromagnetic spectrum of importance in cryogenic insulation, metals are approximately "gray bodies"; that is, their emissivities (and absorptivities) are almost independent of the wave length of the radiation, so their emissivities for one distribution of wave lengths are very nearly equal to their absorptivities for another distribution. Thus the formulae for radiant heat transfer given in Chapter 6 (p. 146), will give acceptable results.

TABLE 10.15.   EMF'S OF SOME THERMOCOUPLE MATERIALS AT LOW TEMPERATURES
(The emf's are for thermocouples made of copper
with the indicated alloy as the other element.)

| Temp., °K | Electromotive Force, microvolts | | |
	Au + 2.11 At % Co	Constantan	Ag + 0.37 At % Au
0	0.00	0.00	
2	2.04	0.70	
4	8.04	2.76	
6	17.76	6.14	
8	37.01	10.79	
10	47.57	16.64	
12	67.23	23.66	
14	89.78	31.78	
16	115.0	40.97	
18	142.9	51.22	
20	173.1	62.48	0.00
25	259.5	95.18	0.65
30	360.1	134.1	2.05
35	472.6	178.6	4.25
40	595.8	228.5	7.40
45	728.3	283.3	11.15
50	869.0	342.8	15.25
60	1171.1	474.7	24.10
70	1495.4	622.4	33.20
80	1836.3	784.4	41.70
90	2190.3	960.5	49.5
100	2555.8	1149.8	57.1
110	2930.5	1351.9	64.2
120	3312.6	1566.5	71.1
130	3700.6	1793.1	77.9
140	4093.2	2031.8	84.3
150	4489.6	2282.4	90.7
160	4888.7	2545.0	96.9
170	5290.1	2819.8	103.1
180	5693.3	3106.7	109.4
190	6098.1	3405.2	115.9
200	6504.0	3714.1	122.4
210	6910.6	4033.3	128.9
220	7317.6	4362.7	135.3
230	7724.8	4702.2	142.2
240	8131.9	5051.9	148.8
250	8538.8	5411.7	155.5
260	8945.3	5781.5	162.3
270	9351.1	6161.5	169.7
280	9756.3	6551.7	177.1
290	10160.	6952.1	184.8
300	10564.	7362.9	192.9

VII. Thermoelectric EMF

10.16. The only practical application of thermoelectricity at low temperatures at the present time is the use of thermocouples for the measurement of temperature. There have been some suggestions that the Peltier effect could be used to produce refrigeration, but a refrigerator using this principle has not yet been developed. Accordingly, the data presented here will be confined to a few metals and alloys which have been thoroughly investigated over the temperature range 4° to 300°K because they have attributes suitable for use as low-temperature thermocouple elements. Bunch, Powell, and Corruccini [46] have measured the thermal emf's of (1) an alloy consisting of gold with an admixture of 2.1 atomic percent cobalt, (2) silver with 0.37 atomic percent gold, and (3) constantan thermocouple wire supplied by the Leeds & Northrup Co. The thermal emf's of these alloys versus copper magnet wire (known to the industry as "electrolytic tough pitch copper") were measured from 4° to 300°K. Table 10.15 was constructed by smoothing the observed data. It is recommended that this table be used as a "base line" and that other thermocouples of the same nominal composition be compared by means of a deviation graph, observed-minus-tabular values versus tabular values of emf. This will produce a complete calibration curve for the new thermocouple (which can be used to construct a table) with a very few calibration temperatures.

Table 10.15 gives the thermal emf's of (1) gold plus 2.1 atomic percent cobalt, (2) constantan, and (3) silver plus 0.37 atomic percent gold, each with copper magnet wire as the other element of the thermocouple.

REFERENCES FOR CHAPTER 10

[1] R. J. Corruccini, *Chem. Eng. Prog.*, **53**, 262, 342, 397 (1957). A three-part article.

[2] A. E. White and C. A. Siebert, "Literature Survey on the Low Temperature Properties of Metals," Edwards Bros., Inc., Ann Arbor, Mich., 1947.

[3] P. Litherland Teed, "The Properties of Metallic Materials at Low Temperatures," John Wiley & Sons, Inc., N.Y., 1950.

[4] Symposium on Mechanical Properties of Metals at Low Temperatures, *NBS Circ.* 520 (1951).

[5] J. R. Watt, Choosing metals for low-temperature use, *Ref. Eng.*, **59**, 751 (1951).

[6] R. M. Brick, J. R. Low, and C. H. Lorig, Behavior of metals at low-temperatures, *ASM* (1953).

[7] Symposium on Effect of Temperature on the Brittle Behavior of Metals with Particular References to Low Temperatures, *ASTM* (1953).

[8] W. F. Giauque, T. H. Geballe, D. N. Lyon, and J. J. Fritz, *Rev. Sci. Instr.*, **23**, 169 (1952).

[9] C. A. Swenson, *Rev. Sci. Instr.*, **25**, 834 (1954).

[10] R. M. McClintock and R. H. Kropschot, NBS. Unpublished data.

[11] J. Dyment and H. Ziebland, *Ministry of Supply, Explosives Research and Development Establishment (Great Britain), Report* 24/R/55 (1955).

[12] B. Vonnegut and J. L. Glathart, *J. Appl. Phys.*, **17**, 1082 (1946).

[13] E. B. Shand, *J. Amer. Ceram. Soc.*, **37**, 52 (1954).

[14] R. H. Kropschot and R. P. Mikesell, *J. Appl. Phys.*, **28**, 610 (1957).

[15] James A. Beattie, *J. Math. and Phys.*, **6**, 1 (1926-7).

[16] K. K. Kelley, *Bur. Mines Bull.* 477 (1950).

[17] C. A. Shiffman, "The Heat Capacities of the Elements below Room Temperature," General Electric Research Laboratory, 1952.

[18] H. L. Laquer, "Low Temperature Thermal Expansion of Various Materials," *AECD*-3706 (Dec. 9, 1952). Available from the Office of Technical Services, Department of Commerce, Washington 25, D.C., 40 cents.

[19] H. L. Laquer and E. L. Head, "Low Temperature Thermal Expansion of Plastics," *AECU*-2161, *LADC*-1230, Los Alamos Scientific Laboratory (1952).

[20] R. B. Scott. Measurements made in 1933 on three tubes of fused silica from different sources.

[21] K. Scheel and W. Heuse, *Verh. Deutsche Phys. Ges.*, **16**, 1 (1914).

[22] L. Pincherle and J. M. Radcliffe, *Advances in Phys.*, **5**, 271 (1956).

[23] J. M. Reynolds, H. W. Hemstreet, and T. E. Leinhardt, *Phys. Rev.*, **91**, 1152 (1953).

[24] Alan W. Smith and Ned S. Rasor, *Phys. Rev.*, **104**, 885 (1956).

[25] J. R. Clement, R. L. Dolecek and J. K. Logan, Resistance-temperature "scaling" of carbon-composition thermometers, C-4, 104, *Proc. 1956 Cryogenics Engineering Conf.* (Boulder, Colorado, Sept. 5-7, 1956), and a paper presented at the Eleventh Calorimetry Conference (Johns Hopkins University, Baltimore, Maryland, Sept. 14-15, 1956).

[26] J. R. Clement. Private communication.

[27] Henry L. Laquer, *Proc. Instr. Soc. Amer.* **11**, Paper No. 56-16 (1956).

[28] H. Kammerlingh Onnes and W. Tuyn, *Leiden Comm. Suppl.* No. **58** (1926).

[29] O. E. Park, M. M. Fulk, and M. M. Reynolds, NBS-CEL. Unpublished measurements.

[30] Norman E. Woldman, "Engineering Alloys," 3rd ed., American Society for Metals, 1954.

[31] B. Serin, in "Encyclopedia of Physics," Springer Verlag, Berlin, Göttingen, Heidelberg, 1956, Vol. 15, p. 210.

[32] J. Bardeen, Theory of Superconductivity, in "Encyclopedia of Physics." Springer Verlag, Berlin, 1956, Vol. 15, p. 274.

[33] B. T. Matthias, in C. J. Gorter (Ed.), "Progress in Low Temperature Physics," Interscience Publishers, Inc., N.Y.; North Holland Publishing Co., Amsterdam, Vol. 2 (1957) p. 138.

[34] F. B. Silsbee, *Bur. Stand. Bull.* **14**, 301 (1917).

[35] W. Meissner and R. Ochsenfeld, *Naturwiss.*, **21**, 787 (1933).

[36] A. Meshkovsky and A. Shalnikov, *J. Phys. U.S.S.R.*, **11**, 1 (1946).

[37] G. T. Furukawa and T. B. Douglas, A compilation, in "American Institute of Physics Handbook," McGraw-Hill Book Co., Inc., N.Y., 1957, Sec. 4, 49.

[38] B. T. Matthias, in C. J. Gorter (Ed.), "Progress in Low Temperature Physics," Interscience Publishers, Inc., N.Y.; North Holland Publishing Co., Amsterdam, Vol. 2 (1957) p. 138.

[39] Robert L. Powell and William A. Blanpied, *NBS Circ.* 556 (1954). For sale by the Superintendent of Documents, U.S. Government Printing Office, Washington 25, D.C.

[40] R. L. Powell and D. O. Coffin, *Rev. Sci. Instr.*, **26**, 516 (1955).

[41] R. L. Powell, W. M. Rogers, and D. O. Coffin, *J. Research NBS*, **59**, 349 (1957) RP 2805.

[42] R. L. Powell, W. M. Rogers, and H. M. Roder, *Proc. 1956 Cryogenic Engineering Conf.*, 166 (1956). Also *J. Appl. Phys.*, **28**, 1282 (1956).

[43] W. J. Hall, R. L. Powell, and H. M. Roder, *Proc. 1957 Cryogenic Engineering Conf.* (1957).

[44] R. Berman, E. L. Foster, and H. M. Rosenberg, *Brit. J. Appl. Phys.*, **6**, 181 (1955).

[45] M. M. Fulk and M. M. Reynolds, in D. E. Gray (Ed.), "American Institute of Physics Handbook," McGraw-Hill Book Co., Inc., N.Y., 1957.

[46] M. D. Bunch, R. L. Powell and R. J. Corruccini, NBS-CEL. Unpublished data

Appendices

CONVERSION FACTORS

TABLE A.1. CONVERSION FACTORS FOR UNITS OF LENGTH*

Multiply by appropriate entry to obtain →	cm	mm	μ	mμ	Å
1 centimeter (cm)	1	10	10^4	10^7	10^8
1 millimeter (mm)	10^{-1}	1	10^3	10^6	10^7
1 micron (μ)	10^{-4}	10^{-3}	1	10^3	10^4
1 millimicron (mμ)	10^{-7}	10^{-6}	10^{-3}	1	10
1 angstrom unit (Å)	10^{-8}	10^{-7}	10^{-4}	10^{-1}	1

Multiply by appropriate entry to obtain →	cm	m	in.	ft	yd
1 cm	1	0.01	0.3937	0.032808333	0.010936111
1 m	100.	1	39.37	3.2808333	1.0936111
1 in.	2.5400051	0.025400051	1	0.083333333	0.027777778
1 ft	30.480061	0.30480061	12.	1	0.33333333
1 yd	91.440183	0.91440183	36.	3.	1

TABLE A.2. CONVERSION FACTORS FOR UNITS OF AREA

Multiply by appropriate entry to obtain →	cm^2	m^2	sq in.	sq ft	sq yd
1 cm^2	1	10^{-4}	0.15499969	1.0763867 × 10^{-3}	1.1959853 × 10^{-4}
1 m^2	10^4	1	1549.9969	10.763867	1.1959853
1 sq in.	6.4516258	6.4516258 × 10^{-4}	1	6.9444444 × 10^{-3}	7.7160494 × 10^{-4}
1 sq ft	929.03412	0.092903412	144.	1	0.11111111
1 sq yd	8361.3070	0.83613070	1296.	9.	1

* Tables of conversion factors for units of length, area, volume, mass, density, pressure, ᵉnergy, molecular energy, specific energy, and specific energy per degree are reprinted from *ᵌbles of Thermal Properties of Gases* by Joseph Hilsenrath, Charles W. Beckett, William S. ᵊnedict, Lilla Fano, Harold J. Hoge, Joseph F. Masi, Ralph L. Nuttall, Yeram S. Touloukian, ᵈd Harold W. Woolley, National Bureau of Standards Circular 564, U.S. Department of ᵒmmerce, Washington 25, D.C., 1955.

TABLE A.3. CONVERSION FACTORS FOR UNITS OF VOLUME

Multiply by appropriate entry to obtain ⟶	ml	liter	gal
1 cm³	0.9999720	0.9999720×10^{-3}	2.6417047×10^{-4}
1 cu in.	16.38670	1.638670×10^{-2}	4.3290043×10^{-3}
1 cu ft	28316.22	28.31622	7.4805195
1 ml	1	0.001	2.641779×10^{-4}
1 liter	1000.	1	0.2641779
1 gal	3785.329	3.785329	1

Multiply by appropriate entry to obtain ⟶	cm³	cu in.	cu ft
1 cm³	1	0.061023378	3.5314455×10^{-5}
1 cu in.	16.387162	1	5.7870370×10^{-4}
1 cu ft	28317.017	1728.	1
1 ml	1.000028	0.06102509	3.531544×10^{-5}
1 liter	1000.028	61.02509	0.03531544
1 gal	3785.4345	231.	0.13368056

TABLE A.4. CONVERSION FACTORS FOR UNITS OF MASS

Multiply by appropriate entry to obtain ⟶	g	kg	lb	metric ton	ton
1 g	1	10^{-3}	2.2046223×10^{-3}	10^{-6}	1.1023112×10^{-6}
1 kg	10^3	1	2.2046223	10^{-3}	1.1023112×10^{-3}
1 lb	453.59243	0.45359243	1	4.5359243×10^{-4}	0.0005
1 metric ton	10^6	10^3	2204.6223	1	1.1023112
1 ton	907184.86	907.18486	2000.	0.90718486	1

TABLE A.5. CONVERSION FACTORS FOR UNITS OF DENSITY

Multiply by appropriate entry to obtain ⟶	g/cm³	g/ml	lb/cu in.	lb/cu ft	lb/gal
1 g/cm³	1	1.000028	0.036127504	62.428327	8.3454535
1 g/ml	0.9999720	1	0.03612649	62.42658	8.345220
1 lb/cu in.	27.679742	27.68052	1	1728.	231.
1 lb/cu ft	0.016018369	0.01601882	5.7870370×10^{-4}	1	0.13368056
1 lb/gal	0.11982572	0.1198291	4.3290043×10^{-3}	7.4805195	1

TABLE A.6. CONVERSION FACTORS FOR UNITS OF PRESSURE

Multiply by appropriate entry to obtain ⟶	dyne/cm²	bar	atm	kg(wt)/cm²	mm Hg	in. Hg	lb(wt)/sq in.
1 dyne/cm²	1	10^{-6}	0.9869233×10^{-6}	1.0197162×10^{-6}	7.500617×10^{-4}	2.952993×10^{-5}	1.4503830×10^{-5}
1 bar	10^6	1	0.9869233	1.0197162	750.0617	29.52993	14.503830
1 atm	1013250.	1.013250	1	1.0332275	760.	29.92120	14.696006
1 kg(wt)/cm²	980665.	0.980665	0.9678411	1	735.5592	28.95897	14.223398
1 mm Hg	1333.2237	1.3332237×10^{-3}	1.3157895×10^{-3}	1.3595098×10^{-3}	1	0.03937	0.019336850
1 in. Hg	33863.95	0.03386395	0.03342112	0.03453162	25.40005	1	0.4911570
1 lb(wt)/sq in.	68947.31	0.06894731	0.06804570	0.07030669	51.71473	2.036009	1

TABLE A.7. CONVERSION FACTORS FOR UNITS OF ENERGY

Multiply by appropriate entry to obtain ⟶	g mass (energy equiv.)	abs. joule	int. joule	cal	I. T. cal	Btu
1 g mass (energy equiv.)	1	8.98656×10^{13}	8.98508×10^{13}	2.14784×10^{13}	2.14644×10^{13}	8.51775×10^{10}
1 abs. joule	1.112772×10^{-14}	1	0.999835	0.239006	0.238849	0.947831×10^{-3}
1 int. joule	1.112956×10^{-14}	1.000165	1	0.239045	0.238889	0.947988×10^{-3}
1 cal	4.65584×10^{-14}	4.1840	4.1833	1	0.999346	3.96573×10^{-3}
1 I. T. cal	4.65888×10^{-14}	4.18674	4.18605	1.000654	1	3.96832×10^{-3}
1 Btu	1.174019×10^{-11}	1055.040	1054.866	252.161	251.996	1
1 int. kilowatt-hr	4.00664×10^{-8}	3,600,594.	3,600,000.	860,563.	860,000.	3412.76
1 horsepower-hr	2.98727×10^{-8}	2,684,525.	2,684,082.	641,617.	641,197.	2544.48
1 ft-lb(wt)	1.508720×10^{-14}	1.355821	1.355597	0.324049	0.323837	1.285089×10^{-3}
1 cu ft-lb(wt)/sq in.	2.17256×10^{-12}	195.2382	195.2060	46.6630	46.6325	0.1850529
1 liter-atm	1.127548×10^{-12}	101.3278	101.3111	24.2179	24.2021	0.0960417

TABLE A.7. (CONTINUED)

Multiply by appropriate entry to obtain ⟶	int. kilowatt-hr	ft-lb(wt)	cu ft-lb(wt)/sq in.	liter-atm	horsepower-hr
1 g mass (energy equiv.)	2.49586×10^7	6.62814×10^{13}	4.60287×10^{11}	8.86880×10^{11}	3.34754×10^7
1 abs. joule	2.77732×10^{-7}	0.737561	5.12195×10^{-3}	9.86896×10^{-3}	3.72505×10^{-7}
1 int. joule	2.777778×10^{-7}	0.737682	5.12279×10^{-3}	9.87058×10^{-3}	3.72567×10^{-7}
1 cal	1.162030×10^{-6}	3.08595	2.14302×10^{-2}	4.12917×10^{-2}	1.558562×10^{-6}
1 I. T. cal	1.162791×10^{-6}	3.08797	2.14443×10^{-2}	4.13187×10^{-2}	1.559582×10^{-6}
1 Btu	2.93018×10^{-4}	778.156	5.40386	10.41215	3.93008×10^{-4}
1 int. kilowatt-hr	1	2,655,656.	18442.06	35534.1	1.341241
1 horsepower-hr	0.745578	1,980,000.	13750.	26493.5	1
1 ft-lb(wt)	3.76555×10^{-7}	1	6.94444×10^{-3}	1.338054×10^{-2}	5.05051×10^{-7}
1 cu ft-lb(wt) sq in.	5.42239×10^{-5}	144.	1	1.926797	7.27273×10^{-5}
1 liter-atm	2.81420×10^{-5}	74.7354	5.18996	1	3.77452×10^{-5}

TABLE A.8. CONVERSION FACTORS FOR UNITS OF MOLECULAR ENERGY

Multiply by appropriate entry to obtain ⟶	erg/molecule	abs. joule/mole	int. joule/mole	cal/mole	abs. electron-volt/molecule	int. electron-volt/molecule	wave no. (cm^{-1})
1 erg/molecule	1	6.02283×10^{16}	6.02184×10^{16}	1.439491×10^{16}	6.24222×10^{11}	6.24017×10^{11}	5.03581×10^{15}
1 abs. joule/mole	1.660349×10^{-17}	1	0.999835	0.239006	1.036427×10^{-5}	1.036086×10^{-5}	8.36121×10^{-2}
1 int. joule/mole	1.660623×10^{-17}	1.000165	1	0.239046	1.036599×10^{-5}	1.036257×10^{-5}	8.36259×10^{-2}
1 cal/mole	6.94690×10^{-17}	4.18400	4.1833	1	4.33641×10^{-5}	4.33498×10^{-5}	0.349833
1 abs. electron-volt/molecule	1.601992×10^{-12}	96485.3	96469.4	23060.5	1	0.999670	8067.34
1 int. electron-volt/molecule	1.602521×10^{-12}	96517.1	96501.2	23068.1	1.000330	1	8070.00
1 wave no. (cm^{-1})	1.985776×10^{-16}	11.95999	11.95802	2.85851	1.239567×10^{-4}	1.239158×10^{-4}	1

TABLE A.9. CONVERSION FACTORS FOR UNITS OF SPECIFIC ENERGY

Multiply by appropriate entry to obtain ⟶	abs. joule/g	int. joule/g	cal/g	I. T. cal/g	Btu/lb
1 abs. joule/g	1	0.999835	0.239006	0.238849	0.429929
1 int. joule/g	1.000165	1	0.239045	0.348889	0.430000
1 cal/g	4.1840	4.1833	1	0.999346	1.798823
1 I. T. cal/g	4.18674	4.18605	1.000654	1	1.8
1 Btu/lb	2.32597	2.32558	0.555919	0.555556	1

TABLE A.10. CONVERSION FACTORS FOR UNITS OF SPECIFIC ENERGY PER DEGREE

Multiply by appropriate entry to obtain →	abs. joule/ g deg C	int. joule/ g deg C	cal/ g deg C	I. T. cal/ g deg C	Btu/ lb deg F
1 abs. joule/g deg C	1	0.999835	0.239006	0.238849	0.238849
1 int. joule/g deg C	1.000165	1	0.239045	0.238889	0.238889
1 cal/g deg C	4.1840	4.1833	1	0.999346	0.999346
1 I. T. cal/g deg C	4.18674	4.18605	1.000654	1	1
1 Btu/lb deg F	4.18674	4.18605	1.000654	1	1

TABLE A.11. CONVERSION FACTORS FOR UNITS OF VISCOSITY*

Multiply by appropriate entry to obtain →	centipoise	poise	g_F sec cm^{-2}	lb_F sec in.$^{-2}$	lb_F sec ft^{-2}	lb_F hr in.$^{-2}$
centipoise	1	1×10^{-2}	1.0197×10^{-5}	1.4504×10^{-7}	2.0886×10^{-5}	4.0289×10^{-11}
poise	$1. \times 10^{2}$	1	1.0197×10^{-3}	1.4504×10^{-5}	2.0886×10^{-3}	4.0289×10^{-9}
g_F sec cm^{-2}	9.8067×10^{4}	9.8067×10^{2}	1	1.4224×10^{-2}	2.0482	3.9510×10^{-6}
lb_F sec in.$^{-2}$	6.8947×10^{6}	6.8947×10^{4}	7.0305×10^{1}	1	1.4400×10^{2}	2.7778×10^{-4}
lb_F sec ft^{-2}	4.7880×10^{4}	4.7880×10^{2}	4.8823×10^{-1}	6.9445×10^{-3}	1	1.9290×10^{-6}
lb_F hr in.$^{-2}$	2.4821×10^{10}	2.4821×10^{8}	2.5310×10^{5}	3.6000×10^{3}	5.1841×10^{5}	1
lb_F hr ft^{-2}	1.7237×10^{8}	1.7237×10^{6}	1.7577×10^{3}	2.5001×10^{1}	3.6001×10^{3}	6.9446×10^{-3}
g_M sec^{-1} cm^{-1}	1×10^{2}	1	1.0197×10^{-3}	1.4504×10^{-5}	2.0886×10^{-3}	4.0289×10^{-9}
lb_M sec^{-1} in.$^{-1}$	1.7858×10^{4}	1.7858×10^{2}	1.8210×10^{-1}	2.5901×10^{-3}	3.7298×10^{-1}	7.1948×10^{-7}
lb_M sec^{-1} ft^{-1}	1.4882×10^{3}	1.4882×10^{1}	1.5175×10^{-2}	2.1585×10^{-4}	3.1083×10^{-2}	5.9958×10^{-8}
lb_M hr^{-1} in.$^{-1}$	4.9605×10^{-2}	4.9605×10^{-5}	5.0582×10^{-7}	7.1947×10^{-4}	1.0361×10^{-4}	1.9985×10^{-10}
lb_M hr^{-1} ft^{-1}	4.1338×10^{-1}	4.1338×10^{-3}	4.2152×10^{-6}	5.9957×10^{-8}	8.6339×10^{-6}	1.6655×10^{-11}

* These conversion factors are based on a tabulation by Hawkins, Solberg, and Sibbitt, *Power Plant Eng.*, **45**, 62 (1941).

TABLE A.11. (CONTINUED)

Multiply by appropriate entry to obtain →	lb$_F$ hr ft^{-2}	lb$_M$ sec^{-1} in.$^{-1}$	lb$_M$ hr^{-1} ft^{-1}	slug sec^{-1} in.$^{-1}$	slug hr^{-1} ft^{-1}	g$_M$ sec^{-1} cm^{-1}
centipoise	5.8016 × 10^{-9}	5.5998 × 10^{-5}	2.4191	1.7405 × 10^{-6}	7.5188 × 10^{-2}	1 × 10^{-2}
poise	5.8016 × 10^{-7}	5.5998 × 10^{-3}	2.4191 × 10^2	1.7405 × 10^{-4}	7.5188	1
g$_F$ sec cm^{-2}	5.6895 × 10^{-4}	5.4916	2.3723 × 10^5	1.7068 × 10^{-1}	7.3733 × 10^3	9.8067 × 10^2
lb$_F$ sec in.$^{-2}$	4.0000 × 10^{-2}	3.8609 × 10^2	1.6679 × 10^7	1.2000 × 10^1	5.1840 × 10^5	6.8947 × 10^4
lb$_F$ sec ft^{-2}	2.7778 × 10^{-4}	2.6812	1.1583 × 10^5	8.3335 × 10^{-2}	3.6000 × 10^3	4.7880 × 10^2
lb$_F$ hr in.$^{-2}$	1.4400 × 10^2	1.3899 × 10^6	6.0044 × 10^{10}	4.3199 × 10^4	1.8662 × 10^9	2.4821 × 10^8
lb$_F$ hr ft^{-2}	1	9.6524 × 10^3	4.1698 × 10^8	3.0000 × 10^2	1.2960 × 10^7	1.7237 × 10^6
g$_M$ sec^{-1} cm^{-1}	5.8016 × 10^{-7}	5.5998 × 10^{-3}	2.4191 × 10^2	1.7405 × 10^{-4}	7.5188	1
lb$_M$ sec^{-1} in.$^{-1}$	1.0360 × 10^{-4}	1	4.3200 × 10^4	3.1081 × 10^{-2}	1.3427 × 10^3	1.7858 × 10^2
lb$_M$ sec^{-1} ft^{-1}	8.6339 × 10^{-6}	8.3333 × 10^{-2}	3.6000 × 10^3	2.5902 × 10^{-3}	1.1189 × 10^2	1.4882 × 10^1
lb$_M$ hr^{-1} in.$^{-1}$	2.8779 × 10^{-8}	2.7778 × 10^{-4}	1.2000 × 10^1	8.6337 × 10^{-6}	3.7297 × 10^{-1}	4.9605 × 10^{-2}
lb$_M$ hr^{-1} ft^{-1}	2.3983 × 10^{-9}	2.3148 × 10^{-5}	1	7.1946 × 10^{-7}	3.1081 × 10^{-2}	4.1336 × 10^{-3}

TABLE A.12. CONVERSION FACTORS FOR UNITS OF THERMAL CONDUCTIVITY*

Multiply by appropriate entry to obtain →	watt cm^{-1} deg K^{-1}	cal cm^{-1} sec^{-1} deg K^{-1}	Btu in. hr^{-1} ft^{-2} deg F^{-1}	Btu ft hr^{-1} ft^{-2} deg F^{-1}	Btu in. sec^{-1} ft^{-2} deg F^{-1}	Btu ft sec^{-1} ft^{-2} deg F^{-1}
1 watt cm^{-1} deg K^{-1}	1	0.239046	693.459	57.7882	.192627	1.60523 × 10^{-2}
1 cal cm^{-1} sec^{-1} deg K^{-1}	4.1833	1	2900.94	241.745	.80581	6.7151 × 10^{-2}
1 Btu in. hr^{-1} ft^{-2} deg F^{-1}	1.4420 × 10^{-3}	3.4472 × 10^{-4}	1	8.33333 × 10^{-2}	2.77778 × 10^{-4}	2.3148 × 10^{-3}
1 Btu ft hr^{-1} ft^{-2} deg F^{-1}	1.7305 × 10^{-2}	4.1366 × 10^{-3}	12	1	3.333 × 10^{-3}	2.7778 × 10^{-4}
1 Btu in. sec^{-1} ft^{-2} deg F^{-1}	5.19137	1.24098	3600	300	1	8.3333 × 10^{-2}
1 Btu ft sec^{-1} ft^{-2} deg F^{-1}	62.296	14.892	43200	3600	12	1

* This table was prepared from the conversion factors listed in Tables A.1 through A.11.

SUBJECT INDEX

NAME INDEX

365